Open Wider, Please

THE STORY OF DENTISTRY IN OKLAHOMA

THE STORY OF DENTISTRY

IN OKLAHOMA

---

by J. Stanley Clark

UNIVERSITY OF OKLAHOMA PRESS
Norman

Library of Congress Catalog Card Number: 55–6361

Copyright 1955 by the University of Oklahoma Press
Publishing Division of the University
Composed and printed at Norman, Oklahoma, U.S.A.
by the University of Oklahoma Press
First edition

DEDICATED TO

Licensed Dentists of Oklahoma, 1891–1955

"The story of man's progress through
the ages is a legend of co-operative effort. From the earliest records of his
struggle to raise himself above his environment to the present, his achievements have been made possible only by
co-operation."

—A. C. Seids, D.D.S.

Acknowledgments

THE WRITING of this account of dentistry in Oklahoma required the assistance of many persons and organizations. To all of them, named and unnamed, I would like to express my thanks. First of all, the favorable co-operative attitudes of the Oklahoma State Dental Association and the University of Oklahoma Press made possible the completion of this story. The Special Historical Committee of the Association—Drs. Harry Sorrels, Noel Kaho, Al Walters, A. B. Walker, W. N. Flesher, Fred Sparks, John Wadlin, Jr., Sam Barrett, and Roy Gravelle—lent assistance and encouragement. Dr. Theo P. Bringhurst furnished supplementary documentary evidence of pre-statehood activities and Dr. W. E. Flesher pointed up the responsiveness of Oklahoma legislatures to conscientious legislation.

Bill Cole, president of the Board of Governors of Registered Dentists, made valuable suggestions relative to the state regulatory agency; Bill Hopkins compiled the roster of Oklahoma dentists in the armed services; Rolla Calkin, A. E. Bonnell, Jr., and D. L. Rippeto responded to every request for corroborative information; and my neighborhood dentist, Dale W. Crowder, was always a willing consultant. Bill Howard, executive secretary of the Association, made available all records and files of the organization.

Tullie Sorrels read and corrected a draft of the chapter on oral hygiene; L. D. Wright and Bob Lochridge furnished guidance on happenings since World War II. RobRoy M'Gregor, head of the Department of History, Oklahoma City University, read the manuscript and gave helpful guidance on that portion not directly related to dentistry. Sumner Russman likewise read the manuscript to review technical aspects of dentistry.

Alfred B. Sears and M. L. Wardell, of the Department of History in the University of Oklahoma gave counsel and guidance to the Special Historical Committee of the Dental Association on how best to proceed in developing the history, and Robert Terrill, graduate student, helped to develop the committee's source records. William S. Burt, of the H. Dorsey Douglas Company of Oklahoma City, kindly lent special recording machines for use in interviews.

Miss Dorothy Cutting, librarian, School of Dentistry, University of Kansas City, filled all requests for archival material from that institution on Oklahoma dentistry; Mrs. O. J. Cook of the Oklahoma Historical Society helped research in newspaper files; and Ralph Hudson, Oklahoma state librarian, and his staff assisted with legal citations. Miss Leona Mahaffey accurately transferred an almost indecipherable scrawl into clean, typed copy. Any omissions in the story are directly my own.

J. STANLEY CLARK

Oklahoma City
January 15, 1955

Contents

Illustrations

Open Wider, Please

THE STORY OF DENTISTRY IN OKLAHOMA

CHAPTER ONE

New Frontiers

— I —

I T IS NOT UNUSUAL for a professional organization to evolve ethical standards and techniques in keeping with scientific and social progress. It is remarkable, however, when a small group of professional men willfully pledge themselves to promote professional growth in the interest of the public. From small beginnings predating territorial organization, members of the dental profession kept that idea before them. With the organization of territorial dental associations the idea grew, and shortly after statehood the force of law made effective this ideal.

When Oklahoma was new and Indian Territory sparsely settled, dentists traveled from place to place visiting cross-roads settlements and small communities, ministering to frontier wants and needs. And as new waves of settlement washed over frontier barriers to white encroachment, the process was repeated—in the Unassigned Lands, the Cheyenne-Arapaho country, the Cherokee Outlet, the land of the Kiowa and Comanche—wherever opportunity beckoned, members of the profession came to take part in community development.

In the time span of a dozen years Oklahoma progressively witnessed the disappearance of America's last frontier within its borders. Small settlements grew into cities with paved streets and board walks and public utilities, while a few miles distant ranchmen, hunters, soldiers, and bands of Indians awaited the inevitable rush of settlement that was to transform the grasslands into farms and communities. Mining development, ranch and farm operations, and railroads drew white settlers to Indian Territory, while in Oklahoma Territory, Guthrie, Oklahoma City, Norman, and King-

3

fisher, established in a day, saw the process repeated at Perry, Enid, Woodward, Lawton, and other places.

Dr. J. E. Wright, McAlester, who retired from active practice in 1919 after fifty-one years devoted to his profession, recorded some of his earlier experiences in Indian Territory:

"In the fall of 1883, I disposed of my team, and paid a long promised visit to a friend, who had moved from our home town (Tyler, Texas) to Caddo, Indian Territory, intending to open an office on my return. Before my visit ended, it became known that I was a dentist—then I was besieged to stay a while longer, and do a lot of much needed work. I had my outfit shipped, and went to work. Then I was wanted at Tishomingo Academy (Indian School). This called for another buggy and team. Then to the Wapanucka Academy; then to Stonewall, where I was engaged for three weeks; then to Johnsonville, White Bead Hill, Pauls Valley, Mill Creek; from there back to Stonewall. But before I got to Stonewall, I got lost trying to find a ranch place six miles off the main road, where I had promised to stop and make an old gentleman a set of teeth, but I never found the place. After traveling six or seven miles up a long timbered ridge, the dim road played out entirely. By this time it was growing late, and I decided the best thing for me to do would be to take a back track, which I did. After traveling about two miles, I thought to save time and mileage, and left the top of the ridge—turning to the right in a northeast direction toward Stonewall, and made a long, slanting drive down the ridge, hoping to get to the prairie before dark. Luckily, I had no mishap in making that perilous drive—not that it was not the roughest drive I had ever made. Reaching the foot of the hill, I landed in the midst of an Indian village. I almost jumped out of that buggy when all the dogs in the village commenced barking at once—the women and children came out, stared and 'made mirations.' I was now on the edge of the prairie, and it was sundown. I saw an old man about three hundred yards away, staking out a horse. I drove my tired ponies to where he was, and asked if he could talk to me. He looked straight at me, but said nothing. I then called out 'Stonewall' to him. He came closer and put one foot on the buggy, while still staring at me—then said 'Stonewall one road,' and pointed the way. He then motioned for me to get out, and commenced unharnessing my ponies, saw I was all right; got to work myself, helping water and stake them out. Got out my grip and we went to his cabin, where he set out a chair for me. I heard him talking to his wife in the cabin, and was soon made to understand supper was ready, which consisted of dried beef, corn bread, and black coffee. The night passed, as all nights do. The same fare for breakfast as we had for dinner, after which he had his old wife to come out and sit down, and he made it known that she wanted teeth pulled. I went to work, and before I got through, I had taken out about a dozen teeth for various ones of that village. When through, the old man brought out his buckskin pouch, poured out a hand full of money, and motioned for me to take my pay. That was one time gratitude predominated. I put the money back into the pouch and handed it to him. The old man helped me to hitch up, got on his horse and piloted me to the Stonewall road, which was four or five miles. Here I got after him to tell me how he knew I pulled teeth, and he said: 'Pull it tooth Bird's Store.' He meant he saw me at work in Bird's Store at Stonewall, which was eight weeks before this."[1]

This trip lasted ten weeks. Dr. Wright was so impressed with Indian Territory that he settled in 1885 in Savanna, Choctaw Nation. His was the first dental office opened in Oklahoma. Savanna at the time was a company-owned mining camp of the Missouri-Pacific interests. More than 300 men were employed in the coal mines. Miners and their families lived in rows of company houses; a company store furnished comestibles and supplies for the miners' wants, issued usually against company script, and a company doctor administered to medical needs. The industrial payroll from coal-mining operations helped sustain the young dentist in his profession. Suddenly, without warning, disaster struck the small community, and the fear, ever present in such a community, that miners "seeking bread will find a grave," filled and overflowed the homes. On a clear, cool evening, of April 4, 1887, a deafening explosion rocked the town. Miners working the night shift in Slope No. 2 were en-

---

[1] J. E. Wright, "Dentistry Fifty Years Ago" in *Hettinger Dental News*, Vol. II, No. 12 (December, 1919) (Hettinger Bros. Mfg. Co., Kansas City, Missouri). Dr. Wright prepared the article at the time of his retirement from fifty-one years devoted to his profession. He began practice before the foot engine was invented in 1872; hand drills, manually operated, furnished power. His first two years of practice were by horseback from house to house; later, by buggy. He was the first dentist to locate permanently in Indian Territory.

trapped, and six were killed. Valiant and heroic attempts were made at rescue, finally achieved through Slope No. 1, but not until an additional twelve intrepid men gave their lives to reach those entombed.

This disaster destroyed productive mining activity at Savanna. Company houses and salvaged operating machinery were dismantled and moved to company property at Lehigh. Dr. Wright moved ten miles northward up the Missouri, Kansas and Texas Railway to McAlester, center of the coal-mining industry. From here he made professional visits to coal-mining camps and communities of the surrounding area. The following incidents are taken from his "horse and buggy" practice: "I was called to attend an Indian with toothache. This Indian lived fifteen miles in the country. I went; I always went. The roads, when there were any, were rough, ditchy, and dim. At last I found my Indian, and I am not sure he did not prefer his toothache to me, and I cannot say that I blame him. I might have blamed him then. I do not now. When he was informed that the doctor had come to pull his tooth, he squinted his eyes, grunted, and said, 'Tooth heap damn hurt all night, no hurt now, no want him pulled.' I might add, there were no teeth pulled in that neck of the woods that day.

"Considerable inducements were made to that same dentist to make a professional visit to the little town of Sans Bois, on one occasion, and finally, with some misgivings and a feeling that he was violating some unknown command, he went. To his surprise, he found things looking prosperous, professionally. But, alas and alack! After doing the natives up brown at the first stop, he went forward with some eagerness to the next victim, and in his anxiety to relieve the sufferers, failed to note surroundings and tied his horses in too close proximity to a yellow jackets' nest. The horses being particular about the company they kept, and not liking that particular portion of the universe anyhow, concluded to move. They did move. They made up their minds suddenly, and without due notice to the dentist. They did not take the time or precaution to sound their alarm gongs or crank their cylinders. They possessed electric starters, and they simply opened the throttle, gave one spurt, and down the shadowy distance they flew. It was rapid transit with a whoop, believe me. They made straight for Sans Bois creek bottom, where the timber was thick, and they must have

6

thought they stood some chance of disengaging themselves from their unpleasant and impolite company. They seemed to have no thought whatever what might happen to the dentist's possessions. They didn't, for I am telling you that there were evidences of dentistry strewn for miles. The old foot engine was a total wreck, and the instrument case looked like a deserted village, and was a sight more vacant. What was left of that buggy is easily told. That was that dentist's last trip to Sans Bois."

Into the twin territories came men of the professions and men of trade and commerce, attracted to established communities or platted townsites portrayed in lavish circulars and brochures which were full grown only in the minds of promoters. Dr. Roy James Rinehart, dean of the University of Kansas City School of Dentistry, has related his experiences with a townsite promoter in lands recently opened to white settlement in the Kiowa-Comanche reservation:

"When I was practicing in Canton, Illinois in 1904, a gentleman who wore a hat somewhat different in style from those in central Illinois, and who possessed an unusually friendly nature, walked into my office with a friend of mine who was in the real estate business in the same building as myself. He said he had a good proposition in Oklahoma. A new railroad was being built through the state en route to Mexico, known as the Kansas City, Mexico and Orient. New towns were being laid out, and great were the opportunities in this new country to be opened where only cattle were then being grazed. Town lots would make a young fortune for early investors. I wish I could recall the name of this particular new city near Hobart, that never was on the map. Well, the old boy, who limped somewhat, sold us lots, and lots of them. I was one of three Canton citizens selected to go to Oklahoma to the drawing. Of course, everyone who bought hoped to draw a corner lot on Main Street. We reached Hobart, a neat-looking western citadel where we met ladies and gentlemen from other places in Illinois and Iowa; quite a delegation. The hotel was ours and the Elks lodge fed the—you know the nickname for people from Illinois—well if you don't know, it's the 'Sucker State.' Sheep were never more closely herded than we were.

"In the morning after we arrived, we were taken in vehicles of various kinds out about twelve miles to the proposed townsite. On

7

the way we were shown oil right on top of water in wells. Yes, there on top of the water they dipped out oil. At the townsite was a general store and a blacksmith shop; a good start for a city. The grading was done as far as we could see in each direction, and ties were strewn all along the grading. Someone in the party suggested we drive for a distance along the right-a-way, but it wasn't good driving, so they said, so we went back to Hobart and engaged in the drawing. Of course, we did not learn until some months later that this was not the course of the new railroad, but to me this was an introduction to a new art—a different art from dental techniques."[2]

Railroad development, the establishment of communities along the right-of-ways, and the always present hope that towns would grow into cities attracted dentists to the territories. Typical was the development of the town of Prague. The banking firm of Hoffman, Charles and Conklin, with Herman Josey, had a contract with the Fort Smith and Western Railroad in 1901 to lay out townsites between the western line of the Creek Nation and Guthrie. The inland villages of Arlington, Keokuk Falls, Bellmont, Dent, and Lambdin were approached by the promoters for concessions to the railroad development. When none were forthcoming, an enterprising Czech farmer gave forty acres to the promoters, on which was developed the Prague townsite. Residential and business lots—for sale at $200 to $700—were advertised in the Guthrie and Oklahoma City papers. In 1902, six months after the railroad reached Prague, the town's population was estimated to number 600. In 1907, when an official census for the territories was completed, its population was 998. Dr. J. W. Huffman opened a dental office in 1903 to serve Prague and the surrounding trade area.

Dr. A. B. Walker, Norman, who practiced at Fairview from 1902–25, has recalled that he was attracted to Oklahoma Territory by advertisements that came to his notice on extension of the Kansas City, Mexico and Orient Railroad through the territory. When Cleo Springs, later to be a contender for a county seat when the state constitution was written, failed to make concessions that would have assured it the railroad, promoters platted the townsite of Fairview in a valley south of the Cimarron River. Walker established

[2] R. J. Rinehart, excerpt from address given before the Oklahoma State Dental Association, Tulsa, April 17, 1950. The typed copy is in the files of the Central Office, Oklahoma State Dental Association, Oklahoma City.

his practice there when it was the railroad terminus. Its location in the beautiful, fertile river valley presaged its growth into a stable trade community.

Similar interests—the growth of towns and the need for professional services—prompted other dentists, still active or recently retired, to stake their future on the growth and development of newly established communities. W. E. Furrow, Guthrie (1891), T. H. Williams, Chickasha (1893), Fred Seids, Perry (1896), Fred Sparks, Ponca City (1896), R. H. Pendleton, Norman (1899), J. A. Wells, Shawnee (1899), R. O. Hirschi, Guthrie (1900), Fred Sims, Weatherford (1903), and I. M. Lightner, Guymon (1907), established a practice, took part in community government and other civic affairs, and worked for the betterment of their profession.

The establishment of a practice was not an easy matter, particularly in the 1890's and early 1900's when money was scarce, agricultural prices were depressed, and recurrent crop failures discouraged so many settlers in the new land. Mrs. A. B. Walker, Norman, has related that when she and Dr. Walker settled in Fairview there was only one water well—and the water, bought by the barrel, was "gyppy." She remembers that milk was delivered by horse-drawn wagon and ladled out from five-gallon containers to the pitchers or buckets of the customers.

Dr. Walker recalled how green the valley of the Cimarron appeared in December, 1902. Wheat was eight or ten inches high, and how lush the valley was in the early spring when rains came! Corn and other row crops burst green shoots through the rich sod, heralding promise of bountiful crops. But the searing heat of summer, the winds of July and August blew and dried and parched and burnt and destroyed. Because of crop failure, money was extremely scarce in the farming communities of the valley. As Dr. Walker related: "Things were pretty slim in those early days. For example, I recall one week in November after I had been in Fairview about a year. My first office in Oklahoma I built myself. It was twelve feet square, unpainted on the outside and unfinished on the inside. I furnished it with a spool case for a cabinet, a jeweler's lathe, a dental chair, and had a second-hand stove in which I burnt blackjack wood. I remember well that cold November week; I sat in the office all week long and nobody came in. On Saturday night when I was about to lock the office to leave, a man rode up on horseback and wanted a tooth pulled. I went back in, pulled the tooth for him, and he gave me all the money he had—which was twenty-three cents. As he rode away, I turned the key in the lock, buttoned up my coat, and went home. There was no need of sterilizing my instruments. There would be plenty of time next week."[3]

Another pioneer of an earlier period has related that when he equipped his first office, he included a dental chair with foot-pump attachment, purchased on credit to be paid for in installments. When the first payment of ten dollars came due, he was without funds. He visited a money lender in the same building who drew up necessary papers for the requested thirty-day loan. But the lender counted out only nine dollars! The young dentist told the money lender he had urgent need of ten dollars—to meet a necessary payment. He was told the loan was for ten dollars, but one dollar was withdrawn for interest charge. Upon further conversation the dentist was invited to take his business elsewhere. This he did. Downstairs was a saloon, which he entered. The barkeeper, noting his dejected mien, prompted him to tell his story. Hearing it and without a word of solicitation, the saloonkeeper handed the young professional man a ten-dollar bill. The dentist stated that this experience taught him a valuable lesson; never again was any dental equipment purchased by him on the installment plan. He remembers how the good-natured saloonkeeper tided him over one of the darkest moments of his professional career and enabled him to continue in practice.

Many licensed dentists, and apprentices, found it profitable to travel from place to place in the territories, taking their practice to the patients. This was not unusual, particularly in the early settlement of Indian Territory. Physicians, lawyers, preachers, and dentists made it a common practice to travel a regular circuit or make emergency trips to distant places when services were needed. Dr. R. D. Seals, who practiced in Fort Smith for thirty years before his death in January, 1901, made regular trips in the 1870's

[3] A. B. Walker, interview at Norman, 1953. During the summer of 1953, tape recordings were made of interviews sponsored by the Oklahoma State Dental Association with selected members of the dental profession, and also with Dr. Everett Lain, dermatologist. Transcriptions were made which furnished the basis for material on Dr. Walker's early-day experiences at Fairview, as well as information by other pioneers which appears in the text.

and 1880's to Childress Station, Fort Gibson, Muskogee, Okmulgee, Tahlequah, and Park Hill.

In August, 1888, young Dr. A. E. Bonnell established an office in Muskogee, prepared to offer his services and make "artistic gold fillings." The Eufaula *Indian Journal* of April 4, 1889, includes this announcement: "Call on Bonnell and get your teeth fixed. He will be at Moore's Drugstore on the 9th to remain for a day or two only." Bonnell extended his practice into communities and settlements formerly served by Dr. Seals.

The experiences of Dr. R. C. West, Oklahoma City, typify those of many early-day practitioners in Indian Territory. West apprenticed himself to a dentist in Schuyler, Nebraska, when he was fourteen years old. By the time he was twenty, West was traveling a circuit out of Schuyler through Nebraska and the Dakotas. At the age of twenty-three, thoroughly trained and experienced, he joined Dr. L. S. Lyle in practice at Tishomingo in 1903 and made regular trips to near-by towns of the Chickasaw Nation.

Practice under pioneer conditions was not always a hardship, but was frequently enjoyed by the younger members of the profession. This was expressed by Dr. A. L. Walters, Tulsa, in relating experiences fifty years ago in the Checotah trade area: "After locating in Checotah I went to Texanna each Saturday. . . . I, too, was on call like the physicians and made trips to the farmers and ranchers throughout the area, and once spent a week at the Cicero Davis ranch, taking care of the cowboys. He preferred to pay me to bring my instruments and be a guest, rather than have the men leave the ranch and come to Checotah. A rocking chair, two pillows, a stick of wood under each rocker, a stand for the instruments, and a bucket for cuspidor was the usual equipment, plus my foot engine and instruments.

"I spent the week working, hunting, and enjoying the boys, the rancher, and his family, and shall always treasure it as one of the most enjoyable I have ever known."

Dr. L. M. Doss, Oklahoma City, has recently recalled how he "bushwhacked" in Indian Territory: "In 1898 I was a traveling dentist in Indian Territory. No license was required; I worked as an assistant to Dr. George F. Dean, Shawnee, but made regular trips to Sapulpa, Wetumka, Holdenville, Ada, Sulphur, and other points, staying a day or two at each place, sometimes a week. I had a fine team of horses and a buggy, a folding chair, and a foot engine. I had two complete cases of operating instruments and dental supplies, but depended on Chicago dental laboratories to do my prosthetic work. When I didn't have my folding chair, I would use a rocking chair that would sit on top of a tub—just a big tub—tie the chair on there and it made a pretty good dental chair. I had little circulars printed announcing the dentist was in town, would be there a few days, then I'd go around and hand notices to the businessmen and meet them in person. In those days I did a lot of work for Indians where an interpreter was necessary."

Hope for an assured income led Dr. T. H. Williams to extend his practice beyond Chickasha:

"When I went to Chickasha, Indian Territory, I had as my objective, Fort Sill, Oklahoma Territory, and hoped I might be permitted to practice in Fort Sill for the army as a civilian. That was about ten years before the advent of the commissioned army dentist. Dr. E. L. Wilson, from whom I had purchased the office in Norman, was making professional visits to Fort Sill, at which time pay day was every two months. I made plans to follow him on these visits, and on July 9, 1894, I made my first visit. My visits there were very pleasant and profitable. My practice increased to such an extent that I was obliged to make Fort Sill my headquarters.

"Fort Sill was a real beautiful post located in the Kiowa-Comanche Reservation, at the foot of the Wichita Mountains. The fort was a small army post; four companies of infantry and two troops of cavalry.

"The pay day before I went to Fort Sill, there were four dentists endeavoring to get permission to practice there. Dr. Wilson, whom I had succeeded at Norman, was the only one doing any practice. When I went into Fort Sill on July 9, 1894, I was the only dentist present. Colonel Smith, the commanding officer, granted me permission to practice. It developed to be a very satisfactory practice.

"In the gay nineties we had a panic or depression, and money was not very plentiful except at Fort Sill. The government, in providing medical service for the army, also provided veterinary service for the horses and mules, but neglected dental service for the army. This seemed to be a very strange arrangement to me.

"In October, 1895, the troops were ordered out for field service, and the camp was located on Cobb Creek, and I elected to go also. I secured a tent; got a road wagon to transport my equipment, and soon was on the camp site, and after a few hours ready for practice. The location of the camp on Cobb Creek was near the town of Colony, and I was in camp two weeks."

— 2 —

BEGINNING in 1891 dentists practicing in Oklahoma Territory were subject to the licensing provisions of a law passed by the Territorial Legislature. The Congressional act of May 2, 1890, provided for the government of Oklahoma Territory, including the right of local choice of a bicameral legislature. The first law-making body, composed of twenty-six members of the House and thirteen members of the Council, convened at Guthrie on August 27, 1890. On the afternoon of the fourth legislative day, Governor George W. Steele delivered before a joint session of the House and Council his message relating to territorial conditions and legislative needs. Even though much time was consumed during the legislative session in considering a permanent location for the territorial capitol, no other legislature has enacted as many laws. By provisions of a bill introduced in the Council, entire chapters of the laws of other states were adopted and enacted without any attempt to consider provisions section by section. Thus was adopted the entire criminal code and criminal procedures from the laws of Dakota, much of the civil code was copied from statutes of Indiana, and laws relating to county organizations were adopted directly from Kansas statutes. Because the Dakota code had been originally written for New York, territorial newspapermen later made merry with those provisions relating to mutiny on shipboard and other problems of navigation!

The legislature completed its six-day-week program at noon, December 24. It enacted special legislation relating to public schools and roads, located territorial institutions, provided for the care and custody of persons convicted of crime, and regulated the liquor traffic. Provision was made, too, for licensing professional groups.

Ethical dentists of the Territory were particularly interested in legislation to regulate the profession. Dr. G. F. Dean, Oklahoma City, and Dr. D. A. Peoples, Guthrie, were selected to draw up proposed legislation.[4] Judge J. L. Brown, Republican member of the Council from Oklahoma County, who had introduced Council Bill No. 7 to locate the capitol at Oklahoma City—the most controversial issue of the session—on November 11 introduced "an Act to regulate the practice of dentistry in Oklahoma Territory." The bill was read the second time and referred to a special committee, whose members were Judge Brown, Charles Brown, Guthrie, and Dr. J. W. Howard, physician-druggist, Edmond. The committee made one minor revision and corrected one obvious oversight in the bill: to be automatically licensed under the proposed law, a dentist, unless he held a diploma from a recognized college of dentistry, must have been practicing three years before passage of the act; no provision for the length of term of the proposed Board of Dental Examiners was provided.

On Thursday morning, November 13, the committee report was adopted, and that afternoon the bill passed by a vote of eleven to none. Two members of the Council were absent. The measure, Council Bill 66, was then referred to the House of Representatives. Because adjournment of the legislature was set for twelve o'clock noon, Christmas Eve, it appeared to the dentists that the measure might perish from legislative delay. Through their influence the House placed it on the calendar for consideration Monday, December 22. After a second reading, Dan H. Peery, member from Oklahoma County, moved to amend line 8, section 8 of the bill. The House approved his amendment, which consisted of adding the phrase "or other persons" to make the sentence read: "Provided, nothing in this act shall be so construed as to prevent physicians and surgeons or other persons from extracting teeth."

[4] Dean and Peoples, if not the first, were among the first dentists to establish practice in Oklahoma Territory. G. F. Dean is credited by an early writer as the first dentist to locate in Oklahoma City. "His elaborate dental parlors," set up within a month of the Run, "are supplied with all the instruments and appliances of the dental profession." See *The First Eight Months of Oklahoma City*, by Bunky (Oklahoma City, McMaster Printing Company, 1890). "Bunky's" real name was Irwin Jeffs.

D. A. Peoples arrived in Guthrie via train from Arkansas City, April 22, 1889, and obtained a town lot. W. T. Little, editor of the *Guthrie Getup*, the first paper published in the Oklahoma country, sold the press to Peoples, who published the paper during the summer and fall of 1889. See Carolyn Thomas Foreman, *Oklahoma Imprints*, (Norman, University of Oklahoma Press, 1936), 324.

Both dentists were college graduates with more than ten years' dental practice.

That afternoon the House took the bill under consideration in Committee of the Whole. Arthur N. Daniels, speaker of the House and representative from Canadian County, moved that the bill be considered section by section. A movement to amend section 1 was defeated; under section 2, which provided in the qualifications for members of the proposed Board of Dental Examiners that they have at least three years' experience as practicing dentists, the House approved an amendment reducing this time to two years. Further reading of the measure by section was dispensed with and the bill passed by a vote of fifteen to six. Governor George W. Steele signed the measure the following day.

Weak as this act proved to be, it was nevertheless an important milestone in the history of Oklahoma dentistry. Pharmacy and dentistry were the only professions for which laws regulating practice and licensing were passed by the first legislature. This is more remarkable when it is recalled that not until after statehood, in 1908, did a law appear on the statute books for the regulation and licensing of physicians.

The dental law, which remained in effect until June 1, 1905, was too mild and general in nature, and lacked enforcement provisions against unethical practitioners. A Board of Dental Examiners, consisting of five practicing dentists or dental surgeons, was to be appointed by the territorial governor. Any dentist who had practiced in the Territory before September 22, 1890, with three years' experience and any person who had a diploma from a dental college and was practicing before September 22 could obtain a license from the Board by the payment of a three-dollar fee and registering within six months after the passage of the act. Dentists who did not meet the qualifications were required to pay a fee of ten dollars in order to be licensed. If the applicant held a diploma, it was made a matter of record; if not, the applicant was subject to examination by the Board. Temporary certificates to practice could be issued by the Board until official examinations were given. The Board was to meet at least once a year, primarily to conduct examinations, check the validity of credentials submitted by applicants, and bring up to date the roster of registered dentists.

The first Territorial Board of Dental Examiners met May 5, 1891, in the office of Dr. Peoples, 201 Oklahoma Avenue, Guthrie.[5]

[5] "Official Proceedings of the Oklahoma Board of Dental Examiners, 1891–1919,"

It organized with Dr. Dean, Oklahoma City, president; Dr. Peoples, secretary; and Dr. J. S. Nicholson, El Reno, treasurer. The Board then crossed the street and climbed steps to the office of Governor Steele, who informed them other members would be appointed directly.

Members of the profession met the following day in Guthrie to organize the Oklahoma Dental Association.[6] Those present at this epochal meeting, in addition to the three members of the Board of Dental Examiners, were W. E. Furrow and J. B. Calmes, Guthrie; W. R. Sheldon, Edmond; and M. L. McConn, Purcell, Chickasaw Nation. They pledged themselves to work in harmony with the Board in developing standards of conduct and practice.

Under the territorial administrative body, so far as the laxity of Council Bill 66 permitted, the dental profession began that long upward surge to better its condition, to raise moral and ethical standards, and to build a firm foundation of professional growth. Each member of the Dental Association, governed only by his limited means, assumed a share of responsibility to its principles by applying them to official administrative duties or private practice. Members of a comparatively new profession, they and their successors were deeply zealous that every step the Association made

on file in the office of the secretary-treasurer of the Board of Governors of the Registered Dentists of Oklahoma, Dr. Robert P. Keidel, Muskogee. This volume contains the typewritten and handwritten official minutes of the Board prepared by the incumbent secretary, countersigned by the president, from the first meeting, May 5, 1891, to December 22, 1919. Included with the minutes are rosters of applicants, copies of examination questions and grades by subjects made by applicants, names of those who successfully qualified for licensing, reciprocity agreements with other states, correspondence with the National Association of Dental Examiners, disciplinary action against members, and other matters pertinent to the actions of the administrative agency. The dental profession is particularly grateful for action taken by Dr. W. E. Cole, Oklahoma City, member of the Board of Governors, who in 1954 had the volume rebound and the contents microfilmed. The minutes are the principal source used by the author for information pertaining to Board activities while it was a territorial agency and from statehood to 1920.

[6] D. A. Peoples to R. L. Pearson & Co., July 6, 1891, in the *Western Dental Journal*, Vol. V (1891), 322–26. The *Western Dental Journal* was a trade publication issued quarterly at Kansas City, Missouri, Vols. I–XXXI for the years 1887–1918. R. L. Pearson & Company were publishers, 1887–96; Pearson-Allendorph Mfg. Co., 1896–98; Hettinger Bros. Mfg. Co., 1898–1918. Until 1929 the company issued it as *Hettinger's Dental News*; after 1928, *The Dental News*. Dr. J. D. Patterson was editor 1887–1907; Drs. F. O. Hetrick, J. R. Root, and F. G. Worthley, 1907–13; Dr. Charles Channing Allen, 1913–18; after 1918, Dr. Hubbard B. Whiting.

be upward, that the taint of quackery and charlatanism be removed from associate members, and that every action taken be in the public's interest.

The Board held its second meeting in Oklahoma City on June 10. W. M. Janney, Stillwater, presented his commission from Governor Steele and joined the other members in the official proceedings. Only Jefferson Ellard and Elbert Ellard, Norman, applied for examination; both were successful.

It was at this meeting that the Board passed upon applications and granted licenses for the practice of dentistry, thus inaugurating regulatory and supervisory control over the profession—controls for the protection of the public and the profession that have continued uninterruptedly and become stronger through the years by increased ethical standards and attitudes.

Licenses were granted as follows:

Number	Name	Location
1	G. F. Dean	Oklahoma City
2	D. A. Peoples	Guthrie
3	J. S. Nicholson	El Reno
4	W. M. Janney	Stillwater
5	J. B. Calmes	Guthrie
6	J. D. Russell	Beaver City
7	Jefferson Ellard	Norman
8	Elbert Ellard	Norman
9	J. G. McCathron	Guthrie
10	D. D. Slocum	Guthrie

The last two licenses were conditioned upon satisfactory corroborating affidavits from the dentists that they were practicing in the Territory at least three months before the dental act took effect.

The Board held its third meeting at Guthrie, June 25, and licenses were issued six applicants, including one woman: W. R. Sheldon, Edmond; A. L. Nicholson, El Reno; Laura F. Davis, Oklahoma City; Henry Davis, Oklahoma City; W. E. Furrow, Guthrie; and A. E. Adams, Norman.

How the Board was evolving administrative procedure in a new area of regulatory commission is recorded in the minutes:

"C. M. Woods made application, accompanied by fee of ten

dollars but not having been in Territory three months previous to passage of Act, as required by same, it was necessary to examine him, and not being present, the examination was passed for present.

"A. A. Scribner made application, accompanied by check for three dollars but it appearing to satisfaction of Board that there existed good grounds for doubt regarding the three month clause, and money tendered being in form of private check, the secretary was instructed to return check to him and demand proof of him being established in business in Territory three months previous to passage of Act, and inform him the Board would not receive personal checks in payment of fees.

"On motion, the secretary was given power to hold examinations of such as might present themselves, mark the papers and forward same to Dr. Dean, who was to mark and forward to Dr. Nicholson, who was to return them to secretary after he had examined and marked the same, whereupon secretary was to issue or refuse license determined by grade and vote of members of Board. Also to issue license to those who filed their diplomas or a duly authenticated copy of same with him upon the payment of fees."

At the first meeting in 1892 the Board decided to issue temporary licenses to graduates of reputable dental colleges who made application after sessions were adjourned. A fee of twenty dollars was established for interim examinations and fifteen dollars for examinations while the Board was in session. The office of the attorney general issued an opinion in 1894, however, that the Board was not authorized to charge for examining applicants for licenses; that a charge could be made only for each license issued, as set forth in the act of 1890. According to this ruling, any applicant previously charged an examination fee could demand a refund from the Board.

Board finances, solely dependent upon license fees, remained in distressed condition throughout the territorial period. Each member supposedly received three dollars a day and expenses for attending meetings held in a member's office or public building. Ledgers, stationery, stamps, application blanks, license forms, and other supplies were purchased from fees received; rarely were sufficient funds on hand to reimburse the members. Typical of the financial straits is the entry in the minutes for the regular session of May 2, 1894, held in the rooms of Professor E. L. Hallock, superintendent of schools, Oklahoma City:

"The expense and per diem accounts of each member were allowed, and the secretary instructed to pay out what moneys were in hand pro rata on back accounts of members against the Board and also pay pro rata what might be received by him during the year until back accounts should be paid in full."

Dr. Levi L. Miles, Kingfisher, appointed by Governor A. J. Seay, attended the session of the Board held May 4, 1892, and for the first time it had its full complement of membership. At this meeting the Board made application for admission to the National Association of Dental Examiners; Dr. Peoples attended the national meeting at Niagara Falls in August. Membership afforded the Board up-to-date ideas and methods on procedures and examinations in effect throughout the country.

It was customary to hold board sessions at the same time the Oklahoma Dental Association met; in many instances the five board members almost constituted a majority of dentists in attendance at the annual convention. By May, 1896, there were forty-three registered dentists in the Territory, thirteen of whom attended the annual meeting. Dentists in attendance were: J. B. Gillespie, Woodward; G. A. Hughes, W. E. Furrow, and D. A. Peoples, Guthrie; A. M. Detrick, W. L. Maupin, and E. E. Kirkpatrick, Oklahoma City; Fred C. Seids and B. H. Seaton, Perry; M. L. McConn and G. F. Dean, Shawnee; J. B. Calmes, Tecumseh, and Jefferson Ellard, Norman.

The roster of dentists in attendance, especially their location, reveals an interesting phenomenon in the expanding territory. Successive openings expanded the Territory to the Texas and Kansas borders, towns were established, and to the newly created county seats moved leaders of the profession from the original territory, seeking new fields of service, ready to face the challenge of establishing a practice and becoming a part of the growth of the community.

Thus, M. L. McConn, early territorial practitioner at Purcell and Lexington, transferred to Shawnee after the Choctaw, Oklahoma and Gulf Railway won the right to by-pass Tecumseh for the new settlement. To Shawnee came G. F. Dean, who had opened the first dental office in Oklahoma City, attracted by new opportunities and the fact that railroad shops were to be established there. Calmes had moved from Guthrie to Tecumseh when the lands of the Shawnee, Potawatomi, and associated tribes were opened to settlement and that town was designated a county seat. A. E. Adams, brilliant leader in the profession, moved from Norman to Ardmore in the Chickasaw Nation, where he was to assume leadership in the Indian Territorial Association and, later, the State Association. Some, not so successful in practice, were continually on the move toward newer communities; records disclose one individual who practiced in Alva, Okarche, Pawhuska, Guymon, and Fairfax within a period of ten years. Others, like R. O. Hirschi, Guthrie, and T. H. Williams, Chickasha, were to register for the land lottery at El Reno and Fort Sill, in July, 1901, then return to their home towns for years of uninterrupted service.

At the meeting held at the Thomson House, Oklahoma City, May 5–6, 1896, Dr. Furrow talked on metal, crown, and bridge work, Dr. McConn on odontology, Dr. Hughes on the use of salol in filling roots, and Dr. Peoples on porcelain, crown, and bridge work. After officials of the Association were elected, the Territorial Board of Dental Examiners met at the Grand Avenue Hotel. Licenses were issued to Fred C. Seids, Perry, and Clinton T. Hart, Newkirk. The Board members had forwarded their resignations to Governor William C. Renfrow, but at this time no action had been taken by him. They had resigned because the dental act of 1890 had been engrossed and printed without any provision for the tenure in office of members of the Board, although the original bill drawn by Dr. Dean and Dr. Peoples had provided that members should serve for a term of five years.

Changes in the national administration at Washington in 1897 caused changes in territorial governmental personnel at Guthrie. The new governor, C. M. Barnes, appointed to the Board of Dental Examiners, Drs. J. Q. Waddell, Kingfisher; L. A. Kelsey, Chandler; W. E. Furrow and D. A. Peoples, Guthrie; and E. E. Kirkpatrick, Oklahoma City.

Subjects were assigned Board members, for the examination of applicants, as follows:

W. E. Furrow: Nitrous Oxide Anaesthesia, Metallurgy, Chemistry, Anatomy.
D. A. Peoples: Pathology, Therapeutics, Prosthetic Dentistry.
L. A. Kelsey: Oral Deformities, Crown and Bridge Work.

Buckboard Dentistry at the Turn of the Century
Dr. F. C. Holmes, of Mangum, setting out to see his patients. Dr.
Holmes would travel from dugout to dugout, staying with each patient
until his work was completed.

Army Dentistry in Oklahoma Territory, 1895
With the Tenth U. S. Infantry from Fort Sill on autumn maneuvers near Colony.

Courtesy Dr. T. H. Williams

J. Q. Waddell: Physiology, Materia Medica, Oral Surgery.
E. E. Kirkpatrick: Operative Dentistry, Dental Science, Dental
  Technique, Histology.

This board re-established the principle of charging applicants
an examination fee, although it was contrary to the ruling made by
the Attorney General's Office in 1894. The fee was ten dollars, the
amount established in the dental law for a license issued on
examination.

The Board, too, in conjunction with members of the Association, made a determined effort to enforce provisions of the dental
law. From information furnished by members of the Association
and from other sources, the Board secretary, E. E. Kirkpatrick,
was kept busy ferreting out violators and preferring court action.
Official minutes for a month-long period in 1901 reveal details of
his activity: April 1, to Norman; April 4, to Edmond; April 30,
to Pottawatomie County; May 1, to Okarche; May 3, to Stillwater to appear in court and present evidence against non-licensed
dentists.

Typical entries in the minutes show that the Board and Association, although intensely zealous in raising professional standards,
dealt as mercifully as possible with fellow-practitioners. Samples
from the minutes, printed below, graphically portray conflicts between duty and justice:

"February 4th, 1898 Dr. ———— who had been arrested for
practicing dentistry without a license by Dr. Ellard of Norman
required my attention. Believing chances for conviction unfavorable, I offered the defendant to dismiss the case if he would pay
all costs and agree not to violate the law anymore. He agreed. The
case cost the defendant for his attorney and costs of case about
$45.00; did not get exact figures.

"Expenses in the case:

One telegram to Norman, Kirkpatrick to J. Ellard	$ .25
Railway fare to Norman and return	1.05
Hotel bill and expense	1.25
Express, on record from Norman	.25
One days time spent on case	3.00

"February 22nd. [The dentist mentioned above] of Norman, O. T. took an examination after making application for license. Applicant failed to make 60 per cent in each branch, and failed.

"Received $10.00 for same $ 10.00

"September 12th. On information I had one Dr. ——— of Newkirk arrested for violating the Dental law. He gave bond and came to Oklahoma City for license, after taking two branches he gave up and asked for a part of his fee of $10.00 back. I returned the fee in full as he was not able to lose so much."

— 3 —

IN ITS annual report to Governor Barnes, December 15, 1897, the Board of Dental Examiners referred to a condition existing in Greer County. This area of some 1,370,000 acres lying between the North and South Forks of the Red River and the hundredth meridian had been settled by veterans of the Texan war for independence on the basis of land-scrip issued to them. In 1860 Greer County was formed as part of Texas, but the claim of that state to the area was disputed by the federal government. When Congress created the Territory of Oklahoma on May 2, 1890, one provision of the act related to the legal determination of the conflicting claims to Greer County. Much to the bitter disappointment of Texas, on March 16, 1896, the United States Supreme Court declared this area a part of Oklahoma, and on January 18 of the succeeding year a land district was established to open unoccupied lands to settlement. With some regard to the current feelings of many Texans who resented the court decision, the secretary stated for the Board: "There are now several dentists in Greer County who are registered in Texas, but not yet registered in Oklahoma Territory and we can easily understand how they look at this matter, but as they are all first class men, I trust we will have matters rightly adjusted satisfactory to them and all interested in the future."

The late Dr. F. C. Holmes of Mangum recorded his impressions of this part of Oklahoma as it appeared on his arrival in 1899.

His reminiscences present a professional man's view of conditions under which dental practice was undertaken far from cities, without adequate professional equipment.

Holmes left Galveston to join two physician friends, Dr. J. C. Baker and Dr. DeWitt Stone, who had come to the Territory. His destination was Wood, now Port, in Washita County.

"After spending the night in Chickasha, I took the Rock Island branch westward to Mountain View, then the terminus. I met Dr. Al Nicholson of El Reno on the train, who seeing my traveling outfit, introduced himself. He was with a party of men who were booming the new town of Mountain View, and had city lots for sale. As we crossed the Washita river on a temporary bridge, we all stood on the back platform of the coach for fear the bridge would give way, and let us down into the swollen stream, which was on a big rise. Arriving at Mountain View, and finding no one to meet me at the new city of tents, I sought out a tent marked 'Restaurant,' had some lunch, and then noticed another tent marked 'Livery Stable,' where I hired a lumber wagon and team with a cow-puncher for a driver and started on my journey westward to Wood, where my medical friends had located. I was surprised to find no established roads, but the driver informed me that he knew where Wood was, and we struck out over prairie trails and through the big ranch pastures forty-five miles north and west. Occasionally we would pass a pile of fresh dirt and upon asking what it meant, the driver would inform me that it was a dugout, where a new citizen had established his home on a claim, to battle with the vicissitudes of a new country and help to establish the commonwealth that we live in today with all the modern conveniences which we enjoy.

"During the afternoon we came to a little rock store and post-office, called Rockey, where the town of Rocky now stands. Upon asking how a store could exist without any town to support it and no human being in sight for miles around, I was informed that the little store often sold several hundred dollars worth of supplies to ranch men and travelers in a single day. After driving all afternoon and not seeing a soul until we met the store keeper at Rockey, I was beginning to wonder where I should find the people who could support a new dentist and where I should find a place to work, if they should need my services.

"About sundown, we arrived at the home of a German homesteader, who was living in a half dugout; a structure dug down in the ground about four feet, with sod walls built up around the edges to support the roof. Here one of my medical friends, Dr. Stone, boarded. After calming down several large fierce looking dogs, which were used to drive up the cattle and as a protection against wolves, we were admitted and enjoyed the hospitality of our host for the night in his, to me, very strange abode.

"The next morning, Dr. Stone, noticing my disappointment at the scarcity of towns and people, suggested that we drive over to Wood, which he intimated was quite a flourishing community.

"Wood consisted of a general store, a post office and a blacksmith shop, a church, schoolhouse and half a dozen residences. These evidences of urban progress did not lessen my disappointment to any great extent. But later when a saloon and a bank moved in, Wood began to assume metropolitan airs. I remember the local undertaker, a tall rawboned Arkansawer, who went barefoot all summer. His place of business was an unpainted board shanty about ten feet square, with a sign painted over the door, 'Cold Drinks and Coffins'; quite a combination of wares it seemed to me. He could refresh the weary wayfarer on his journey, and help put him away at its end. This good citizen seemed to have some very pronounced views on matters educational. He threatened to take his boy out of school if the teacher insisted on his spelling taters with a 'p'. . . .

"One day while working for a family, who lived in a half dugout and kept the postoffice in a little community near where Sentinel now stands, I was summoned by a man, who rode up on horseback, to come over to Head Quarter Mountain, a point several miles northwest of the present town of Granite, to see a man with a broken jaw. Upon finishing my work for the postmaster's family, I packed up my outfit and proceeded to Head Quarter Mountain about twenty miles westward. I found my patient and his wife living in a little one room rock house which some sympathetic and hospitable neighbor had donated for the duration of his illness.

"He, his wife, his son-in-law and daughter were traveling from Texas up into northwest Oklahoma, where they had filed on homesteads. And engaging in a fight over some disagreement, the son-in-law struck the old man with his fist on the jaw, fracturing it

24

through the lower right cuspid socket downward and backward. A local physician had treated him for three weeks without much success, and learning of my presence in the land, he called me.

"My patient was a tall spare elderly man. A preacher, I was told, who talked with a hypocritical whine, as he told me his troubles, trying to exonerate himself from blame in the affair. My antipathy steadily increased as he talked until I was convinced that the son-in-law might have been justified even in the use of brass knucks as was claimed.

"Realizing my obligation to humanity and casting aside my repugnance, I started to make him a splint, according to the approved methods of that day. His jaw was badly swollen and painful. A cartilaginous union seemed to be taking place. The ends of the fracture were not in apposition. The cuspid in the line of fracture and one bicuspid had to be removed as they had been loosened by the impact. I had him bite into some softened compound, holding the ends of the fracture in their proper relation as near as I could judge. Reproduced the compound in rubber, leaving an opening in front for the intake of liquid food, placed the splint with depressions for the upper and lower teeth, in place, and finally a bandage fastened with a buckle cut from my vest to fasten it firmly on top of his head.

"I was about three days making the splint, during which time I partook of the food that kind neighbors sent in to the stricken family. The house having only one room and devoid of furniture, I slept in the yard, the weather being mild, on some bundles of fodder that had been brought along to feed his team. . . . The old man had informed me at the start that he had only enough money to enable him to finish his journey, but would pay me some day, if he lived. My fee was to be $25.00, the price of a set of teeth at that time.

"After I had been in Mangum about a year, one of his neighbors, a lawyer, possibly with the idea of a fee in his mind, sent me word that the fracture had healed as a result of wearing my appliance and suggested that I send him a bill. I did. He sent me $10.00, all that he ever paid me for my trouble. But to show, in his way, some appreciation for my efforts he sent his wife down to Mangum to have a set of teeth made, for which he paid me. . . ."[7]

[7] F. C. Holmes, "Reminiscences of an Early Dental Practitioner in Western Okla-

— 4 —

IN THOSE depression-ridden years when money was scarce, Populism flourished, and a series of crop failures brought hard times and disappointment to the people of the Territory, it is little wonder that a new Board would question meager expenditures passed upon by the outgoing Board, particularly since it represented changes in political administration. "The old Board," so it was reported to Governor Barnes, "conceived of an idea by which they could liquidate its indebtedness by drawing orders on the treasurer of that and succeeding Boards. One of these warrants is causing its owner a great deal of anxiety, evidenced at present by very numerous letters urging his alleged claim. If the records of the old Board can be relied upon, the money expended for stamps alone would go a long way toward buying up these warrants. The warrants with the interest, would amount to about $140.00 and as they held but ten meetings, one who did not understand would naturally ask, what did they do with the money? The expenditure of the money does not show so much extravagance as the carelessness in the appropriation thereof. The records of the Board show they have not one dollar due them."

Principal target in the weak law administered by territorial Boards was that provision for the automatic granting of a license to any applicant who presented a college diploma. When the Board of Dental Examiners met at Kingfisher May 3–5, 1898, only eleven applicants appeared because of heavy rains that delayed train schedules and made other types of travel impossible. The secretary reported: "Most applicants hold certificates from dental colleges which are very numerous in this country. Many of the colleges are nothing more than large dental offices owned and controlled by a few resident dentists who, for a consideration, after a prescribed time, issue certificates which the law of the Territory recognizes.

homa," in the *Bulletin of the Oklahoma State Dental Society*, Vol. XXIX (October, 1940), 43–46, and (January, 1941), 90–92. The *Bulletin*, official publication of the Oklahoma State Dental Association, 1911–51, when the name was changed to the *Journal*, has been issued quarterly and is the principal source of news pertaining to activities of the Association and its members. In former years it was published in the home town of the current secretary-editor; with the establishment of the Central Office, Oklahoma City, in 1947, it has been published at that place.

"We have been asked to register diplomas from reputable colleges when the applicant is under 21 years of age, and at another time when the holder of a license had been in attendance only three weeks but had paid $100 to the college and received a certificate for full attendance."

Two years later sixty-six applicants appeared before the Board, most of whom failed to receive licenses. The secretary reported many of the applicants apparently did not possess a common school education "making it impracticable to study and practice a science." It was his belief that many of the proprietary colleges were in business merely for fees received from enrollees, and had little regard for technical and scientific training. "The word 'Dental College,' " he wrote in the annual report, "should be stricken from our law and we be permitted to examine every applicant."

Although many of the early-day proprietary dental colleges merited the criticism levelled by the Board, two distinguished colleges of outstanding merit established in near-by Kansas City graduated students thoroughly trained in the profession.[8]

The Kansas City Dental College was originally established in 1881 as the dental department of the Kansas City Medical College, but in 1891 it was reorganized as an independent school. Originally the length of the course offered in dentistry was two years, as it was in all similar schools accredited by the National Association of College Faculties. Requirements for entrance were no more than a good English education: this was a period when many young men "read law" in a practicing attorney's office in order to meet bar qualifications, or "studied medicine" with a practicing physician on the way toward an M.D. degree, or undertook a preceptorship with a dentist in order to master that profession. Stricter, more stringent qualifications for matriculation in professional schools were still some years distant. At this time, the Kansas City Dental College would permit an applicant who possessed a medical diploma to substitute it for one course in dentistry. The faculty established rigid requirements for graduation. President John D. Patterson, Dean Charles Channing Allen, and other faculty members appeared on many programs of the territorial and, later, the state association meetings.

[8] Joseph F. Jacobs, *History of the University of Kansas City School of Dentistry* (Kansas City, 1949), 10–28.

The Western Dental College in Kansas City was established by Dr. Drury J. McMillen in 1890. In its second announcement published in 1891 appears this statement: "The successful work of the past year fully confirms the position then taken by the college—that its faculty should be composed of practical men, who are able and willing to go with the student from the lecture room into the infirmary and instruct with their hands in that which they have taught from their chairs." Students were given intense, practical training in oral surgery, prosthetic and operative dentistry, dental pathology, therapeutics and metallurgy, and other related courses that met national standards. It was the first college to advocate the carving of bone teeth to be used in the teaching of dental anatomy and for the purpose of preparing cavities for students to insert fillings as requirements for classwork in operative technique. Dr. McMillen and other faculty members, which at a later period included Dr. W. J. Brady, Dr. Hugh Tanzey, and Dr. R. J. Rinehart, often appeared on programs for meetings of the Oklahoma Dental Association. In 1891, in keeping with standards set by the National Association of College Faculties, professional training at both Kansas City colleges was increased to three years' time.

— 5 —

THE EIGHTH annual meeting of the Oklahoma Dental Association was held at Oklahoma City, October 10–11, 1898, dates set for the free street fair which attracted exhibitors and record-breaking crowds. Railroads granted reduced rates of a fare and a third, but inclement weather on the opening day caused a disappointing attendance at sessions held in parlors of the Grand Avenue Hotel.

At this time there were seven practicing dentists in Oklahoma City.[9] Six had offices upstairs in the 100 block on West Main while the second woman licensed to practice in the territory, Miss Irene Yoakum, had recently opened an office at 15½ North Robinson.

[9] See *A Complete General and Business Directory* of Oklahoma City for 1898, compiled by John W. Nicely (Oklahoma City, 1898). Minutes of the Board of Dental Examiners, for October 15, 1898, refer to the street fair; news columns in reference to the fair appear in issues of the *Daily Oklahoman*, October 2–October 16, 1898. The anecdote credited to T. H. Williams was related by him in the course of a recorded interview, in July, 1953; the one credited to J. Q. Waddell appeared in the sixtieth anniversary edition of the Kingfisher *Free Press*, April 18, 1949.

Within one and one-half blocks of the corner of Main Street and Broadway there were eleven saloons. The Hub, 108 West Main, was the principal store for men and boys, while the Lion Store, at the corner of Main and Robinson, was the largest department store in the Territory. The brick two-story Grand Avenue Hotel, with 100 guest rooms, first built in 1890 and added to several times, offered guest accommodations for seventy-five cents a night; the Choctaw Hotel and Restaurant, 28 First Street near the Choctaw Depot, served meals for fifteen cents and offered lodging for fifteen and twenty-five cents; the McGregor Hotel, near the Choctaw, had a ladies' parlor on the ground floor, and the Pickwick Café advertised as the only first-class restaurant in the city: "We keep our own cows and furnish you the freshest of sweet milk and buttermilk. All vegetables come from our farm fresh every morning." W. T. Hales, dealer in horses and mules, ran the livery barn and stables on East Main near the Santa Fe tracks.

Papers carried a news item that Judge Hosea Townsend had sentenced Al Jennings for his part in the robbery of a Rock Island train near Chickasha the previous October. The express car had been wrecked and $7,000 taken from the way safe, but the through safe which had in it $90,000 "grass money" for the Indians at Anadarko, though cracked, could not be opened. Some 300 passengers were then robbed.

The newspaper account of the robbery might well have prompted Dr. T. H. Williams to relate the following to members of the Association: "At that time I was making a professional trip to Minco; I had finished operations for all patients presented, and was packing up to take the first train to Chickasha when a patient came in from the Half-Moon Ranch who especially desired service. I made an examination and found it would take an additional day to complete the necessary operations. Staying over proved a great blessing to me; if I had left on the train as first planned I would have been on the train which Al Jennings and his gang held up at Siding Number One. They failed to blow the safe, then proceeded to march the passengers out of the cars and required them to surrender money and valuables. I was lucky to have missed the hold-up; money was at a premium, and it saved me my nerves and financial embarrassment."

And, perhaps at this meeting, J. Q. Waddell, president of the Oklahoma Territorial Board of Dental Examiners, told his associates the following story related years later by his daughter, Mary Waddell Jeffery: "My father's favorite story of early Kingfisher was the one concerning his attempt to disarm one of the notorious Dalton boys. Father had opened an office in Kingfisher and had used all his available funds to buy a chair and necessary instruments. His office was over a saloon and one day he was sitting in his office wishing someone would feel the urge to have some sort of dental work done. About that time the saloonkeeper brought a nice-looking man in and the prospective patient showed the aching molar to father and asked if he would get it out quick. Father did not notice a six-shooter in a holster until the man was seated. As was his custom, father asked him to remove the gun, having learned that under stress and strain a man and a gun might prove a bad combination. The man said, 'Doc, I never take this gun off and I am never careless with it,' so father pulled the offending tooth and told the patient that was all while breathing a silent prayer he would get the usual fee of $1.00. The man got up from the chair and said, 'Well, maybe I can keep my mind on my work now, how much do I owe you, Doc?' My father replied, 'Stranger, whatever it's worth to you.' At that, the stranger began pitching silver dollars to father until he had $10 and then asked if that would pay for the job. My father was so overcome he could hardly thank him, but remembered in time to ask him his name. 'I've paid you, the tooth's out, and the name doesn't matter and we're all square' was the reply as the stranger walked out the door. Later in the day the saloonkeeper came back to the office and asked father how he liked his friend, to which query father replied he wished the entire community was settled by men like him, and also inquired as to the name of the unidentified gentleman.

" 'Feller by the name of Dalton,' the saloonkeeper replied. Father then realized his patient was a man on whose head there was at that time a price, and father always said his attempt to disarm a Dalton was about on the par with some attempts made by others to do the same thing."

Dentists of the Territory had planned well in setting dates for the annual convention at the time of the street fair. Wide publicity, careful planning by civic leaders, a good crop yield, and business prosperity made the fair one of the most enthusiastic events of the decade. Several days before the opening, pupils of Washington and Emerson schools began marching and drilling in competition for a library of books to be awarded for the best performance in the parade; dogs were scrubbed and preened for the bench show; equestriennes were seen riding on side-saddles along country roads, getting ready to compete for a fine riding habit to be given the most graceful and skillful rider. Prizes aggregating fifty dollars were to be awarded the champion lady bicycle rider; seventy dollars would go to the gentleman.

The October 4 issue of the *Daily Oklahoman* announced: "One day at the fair a tramp convention and parade will be held at which bums from all over the country will be present. Mr. George Barnett, who has an extensive acquaintance among this class, is marking gates that are good for handouts."

Heavy rains Sunday night, October 9, turned streets into quagmires, and many booths moved into the lobby of the Grand Avenue Hotel and store fronts in the block between Robinson and Broadway on the avenue. Despite muddy streets and lowering weather in the forenoon, throngs of the curious beat a path to the exhibits the next day. During the afternoon, from elevated platforms at street intersections of Grand Avenue with Broadway and Robinson, and at Main and Broadway, there was vaudeville entertainment consisting of song and dance artists, contortionists, and blackface comedy. Three band concerts were given at a stand erected in front of the Grand Avenue Hotel. But the principal attraction on opening day took place at 3:30 P.M. at the near-by intersection of Grand and Robinson. Professor Baum and his wife gave an exhibition of riding a bicycle on a tight wire stretched between two three-story buildings opposite the intersection. "It was a daring and skillful performance and attracted a multitude."

Tuesday was warm and bright; performances of the day before were repeated. Concerts were given all day long in front of the hotel and at the intersection of Main and Broadway where thousands gathered to see Ida LeRoy's balloon ascension: "At 4:30 P.M. the big balloon shot upwards. At a height of 2,000 feet the female aeronaut dropped in her parachute. She landed safely in a peach tree on West Main Street."

And on West Main was held the hog show, while booths in

the Grand Avenue and Main Street area, and on Broadway and Robinson between these limits, held 123 exhibits of fruit, 129 of grain, 32 of vegetables, 50 of cotton, and 62 of poultry. All week the street fair continued and attracted thousands, including Governor Barnes and staff from Guthrie, as well as trainloads of excursionists from the twin territories. Victor Murdock of the *Wichita Eagle* reported there were too many in attendance to estimate; C. G. Jones placed daily attendance from 10,000 to 20,000.

This was a tribute to business and farm recovery, a promise of territorial growth and prosperity. The fresh newness of the land, the generous vision for new opportunity and life, land openings peopled by restless, ambitious Americans, the tremendous bustle in a land of fabulous possibilities—the vitality of it all made growth inevitable. The census of 1890 listed a population of 61,834 for Oklahoma Territory; township appraisers in 1896 raised this number to 275,587; in 1898, to 311,400; and the official census of 1900 listed 398,331. The special census to be made at statehood was to list a combined population of Oklahoma Territory and Indian Territory which exceeded that listed for twenty states of the Union in the official census of 1900.

Although members of the Association took time to visit booths, to enjoy the band concerts, and to watch the balloon ascension, they gave serious consideration to inadequacies of the dental act of 1890. Deletion was approved of the provision that persons other than dentists and physicians could extract teeth. Stricter penalties against violators of the act and the right to charge for examinations also won approval.

After the legislature convened in 1899, House Bill 212 was prepared incorporating these suggestions. Not until March 4, however, was the bill introduced by T. H. Doyle, member of the House of Representatives from Perry. The measure was referred to the Sifting Committee two days later and was recommended for passage in Committee of the Whole on March 10. Action came too late. The legislature adjourned *sine die* before further consideration.

Two years later a similar attempt was made to enact a better law. House Bill 205 was introduced by C. G. Jones, Oklahoma City, on the thirty-eighth legislative day, and Council Bill 184, similar in intent, on the fifty-second legislative day by George W.

Bellamy, El Reno, president of the Council. Neither bill reached consideration for final passage.

At the Board meeting in Guthrie, November 5, 1901, the membership split on the question of sending a delegate to the annual convention of the Board of Dental Examiners. The meeting adjourned, and the members called on the Attorney General to ascertain if funds received in fees to the Board could be used to defray expenses to the national convention. He held that there was no provision in the law to use Board funds for such a purpose; furthermore, that Dr. Kirkpatrick was liable to the present Board for funds spent to send him to the meeting at Niagara Falls in May, 1899.

— 6 —

Towns in the Territory were beginning to recover from the depression years, picking up momentum from railroad development, new industries, and business expansion. Guthrie grew from 5,333 in 1890 to 10,006 in 1900 and 11,652 at statehood. The college towns of Stillwater and Norman experienced similar growth: Stillwater from 480 to 2,431 and 2,577, and Norman from 787 to 2,225 and 3,040 for the corresponding period.

None grew so fast as Oklahoma City. Numbering 4,151 in 1890, the completion of the Choctaw, Oklahoma and Gulf Railroad from the east in 1895 and the St. Louis and San Francisco Railway from Sapulpa in the early spring of 1898 boosted its growth to 10,037 by the census of 1900. Advertised as "the fastest growing city in the fastest growing state in the Union," the population by 1907 had leaped to 32,452 and grew to 64,207 at the next decennial census.

This was the period of greatest, unceasing rivalry between Guthrie and Oklahoma City. Guthrie lost the battle to C. G. Jones, Henry Overholser, and other civic leaders of the rival city for the trunk line of the Frisco, but became the center of eight branch lines and competing railroads. It had more manufacturing and processing industries; it felt secure as the political capital of the Territory. But Oklahoma City, smarting under the rebuff that denied it the capitol in 1890 and also from the later Congressional act that forbade its transfer, played a waiting game for this prize while building itself into the retail and distributing center of the Territory.

Towns in the Indian country, likewise, grew with the return of prosperity and the work underway to dissolve tribal government. From the time the special census of Indian Territory was made in 1890 to 1907, the population of Ardmore increased from 2,100 to 8,759; McAlester, 3,000 to 8,144; Muskogee, 1,200 to 14,418. Tulsa, unlisted in 1890, had grown to 1,390 in 1900 and 7,298 in 1907.

Civic improvements were going forward in towns all over Oklahoma and advances made in its three leading cities typify advancements going on throughout the territories.

Early in its history Guthrie had installed a water-works system and electric lights. The city directory for 1894 lists seventy-eight subscribers to the Missouri and Pacific Telephone Company. By 1904 there were two telephone systems, a gas-distributing system, and new water lines and sewer system had been installed. More than fifty miles of brick and concrete sidewalk had been laid. The city director for 1892 listed four dentists: W. J. Broadfoot, W. E. Furrow, D. A. Peoples, and D. D. Slocum. In 1908 seven were practicing.

Oklahoma City, struggling for an adequate water supply all through the 1890's, was considering abandoning wells for a projected reservoir; franchises for gas and telephone systems were let in 1891. In November, 1900, the city council passed an ordinance to pave Main, Grand, and First streets between the Santa Fe right-of-way and Harvey, and Broadway between California and the Choctaw, Oklahoma and Gulf right-of-way. Disputes concerning the merits of concrete and asphalt delayed completion of the project until the following year. As evidence that the council was broadminded about the use of walk material, the *Times Journal* reported on January 1, 1901, that "within the past three months there has been laid 18,179 feet of board walk, 1,225 feet of stone walk, 4,150 feet of cement walk, 4,650 feet of brick walk, and 5,550 feet of asphalt walk." In 1902 four miles of street railway were laid; a city ordinance forbade the use of horse-drawn cars by the traction company. In 1903 the line was extended southwest to Delmar Garden and northwest to Epworth University. In 1906 the Oklahoma Railway Company was granted a charter to construct interurban lines to neighboring cities. By 1907 twenty-five dentists were practicing in Oklahoma City.

Muskogee, likewise, experienced growing pains. Speculators, grafters, and city builders were attracted by its development, the promise for business development and growth. In 1903 additional streets were surveyed and opened. M. L. Moore, publisher of the city directory, reported that because of the crowded condition of the town, chronic for at least two years, it was difficult to trace and find the place of many residents who had to resort to stores and other places of business for space to sleep. On April 21, 1904, millions of dollars were put in circulation in the Muskogee area when restrictions were removed from the disposition of land by Creek freedmen. An editorial in the Muskogee *Democrat* on May 10 suggested that a fire department needed to be built up and equipped, that Muskogee was sufficiently important to justify a paid department. The hope was expressed that the water would not remain muddy long and . . . "probably the reason so little is said about Muskogee water is that it ain't worth talking about." As early as 1892, E. R. Rulison, druggist, installed a dynamo and strung electric lights along his block on Main Street; not until 1900 was citywide distribution of electric power installed. Dr. A. E. Bonnell in 1899 bought a Columbia Electric Engine, operated by a dynamo which, according to the Muskogee *Phoenix,* August 31, was "a very handy affair, and does away with the foot power so much used around the operating chair, the engine being suspended from the ceiling, thus using the same power to run the laboratory lathe and a fine fan he now has in his office."

By November, 1897, the Indian Territory and Northern Telephone Company had completed a circuit from Muskogee as far north as Wagoner. Eufaula, Enterprise, and Brooken were connected and the line was progressing towards Sans Bois, the home of Governor Green McCurtain of the Choctaws. The following year the line was extended to Fort Smith by way of Skullyville, with another branch from Sans Bois to McAlester. At statehood 375 telephone companies were operating in Oklahoma with approximately 60,000 subscribers; the Pioneer Telephone Company, Oklahoma City, served 3,800 outlets.

In July, 1904, the Muskogee Electric Traction Company was incorporated; the first streetcars were put into operation the fol-

lowing March. Not until January, 1907, did Muskogee have natural gas piped for domestic consumption.

Four dentists were permanently located in Muskogee in 1903;
A. E. Bonnell, W. T. Jacobs, E. E. Overmyer, and M. E. Tarvin.
Two years later, nine additional practitioners were sharing the
practice.

Let us turn hurriedly through the city directories and newspapers of the period and seek out advertisements of dentists. Here
is the business directory of Guthrie, 1894. Turn past the listings of
twenty-two saloons, the Missouri and Kansas Telephone Company,
over the Bank of Indian Territory, but note that there are three
veterinarians, seventeen physicians, four of whom have office
phones, that Rachel A. Wright, the Magnetic Healer is now at
the Guthrie Hotel ready to treat cancer, catarrh, bronchitis, toothache, headache, sore eyes, and all chronic diseases. Let your eyes
rest on the advertisement of the leading brewery of the Territory,
an important industry of Guthrie: "Physicians prescribe Anheuser-
Busch beer for Oklahoma malaria." Three dentists advertise.

Dr. D. A. Peoples, secretary of the Board of Dental Examiners
has his office at the corner of Oklahoma Avenue and First Street.
A roof-high room-length sign bearing his personal advertisement
decorates an outer side of the office building. You read his announcement on the back cover of the directory: "Thoroughly educated up
to the times, with 15 years' experience, supplemented with special
post-graduate courses in the best colleges of the United States. Performs thoroughly and skillfully every operation known to the profession. Inserts artificial teeth on continuous gum, gold, aluminum
and rubber plates or without any plates (bridge work). Best work
and lowest prices in the city."

On page 42 appears the advertisement of G. A. Hughes, surgeon dentist. "Every operation guaranteed to be first class. Charges
reasonable."

Included on page 30 is the modest notice of Dr. W. E. Furrow,
surgeon dentist, 111 West Oklahoma Avenue, prophetic in the
light of modern knowledge that by the time a child is seven years of
age crowns of permanent teeth are already formed, that abscesses
may come from baby teeth, creating malocclusions, that well-
aligned deciduous teeth are guides to permanent oral formations.
Furrow, after his title and address, included this announcement:

"Irregular teeth are caused very often by parents neglecting to take their children to a careful and competent dentist while the permanent teeth are erupting."

You wonder which dentists might be advertising in the Oklahoma City papers during the period of the annual convention of the Association in 1898. You find in the issues of the *Oklahoman* for October 1 a card advertisement for Dr. H. T. Wells, 108½ West Main Street. You are puzzled about this because memory does not include his name on the roster of registered dentists. But a search of the minutes of the Board of Dental Examiners reveals that on October 15 Dr. Wells applied for and was granted a license on presentation of his diploma from the Philadelphia Dental College. His newspaper announcement reads: "All kinds of dental work done at moderate prices. Satisfaction guaranteed or money refunded. Painless extraction of teeth and crown work a specialty."

Here are files of Muskogee papers and business directories. Note how markedly dentists point out that they have become members of the city professional life and understand that the "bushwhacker" or traveling dentist remains a competitor. Turn the pages of the April 27, 1893, issue of the Muskogee *Phoenix* and see the announcement of Dr. A. E. Bonnell that appears in this and successive issues: "Dr. A. E. Bonnell, Dentist, with offices in First National Bank Building, 'Having permanently located in Muskogee, respectfully solicits a trial, and by prompt, reliable and honest work hopes to merit a continuance.'"

The issue of July 5 for the next year reports: "Dr. G. A. Major, late of Sedalia, Missouri, with office at Wellington Hotel, will permanently locate in Muskogee. Teeth extracted without pain. Crown and bridge work a specialty."

Examine the Muskogee *Times* of November 25, 1897. Turn to the medical and dentist directory and read the announcement of a recent arrival: "Dr. M. E. Tarvin, Resident Dentist. Regular graduate Baltimore College of Dental Surgery. Office at residence, corner of Gibson and N. Cherokee Streets. All work guaranteed first class."

Several advertisements appear in the *Democrat* in 1904. Here is the photograph of a proper-looking young brunette dentist. Pause and read: "F. E. Fisher Dental Parlors. Corner Third and Okmulgee. Specialist in crown, bridge, and plate work of all kinds. We are located here permanently and from the best dental college at Louisville, Ky. Gold fillings $2.00. Cement fillings $ .90. Amalgam fillings $1.00. Bridge work $5.00. Plate work $10.00."

No advertisements holds your attention so long, however, as this: "U. S. Dental Company, Oklahoma Bld. Teeth extracted without the least annoyance to the patient. Always a lady in the office. *After meals* do you feel a heaviness in your stomach and mornings a disagreeable taste or breath? If so you should consult a dentist." Curious, you run the classified section of the city directory where through the years 1904–1909 an increasing number of dentists' names appear. But look! Initials appear with proper names for all listings except this: "Copus the dentist." More curious, you run the telephone directory and finally match "Copus the dentist" with the "U. S. Dental Company." Not until you have turned through the 1910 directory do you identify J. A. Copus.

And in any issue of the Muskogee *Times Democrat* 1906–1908, inclusive, and several times in the Muskogee telephone directory for 1910 appears this ad: "Dr. G. L. Knebel, Painless Dentist." Dentists who advertised themselves as "painless" were the *bête noire* of more ethical practitioners who looked forward to the time when such advertisements would be illegal. As late as 1912, nevertheless, the city directory of Oklahoma City carried an advertisement for "Painless McArthur," and not until 1918 did the ad of the "Union Painless Dentist" disappear from its pages. Statutory control of advertising was still some years distant as the 1890's drew to a close; members of the profession new to the land were busy establishing their practice, learning new techniques, and improving the Association.

CHAPTER TWO

Dentistry in the Territories

— I —

WHAT DENTISTRY was like and conditions of practice in the territories at the turn of the century is still vivid in the minds of men grown old in the profession: Lewis R. Richardson, Enid; Fred B. Allen, Okeene; Thomas A. Myers, J. V. Cruzan, T. A. Jones, John T. Miller, Harry P. Oliver, Oklahoma City; W. E. Furrow, Guthrie; T. P. Bringhurst, Shawnee; Fred C. Seids, Perry; Fred D. Sparks, Ponca City; F. D. Stalford, Walters; W. M. Wilson, Tulsa; G. R. Smith, Duncan; F. D. Dole, Lawton. Some of their colleagues through the years recorded their impressions in the summer of 1953 of dentistry in the 1890's and early 1900's.[1]

Dr. H. L. Entriken, who has practiced at Enid since 1900, stated:

"I had an uncle who came here at the Opening and started a bank with H. H. Champlin, now president of the Champlin Oil Company. Some two years after the Strip opened, I came down to attend the wedding of my uncle. This took place in a dugout six miles north of town. I thought at the time I would return to Enid sometime.

"I became interested in dentistry through Dr. E. J. Husband, McPherson, Kansas; served a preceptorship, entered Western Dental College and finished there in 1900. . . . My first office was in the first two-story building built on the north side of the square. The square, then, did not have a street bisecting it east and west, and there were no trees in it. Most of the buildings around the square had wooden awnings that extended out to the curb."

[1] The quoted material that follows is from statements made in recorded interviews June–August, 1953.

Dr. J. A. Wells, who came to Shawnee in 1899, stated:

"I graduated from the Chicago College of Dental Surgery and came to Shawnee right from College. They were running excursion trains from my home town in Missouri to attract settlers, and I came to Oklahoma with one of those groups. There were just two temporary dentists there—I don't recall their names, but apparently they didn't get along. One had a long beard and carried a loaded cane; the other wore a wig and had a long sharp knife. When one saw the other coming, he crossed the street so they wouldn't meet. The real estate and business men of Shawnee said, 'Well, we have plenty of doctors, but we could sure use a dentist.' So I rented an office and started practicing.

"We had few facilities. We carried water from across the street. Had a spittoon fastened on the arm of the chair. When it filled with saliva we'd empty it in the slop can. When that got too full, for sanitary facilities we had a Chic Sale in the alley and we'd take the can out and empty it. We had kerosene lamps for emergency night work. At that time—my first year—I pulled thirty-two teeth for one lady without using an anaesthetic of any kind. When we got through, all she said, turning to her husband, was, 'Well, Richard, fix the pipe and I'll smoke.' And she recovered very satisfactorily and went home in a short time.

"The only anaesthetic we had was cocaine. A doctor one time said, 'Why don't you use cocaine?' I said, 'You fix some up and I'll try it.' He sent it over with a syringe all ready to use. When I injected a few drops in a lady's gums she commenced to scream and turn blue, exclaiming, 'Oh, Mary, take it off, take it off! It's choking me, it's choking me!' There was a man in the office and I sent him running across the street for the physician who had given me the cocaine. He gave her a hypodermic and soon brought her out of it. That was my last use of cocaine. Later we used eucaine. Once in a while we would anaesthetize a patient to remove all his teeth."

R. H. Pendleton (1899), Norman:

"I studied dentistry in the Kansas City Dental College and graduated in 1897. I came to Oklahoma Territory July 14, 1899, after practicing a year in Billings, Missouri. There were two dentists in Norman, Dr. Jefferson Ellard and Dr. J. B. Worley. I bought the office of Dr. Worley over the Farmer's National Bank.

"Norman was a typical early-day town of about 1,800 people,

board sidewalks, hitching posts, open saloons, livery barns. Wooden store buildings extended three blocks. These included three drugstores which were combination drug and jewelry stores. The hotel rang a big bell to call guests to lunch and supper. Lights were kerosene lamps, and people, of course, rode in wagons and buggies.

"My chair was a Harvard chair. A wall bracket, small cabinet, and foot drill furnished the operating room. The laboratory was complete for those days with foot lathe and a bellows to use in soldering. I used the Hollingsworth system for making crowns and bridges. The best teeth used in plate work were S. S. White and Old English. Most of the fillings were amalgam and gold. Gold was put in with a mallet. Extracting a tooth cost fifty cents then. We injected a weak solution of cocaine to deaden the pain of extraction.

"Garretson's *Oral Surgery* and Harris's *Principles and Practice of Dental Surgery,* two texts of college days, were old standbys. Helpful professional journals were *The Texas Dental Journal, The Western Dental Journal,* a journal called *Items of Interest,* and L. D. Caulk's *Dental Brief.*

"Dentistry has developed many new improvements in my time —the gold inlay, synthetic cement fillings, nerve blocking, partial plates, and porcelain jacket crowns. The development and use of electricity has been one of the greatest factors in the improvement of dentistry, with new instant lights, and instruments and X ray, and the convenient arrangement of equipment has made work easier."

R. O. Hirschi (1900), Guthrie:

"In 1893 my mother had a sale of farm implements and livestock, and we moved down to St. Louis, Missouri. I went to the public schools. During the summer months I had to find some work. We were taught to work and be thrifty and I tried to get a job. It was a period of depression and it was hard to find anything to do—even manual labor. But I recall very distinctly at Mother's urging for me to look for something to do, I went downtown to an employment agency and signed up as a news butch on a train, deposited $2.50, and came home with a cap. My mother saw that and she said, 'Aw, son, you don't want to do that! Aim a little higher!'

"Well, I looked around trying to get different things—like a young fellow, not knowing what I wanted—and finally fell in with a dentist of our neighborhood, Dr. Robert Summa, who said, 'Why, you come help me at my office these summer months and if you like dentistry, enroll in the fall.'

"In the fall of '97 I enrolled in Washington University. It was a three year's course. There were no requirements at all. When I finished in 1900, my preceptor said, 'Young man, St. Louis is overcrowded with dentists. Why don't you go West?'

"I had a brother in Guthrie in the hardware business—an eighty-niner. So, never having been away from home, I decided to come down here where, at least, I would have a place to stay.

"Now I want to tell you that in those days dentistry wasn't one glorious thing in money matters. Money was tight. Fees were low and it was a little hard struggling. But I opened an office in July, 1900, and I've been practicing ever since.

"My office was on the second floor of a newly constructed brick building over a drygoods store. It wasn't wired for electricity. There was water at the back of the building, but no sewer connection. The dental chair had a cuspidor you had to empty. You had a foot treadle engine, foot power, and you had a vulcanizer. You did your own laboratory work. There were no commercial laboratories. In fact, you had to do all your work, and it was work, now, to construct a plate, and do the polishing with foot power. At that time we employed no local anaesthetics unless it was a two or three per cent solution of cocaine which was toxic in itself.

"I got a temporary license in 1900, then appeared before the dental board in Oklahoma City the next year. The license fee was ten dollars and it took some scraping to get that much ahead. The board met in Dr. E. E. Kirkpatrick's office. Other members were Dr. W. E. Furrow, Guthrie; Dr. John Q. Waddell, Kingfisher; Dr. R. Wilson, Arapaho; and Dr. L. A. Kelsey, who had a chest-length beard, Chandler. They accepted my diploma from Washington University and I did not have to take an examination.

"My first trip to Oklahoma City was in July, 1900, when Teddy Roosevelt appeared there at the Rough Riders' Reunion. We went down on a special train from Guthrie. At that time there were cotton fields east of the Santa Fe tracks almost to the depot."

Fred E. Sims (1903), Tulsa:

"I chose medicine for my profession, but after completing one year of medicine, I decided to specialize in dentistry. After my junior year in dentistry, I secured a certificate from the Oklahoma Board and located at Weatherford, Oklahoma, in 1903. After one year my brother, E. E. Sims, took my office while I went to Western Dental College in Kansas City and graduated in the class of 1905. My brother then returned to Kansas City and completed his course.

"My first office was in the parlor of the hotel where I stayed until office space could be secured. One other dentist was located in Weatherford, which was enough for a town of that size. Small towns were starting in the surrounding country, but dentists were few and we found it necessary to visit these communities periodically to give them dental service.

"In those days itinerant dentists would come through the district, advertise elaborately, reap what fees they could, then depart to another community."

A. L. Walters (1903), Tulsa:

"My choice of dentistry was perhaps due to the fact my older brother was a dentist and, in a sense, he inspired me with a desire to take it up. My early schooling or training was primarily a preceptorship under Dr. H. C. Jones, Perry, Iowa, who was one of the demonstrators at the State University of Iowa. After I had passed examinations to enter the university there, he advised me, poor as I was, it would be silly for me to attempt to go to school, inasmuch as I already had a good foundation knowledge. And since most of the states did not require a diploma prior to examination, I took him at his word. Later on I passed the State Board of Texas and the Missouri State Board. And some years ago the dental department of Lincoln and Lee, now the College of Dentistry, University of Kansas City, conferred on me degrees—Doctor of Dental Surgery and Doctor of Dental Sciences. I was offered a professorship there on the subjects of nutrition, prophylaxis, and peridontia.

"I tried Texas and liked Texas all right, but decided Indian Territory had a future, decided to come here. I practiced in Kiowa and Hartshorne and traveled around and ultimately decided to locate in Checotah. There were two reasons for that. I liked to hunt. It was a lovely place insofar as its environment was concerned, largely a cattle country, and there was plenty of game. And there was an attraction that would be hard to put into words. My baby was born there. Perhaps that's one of the reasons. But having gone there a young man and having lived there until I promised Dr. Shobe, who was then in Bartlesville, that I would come to Tulsa with him, I was very happy because I had a good practice and lovely friends.

"When I went to Checotah, they were putting in the telephone system. We had no utilities insofar as lights and water were concerned. It was my privilege to serve as president of the Chamber of Commerce while most of the city improvements were made.

"When I first came to Checotah, the Creek Nation had a law that you had to register and the United States government conferred a licentiate of dental surgery on all those permitted to practice in the Creek Nation. I was privileged to have that."

W. E. Flesher (1907), Frederick:

"I chose dentistry as a profession in order to be my own boss; to be in a progressive, recognized profession serving the public. After three semesters at Central Teachers College, Edmond, I spent three years in attendance at the Dental College, Keokuk, Iowa. Between their junior and senior years many student dentists found or made opportunities to do some dental practice, on the side —bushwhacking, as it was called—for experience. A brother suggested I go to Wewoka; I bushwhacked there the summer of 1906. That fall I returned to college and graduated in 1907. I returned to Wewoka to await the announcement of my passing the dental board and being licensed. If I had decided to continue my practice in Wewoka, it would have not been necessary for me to take the board examination, for I had been in practice in Indian Territory when the Enabling Act was passed by Congress in June, 1906. A sister at Frederick told me of opportunities there, and I moved to Frederick and opened an office July 22, 1907, succeeding a dentist who moved to Grandfield, where he proved up a homestead in the Big Pasture, newly opened to settlement.

"Frederick was a center of an excellent farming area. That a fine moral atmosphere existed in this community was evidenced by the fact that all regular church organizations were active and well attended and represented almost all faiths. Later fine church edifices were erected, for one of which as chairman of a committee I purchased an Estey pipe organ, the first pipe organ in Southwestern Oklahoma. The moral attitude of the citizenship in a local option vote was effective in closing the saloons. This action took place prior to the date of statehood.

"Church and lodge activities provided outside interests and 'forty-two' was the chief entertainment at social gatherings. A new make of car in town, Ford, Maxwell, Saxon, Buick, Overland, drew the attention of all; it was an event; crowds gathered to inspect the novelty.

"My office was two rooms over the First National Bank on the corner of the busiest street intersection. My name and profession were lettered in gold with black trim on the windows and could be read easily from all directions.

"My operating-room equipment consisted of a Wilkerson Dental Chair, the most modern and expensive of the period, with pumping pedal which controlled raising, lowering, and rotating movements, or used to lock it in rigid position. A stationary cuspidor was attached which required frequent cleaning and careful disinfection. I had an up-to-date operating cabinet, a rustic type, and a swinging bracket-table for operating instruments. Since there was no day electric current, I used the foot-power dental engine of my college days. The foot-engine was used several years until twenty-four-hour electric service was available.

"An ordinary light bulb furnished illumination for dental operations. A one-burner gasoline stove served for heating. For some time I did my own maid and janitor service and had no assistant.

"The reception room was furnished with an ordinary dark oak dresser with mirror, straight-back chairs and throw rugs. Here, too, was a modern coal heating stove, coal bucket with shovel, and a floor spittoon, the latter to serve as a decoy to the tobacco chewer rather than the too often used coal bucket or stove door. For wall decorations, calendars were very useful, especially if the likeness of a beautiful girl was part of the display.

"The sterilization of instruments was quite a consideration in the early practice. A Lysol solution in a tall glass container was used for most operative instruments. The modern sterilization procedure has been an evolutionary development over a half-century or more.

"In the hot summer months the only relief afforded from the heat was an open window and a palm leaf fan in the hand of the patient. After we received daytime electric service, I installed an eight-inch fan, non-rotating, which was bracketed in the corner of the operating room directed toward the patient with the hope part of the flow of air would fall upon the operator. This electric fan was as welcome in those days as the modern air-conditioning equipment of today.

"My first homemade laboratory bench was equipped with an alcohol lamp for heating spatulas, boiling water, and heating wax for setting up artificial teeth. A gasoline vaporizing jar with air pressure from a foot bellows and blowpipe furnished the heating-torch flame for soldering bridges, etc. A foot-power lathe was used to polish dentures and bridges. At that time most dentists did their own laboratory work, but Hettinger Brothers Dental Supply House in Kansas City served most of the needs of Oklahoma in dental supplies and laboratory service."

C. H. Kibler (1908), Oklahoma City:

"My father was a physician in Dayton, Virginia, and on his death I went to live with my uncle, J. F. Butts, D.D.S., Charleston, West Virginia. There I received apprenticeship in dental laboratory work, and assisted at the chair. Through my uncle I met a dentist acquaintance of his on vacation in West Virginia, Dr. R. C. Snodgrass of Okemah, Indian Territory. I returned with Dr. Snodgrass to Okemah in August, 1907. He accepted me in equal partnership, and the agreement was that I would do the laboratory work and he the chair work. It turned out, though, at times I would do some chair work, like trying in teeth, making gold crowns, treating a tooth, and occasionally extracting one.

"Okemah then was only four years old and strictly a frontier town. We had space with an M.D., two rooms in a small frame building built with boards straight up and down with cleats over the cracks and the inside finished with building paper covering the inside of the outside walls and rafters.

"Our water supply was a cistern; no gas, no electricity. The dental chair was a student-type wooden folding chair with ordinary cuspidor attached to the arm. A foot-type dental engine was used. At that time fixed bridgework with gold crowns for abutments was universally used for partial replacements and rubber dentures for full cases. It was not uncommon to make fourteen-tooth bridges where four teeth were left for abutments. Crown and bridgework were made with a gasoline torch and blowpipe. All lathe work was done with a foot-pedal wheel. The vulcanizer was heated with a kerosene wick-type burner.

"While at Okemah, one day handbills were passed around the town that for a week Dr. L. M. Doss would do dental work at the Broadway Hotel. I met Dr. Doss. He was a dashing young dentist and proved to be a wonderful friend. He had recently moved to Oklahoma City and told me of the wonderful city it would be. He was a good salesman for the city, and I soon followed him here. So in May, 1908, at the age of nineteen, I came to Oklahoma City. I wanted to go to work for some dentist, doing laboratory work, but my youth kept me from getting a job. I called on Dr. Detrick, who did not have a job for me but seemed interested and took time out to take me to the dental supply firm of C. D. Coil and Company to meet the owners, Drs. C. D. Coil and G. A. Nichols. After talking to them, they offered to rent me their laboratory space and equipment.

"I had to wait about ten days for a partition to be put up. Dr. Doss had a patient from Shawnee to make a bridge for on a Sunday while I was waiting for my room. He and I worked all that day getting the bridge made. When we got through, he asked what he owed me. I said, 'Whatever you think it's worth.' He gave me five dollars so I knew then I was on the road to prosperity!

"When my room was ready, I opened the first commercial dental laboratory in Oklahoma, under the name New State Dental Laboratories, May, 1908. This was in the Bassett Building, 115½ North Broadway, now the Egbert Hotel.

"Near by, at 111 North Broadway, was a very fine restaurant, Rueb's Café, where regular meals were served for twenty-five cents. Across the street was a nickelodeon for motion pictures, and out of the window aperture was extended a gramophone horn. Music blared to passersby continuously; the sound reached my laboratory.

"Dr. Nichols was a good trader. Quite often he would have a man bring one of his horses or mules down, tether it near the nickelodeon and go down to swap it off or make a trade. I believe he hurt his back about this time on a trip to Shawnee with a railroad car of horses and mules. He disposed of his interest in the dental supply house and shortly afterwards began building houses, the first, I believe, on West Twenty-fourth Street near Western Avenue."

L. M. Doss (1898), Oklahoma City, after describing early experiences as a "bushwhacker" in Indian Territory and final graduation from the Chicago School of Dentistry said:

"The early-day experiences of practicing were pretty rough compared to modern methods and equipment. We received fifty cents to one dollar for extracting a tooth. If you made a denture, you wouldn't charge for the extraction at all, which is one of the hardest parts of the work.

"I used to give general anaesthetics when I couldn't get a physician to help me, ether or chloroform, which I didn't know a thing in the world about. I just had nerve enough to tackle it, which I wouldn't do at all now, you know. I sometimes wonder how we got along as well as we did.

"We had some interesting experiences in dental clinics in the early days at Association meetings. I recall one time in trying to give somnoform to a patient to put him to sleep. A couple of dentists knew who my patient would be so they gave him an overdose of liquor. Naturally when I tried to put this patient under the anaesthetic in front of all the dentists, with reporters sitting around watching the demonstration, the fellow became unmanageable and he started kicking. He kicked all the instruments off the bracket down into the alley. It took about four men to hold him! So next morning, even with all that bad luck of not being able to hold a man let alone extract a tooth, I was almost turned out of the Association when my name appeared in the paper with mention my clinic was one of the leading features of the work done at the meeting. I had an awful time convincing associates I wasn't doing some self-advertising.

"I had had a previous experience with somnoform on the corner of Main and Broadway in 1906 when a big, strong man just got up out of the chair and walked downstairs all covered up after the extraction. It took about three men to haul him back to the office. We finally learned better than to give that stuff. It was very effective for children, but we did away with it. Of course nitrous oxide is still used. Many extractions were made with nothing at all, just go in there and pull them, and if the head didn't come off the tooth usually came out."

I. M. Lightner (1907), Guymon:

"I graduated from the school of Dentistry in Kansas City, 1905, and began practice in Carthage, Missouri. After the second year there my physician told me I was developing a lung condition and should go into the High Plains country. I wrote my supply house and asked if they knew of a location. Hettinger Brothers wrote me a nice letter and said, 'No, they had no leads.' But a postscript in longhand was added to the letter that said Dr. A. B. Tull at Guymon wanted a man.

"I bought a ticket immediately and landed here the next day. I stepped off the Rock Island about 3:30 P.M.; knew nobody, not even the dentist I'd come to see. So I walked uptown, found the location, went in, and there was a man lying on the lounge, in a drugged or very drunken condition. I asked him if he was Dr. Tull. 'No, no,' he said, 'I'm not Dr. Tull. He's working on my teeth. He's gone downstairs to the bank to see if I have any more money!'

"Dr. Tull turned his practice over to me. There was no other dentist in Guymon. There was no dentist from Dalhart, Texas, to Liberal, Kansas. The territory I served was something like eighty miles square, and in instances patients came from greater distances in horse-drawn vehicles and stayed at the wagon-yard. Guymon was just a little village serving the ranchmen, helping a few farmers get started; homesteading was going on. It was a busy little place, most buildings frame, no pavement, no sewage, and the electric plant was not dependable in any way. Water came from a tank car of the Rock Island.

"A few weeks after I came, my wife was able to get out here. We had very little money and it was tied up in the panic at that time. Through the kind aid of friends in Carthage she was able to get enough money to get out here. We homesteaded a claim six miles out of town. I had two horses, would alternate riding them to the office, and in those years of exposure enjoyed the best of health."

Although the dental supply firm of C. D. Coil and Company, established in Oklahoma City in 1903, was the first in Oklahoma Territory, it served only a local need. The Territory was served primarily by the Hettinger Brothers Manufacturing Company, Kansas City. Howard H. and Isaac F. Hettinger opened a retail drugstore in Wichita, Kansas, in 1889. Because of many calls for dental items, they stocked a supply. After the Cherokee Outlet opened to white settlement in 1893 and towns were established along the Santa Fe Railway, Isaac Hettinger made a number of trips into Oklahoma Territory with a grip line of dental supplies, calling upon dentists at Blackwell, Ponca City, Tonkawa, Perry, and Guthrie.

The Hettinger brothers sold their drugstore in 1898 and bought the R. I. Pearson Dental Supply Company, Kansas City. Salesmen were sent throughout the Western states and territories as far from Kansas City as El Paso, Texas, and Salt Lake City, Utah. Their first traveling representative in Oklahoma and Indian territories was a third brother, Calvin H. Hettinger. He or John Russ, Walters, Oklahoma, had charge of the territory until 1908, when Clay Jewett transferred to Oklahoma to supervise sales operations and maintain a friendly, working relationship with the dental profession until his retirement in 1951.[2]

In pre-statehood days and for some years afterward dental salesmen carried a substantial line of supplies, gold, instruments, and teeth in specially designed trunks. These were usually displayed in hotel sample rooms so that dentists had an opportunity to select goods or supplies desired from trunk stocks. A cigar, a dinner, or a drink at the bar if in Oklahoma Territory, and a fund of ready stories were good-will offerings of the traveling salesmen, who not only peddled dental supplies but scientific knowledge on all dental advances and gossip of the profession. They knew how to gauge credit lists; they knew when dentists died, or moved from a community, or quit the profession. They ran an unofficial placement bureau for dentists seeking a location, and many dentists came into the territories to establish practice directly as a result of leads furnished by a dental supply company's representative.

— 2 —

THE ELEVENTH annual report of the Board of Dental Examiners was made November 30, 1902. Through the years the Board had

[2] Clay Jewett, who retired January 1, 1951, after forty-five years' service with Hettinger Brothers Manufacturing Company, submitted a brief history of the company to the Oklahoma State Dental Association on December 16, 1953. Jewett became Oklahoma representative of Hettinger Brothers Manufacturing Company in 1908; in 1932 he was transferred from Oklahoma City to Kansas City; in 1938 he returned to Oklahoma City. His manuscript is on file in the Central Office, Oklahoma State Dental Association, Oklahoma City.

raised examination standards and had become aware of the need to revise the dental law in conformity with wishes of the Association.

The Board members reported that, because of the laxity of the law, remote districts of the Territory were flooded with incompetent, unrecognized dentists who could not obtain proper recognition elsewhere. Under the dental act they had been obligated to license forty-four applicants who presented diplomas from dental colleges although they believed that all applicants should be required to take an examination. Seven applicants had applied for licenses on examination, only two of whom met required qualifications. They admitted that there had been considerable adverse criticism from members of the Association because of apparent negligence in bringing violators of the law to justice, "when in reality, owing to the inadequacy of the present law, which not only fails to specify the procedure, but also fails to provide funds for the carrying out of such work, it is not possible to accomplish much in this direction. The present statute governing the practice of dentistry is not by any means what it should be for the protection of the people."

Subject to censure by the Oklahoma Dental Association, too, was that provision of the law which provided that nothing in the act should be construed to prevent physicians and other persons from extracting teeth. Many of the professionally trained dentists had attended college courses with young men studying medicine and received instruction in anatomy, physiology, chemistry, materia medica, and general surgery. In many of the smaller communities of the Territory the country doctor was the only scientifically educated man, serving a wide area and whether jogging by horseback some uncharted course to a lonely settler's home or traveling by buggy, experience taught him to include dental forceps in saddlebags or medicine kit for emergency use. The Association had no quarrel with the provision of the law which permitted physicians and surgeons to extract teeth; rather, its obloquy was reserved for those who came under the classification, "and other persons."

At the turn of the century, when communication was slow and travel difficult, the dread monotony of limited amusements was seasonally enlivened in outlying towns of the territories by traveling medicine shows. The black-faced attendants and the medicine show doctor brought colorful entertainment plus a compelling lecture on real and imaginary ailments of the human body. And after the showman had explained all the maladies and afflictions his product would correct, the crowd surged forward to be among the first to buy a bottle of the magical cure. After the crowd was properly mulcted and partially cleansed of real and imaginary evils, lights were extinguished and the doctor and his troupe took the wagon road to a neighboring town to offer his wondrous cure.

Or any Saturday afternoon there might appear at a congested street corner a bearded, frock-coated itinerant preacher of loud voice and baleful eye to enlarge upon some controversial point of theology. Out of the crowd a local champion would come forward to confute and dispute and quote learnedly from Scriptural writings. As the argument grew louder and longer, the restless mother at the wagon-yard would send small fry to tug at their father's overalls or querulously implore his leave-taking while cows and chickens and stock on the farm impatiently sacrificed their evening attention to his intellectual nourishment.

These were conditions of the times which dentists accepted. Not so acceptable to them were the nonresident dentists who hawked their services from the street in direct competition with established practitioners. Dr. Holmes, Mangum, has described methods used by a traveling dentist:

"When I located in Mangum in the spring of 1900, the town had a population of about seven hundred. Some of the people lived in tents and some in dugouts. The town had been called 'tin can town' by the cowmen because many of the box houses, then the prevailing style of architecture, had been weather-stripped with tin cans flattened out and nailed over the cracks.

"A few traveling dentists coming through the country at long intervals provided the only dental service for the community. And unfortunately some of the dentists had not dealt fairly with the people, exacting large fees for inadequate service, departing between suns, leaving their board bills unpaid and defaulting on other obligations.

"By the time I arrived, the people were becoming rather suspicious of the traveling practitioner and would usually ask me how long I intended to stay in Mangum before entrusting their work to me. Realizing that I would have this distrust to overcome, I would look the questioner straight in the eye and tell him in a very

Indian Territory Dental Association

Courtesy Dr. Albert E. Bonnell, Jr.

First Meeting of the Oklahoma State Dental Association
Muskogee, 1908

solemn manner, 'I expect to remain here for seventy-five years.' This statement seemed to restore confidence; it amused those who had a sense of humor, and properly impressed those who could never take a joke. So they quit traveling several hundred miles to find a dentist and came to me, their first resident dentist.

"Dr. Laird, who then lived in Oklahoma City, was known as a picturesque street vendor and is remembered by many. He wore a ten-gallon hat and long hair hanging down over his shoulders. He extracted teeth with his fingers, the teeth having previously been loosened by pyorrhea, before the awed crowd. He was a force to be reckoned with in the early days as people accredited him with all but supernatural power because of his ability to use his fingers rather than the 'dreaded' forceps.

"I cultivated the doctor's acquaintance to learn, if possible, the secret of his success as an extractor. I was just beginning the use of cocaine, which did not give perfect anaesthesia in many cases and often caused nausea and fainting. I could hear occasionally of one of my patients going to Dr. Laird for an extraction. He confided in me that he depended more on rapid skillful technique, using a little campho-phenique on the gum for its psychological effect.

"He injected no anaesthetic and if extracted on the street before a crowd, who were eagerly waiting to give the victim the 'horse laugh' at the first sign of weakening, his black-face artists kept up a running fire of jokes. The doctor's wife, a pretty little woman wearing a fancy costume, stood in front of the victim urging him to keep smiling. All this served to keep the patient's mind diverted until, suddenly, the tooth was out without one having had time to dread it.

"The doctor never performed a difficult extraction before the crowd if he could help it. And should a tooth break, he would conceal the fact from his audience. Some dentist would get the patient later and remove the roots with the aid of cocaine as an anaesthetic."

— 3 —

THE YEAR 1902 marked a turning point in the history of the Oklahoma Dental Association. The society was growing in membership and at its annual meeting conducted programs of technical instruction for its members. For the first time outstanding professional leaders, including Dr. D. J. McMillen, dean and founder, Western Dental College, Kansas City, and Dr. J. R. Pendleton, of the dental faculty, Washington University, St. Louis, brother of Dr. R. H. Pendleton, Norman, secretary-treasurer of the Association, accepted invitations and appeared on the program. Others came from Indian Territory to learn, discuss, and practice new techniques. This important meeting, held at Guthrie, May 6–7, offered the following program:[3]

First Day, Tuesday, May 6, 1902

9:00 A.M. President's Address, G. A. Hughes, D.D.S., Guthrie, Okla.

9:30 A.M. Arthur L. Nicholson, D.D.S., El Reno, Okla. Clinic Vernons Gold

10:30 A.M. S. A. Long, D.D.S., South McAlester, I. T. Clinic

1:00 P.M. D. J. McMillen, M. D., D.D.S., Kansas City, Mo. Clinic Seamless Crown

2:00 P.M. A. F. Griswold, D.D.S., Holdenville, I. T. Clinic Crown and Bridge Work

3:00 P.M. J. R. Pendleton, D.D.S., St. Louis, Mo. Clinic

4:00 P.M. C. L. White, D.D.S., Granite, O. T. Clinic Crown Work

5:00 P.M. J. A. Wells, D.D.S., Shawnee, O. T. Clinic Griswold Bridge

Evening of the 6th
8:00 P.M.

B. F. Michael, D.D.S., Pond Creek, O. T. Hypnotism in the Practice of Dentistry

E. E. Kirkpatrick, D.D.S., Oklahoma City, O. T. Paper: Honorary Degrees for Old Practitioners

C. H. House, D.D.S., Newkirk, O. T. Paper: Symptoms and Treatment of Disease Maxillary Sinus

R. S. Parsons, D.D.S., Oklahoma City, O. T. Paper: Pulp Mummifications

[3] Program, Twelfth Annual Meeting of the Oklahoma Dental Association at Guthrie, Oklahoma, May 6, 7, Tuesday and Wednesday, 1902. Also *The Eleventh Annual Report of the Oklahoma Board of Dental Examiners, 1901–1902* (Guthrie, State Capitol Company, 1902). The program and report were presented the Oklahoma State Dental Association by Dr. R. H. Pendleton, Norman, in July, 1953.

D. J. McMillen, M.D., D.D.S., Kansas City, Mo. Lecture on Fracture of Maxillary

A. D. Cage, D.D.S., Stillwater, O. T. Paper: Care of Children's Teeth

F. D. Sparks, D.D.S., Ponca City, O. T. Paper: Noncohesive Gold in Combination with other Fillings.

Second Day, May 7, 1902

9:00 A.M. Price Cheaney, M.D., D.D.S., Dallas, Texas Clinic: Reproductions and Impressions of the Face in Plaster Paris, also Seamless Crown

10:30 A.M. A. B. Potter, D.D.S., Chandler, O. T. Clinic Covering Cusps

11:00 A.M. M. C. Marshall, D.D.S., St. Louis, Mo. Clinic: Detrays Gold in Cervical Cavities without the Rubber Dam

1:00 P.M. D. O. M. Le Cron, D.D.S., St. Louis, Mo. Clinic: Porcelain Work

2:30 P.M. F. D. Stalford, D.D.S., Perry, O. T. Clinic: Painless Extraction of Teeth the Uses and Abuses Local Anaesthetics

3:00 P.M. T. F. Clifford, D.D.S., El Reno, O. T. Clinic: Noncohesive, Gold Filling

4:00 P.M. M. B. Crumbe, D.D.S., Kansas City, Mo. Clinic: Western Seamless Crown

7:30 P.M. A.A. Maupin, D.D.S., Perry, O. T. Paper: The Law and Protection of Dentistry in Oklahoma

8:30 P.M. F. P. Hulen, M. D., D.D.S., Pond Creek, O. T. Dental Reflexes from a Medico Dental Stand Point

Besides benefits received from technical instruction at the meeting and from informal discussions afterwards in hotel rooms, members of the Association were to benefit by two important occurrences.

National leaders in attendance at the convention were impressed with the serious attitude of Association members and their attempt to raise their professional standing. The members elected Dr. R. H. Pendleton as delegate to the annual meeting of the National Dental Association, Niagara Falls. Through the intercession of Dr. D. O. M. Le Cron, St. Louis, an officer of the national association who presented a clinic at the Guthrie meeting, and Dr. J. D. Patterson, president of the Kansas City Dental College and former president of the National Dental Association, territorial members were admitted to membership.[4]

The other event occurred in Indian Territory. For years the only qualification to practice medicine or dentistry in the Indian nations was the payment of a fee, with the result that Indian Territory served as a dumping ground for unqualified and unethical practitioners. It was not uncommon for applicants who failed to pass examinations given by the Oklahoma Board of Dental Examiners to move on to the Indian country and establish a practice in one of the rapidly growing towns there.

Ethical dentists resented these intrusions and by precept and example raised standards in local communities. In larger cities of the Territory a professional group would call upon a recent arrival, apprise him of dental standards, and, in most instances, if the newcomer were an untrained, unethical practitioner, he moved to remote towns of the Territory or on to another field.

One sultry August day shortly after the Guthrie meeting, Dr. Albert Bonnell, Muskogee, and Dr. J. E. Wright, South McAlester, stood at the station in the latter city where the Kali-Inla Railway and the Katy crossed. Wright had come to the Choctaw Nation twenty years before and could recall his early days of horseback practice when his saddlebags carried a head rest, hand drills, excavators, and forceps. Bonnell could look back on his years of apprenticeship at Cherokee, Kansas, his fifteen years of practice in Muskogee, interrupted only by study at Western Dental College in the 1891–92 term when he received the gold medal award to the student most proficient in crown and bridgework, as well as the highest award offered the class of fifty members in laboratory and operative work. At one time they were the only dentists west of Arkansas, between Kansas to the north and Texas to the south. Both took a deep interest in professional advancement. Since 1890 both had been in attendance at dental association meetings in Missouri, Arkansas, Texas, and, more recently, Oklahoma Territory. While Dr. Bonnell was waiting for the train to arrive for his homeward trip, their discussion turned to dental associations, and out of that event was conceived the idea for an Indian Territory Dental Association.

[4] In 1897 the American Dental Association and Southern Dental Association combined to form the National Dental Association; in 1922 the name of the organization was changed to the American Dental Association.

There was need for a territorial organization; both territories were almost equal in size and population, and number of dentists. The official census of 1900 listed 398,331 inhabitants of Oklahoma Territory; 391,990 in Indian Territory. There were 23 dentists in Oklahoma Territory in 1893; 29, in Indian Territory. By 1904, the numbers were 181 and 188 respectively.[5] The majority of those

[5] *Polk's Dental Register and Directory of the United States and Canada,* sixth edition (Chicago, R. L. Polk and Company, 1904). The *Register* lists each dentist by location and a code relative to registration, membership in an association, and whether or not a college graduate as well as date of graduation. General information on each state and territory is included, and population for each town or city based upon official census data of 1900. Current officers of territorial and state associations are listed, as well as dates when the associations were founded. For example, Arkansas, which became a state in 1836, organized a dental association in 1890; Kansas, admitted to statehood in 1861, did not form an association until September, 1891, four months after the Oklahoma Dental Association was formed.

Most listings for dentists are brief; some contain more information as the following examples show:

ADA, CHICKASAW, 2,580
Babcock, Francis V., D.D.S., Chicago Coll. of Dental Surgery (Dental Dept. of Lake Forest Univ.), Chicago, Ill., 1903; Mem. Ind. Ter. Dental Assn. Office hours 9 to 11:30 A.M. and 12:30 to 5:30 P.M., Sundays, call only; Tel., Office 1, Res. 38.
Doss, L. M.
Emnis, J. A.
Ezell, E. R.
Nowlin, Fred H.

NORMAN, CLEVELAND, 3682
Ellard, Jefferson
Pendleton, Robert H., D.D.S., Kansas City Dental Coll., Kansas City, Mo., 1897; Vice-Pres. Oklahoma Dental

Assn.; Mem. National Dental Assn. and Dental Protective Assn. of U.S.A.

SHAWNEE, POTTAWATOMIE, 10,350
Bringhurst, Theodore P., D.D.S., University of Tenn. (Dental Dept.), Nashville, Tenn., 1900; Sec. and Treas. Okla. Dental Assn.; Mem. National Dental Assn. and Southern Branch of same.
Edminston, Richard J.
Jordon, Cyrus A., 282, 1889
Rogers, Carroll, 265, 1903
Wallace, Gilbert C., 265, 1901
Wells, James A., 152, 1899
Youmans, Charles C., D.D.S., Western Dental Coll., Kansas City, Mo., 1903.

[The codes, 282, 265, 152 refer to New York College of Dentistry, Western Dental College, and the Chicago College of Dental Surgery, respectively; the dates, to years of graduation.]

The earliest copy of Polk's *Dental Registry* in any public library in Oklahoma is the 1914 issue in the Medical Library, Oklahoma City. The 1904 directory was lent to the Oklahoma State Dental Association by Dr. T. P. Bringhurst, Shawnee. Miss Dorothy Cutting, librarian, the School of Dentistry, University of Kansas City, furnished requested information from earlier editions; namely, available listings of officers of the Oklahoma Dental Association, 1891–1906, and dentists in Oklahoma and Indian Territories for the year 1893.

practicing in Oklahoma Territory, however, were college graduates, whereas less than one in six in Indian Territory held college diplomas. Many of the partially educated men in the profession speedily recognized their deficiencies and either enrolled in colleges for intensive training or joined Bonnell and Wright in their movement to associate and bring recognized leaders to annual meetings.

Three dentists were practicing in Tulsa at this time. Ardmore, largest city of the Territory with a population of 8,800, had ten. Ada, Bartlesville, Bearden, Checotah, Chelsea, Chickasha, Cumberland, Duncan, Durant, South McAlester, Tahlequah, Tishomingo, Vinita, Wapanucka, Wilburton, and Wynnewood had as many dentists as Tulsa, or more.

An optimism pervaded the Indian country toward its future development at this time as the Indian nations were surrendering communal land rights and tribal government. The belief that crossroads settlements, platted to include surrounding forests and prairies, would grow into populous centers attracted men of the dental and other professions to the Territory. Trading centers no longer in existence or towns with population fifty years later less than that of 1903 had one or more dentists. In the Choctaw and Chickasaw nations, for example, each of the following places had from one to three dentists: Bebee, Center, Chickiechockie, Cumberland, Enterprise, Erin Springs, Juanita, Kemp, Leon, McGee, Midland, Red Oak, Sterritt, and Wapanucka.

Among those practicing were men who in later years were leaders in Oklahoma dentistry: J. E. Wright, dean of practitioners in the Territory; S. A. Long, A. L. Walters, W. T. Jacobs, A. E. Bonnell, E. E. Overmyer, C. W. Day, N. C. Wood, L. M. Doss, and T. H. Williams, honored by the presidency of the state association. The Muskogee Dental Association had five members: Bonnell, Overmyer, and Jacobs had as colleagues F. A. Stickel, Jr., who became the first secretary of the state association, and the distinguished Marion E. Tarvin, who graduated from the Baltimore College of Dental Surgery in 1867. At Ardmore practiced J. G. Abernathy, president of the Dental Society of the Chickasaw Nation, Aaron E. Adams, who had been granted license number 16 in Oklahoma Territory, and William H. Enloe, old enough to remember happenings in the Civil War.

In practice at Tishomingo was E. E. Heflin, who, later, was to serve on the State Board of Dental Examiners; at Claremore, W. W. Bryan, who became president of the first State Board of Dental Examiners, and H. H. Kaho, who, like the others, devoted years of service to his profession. Pauls Valley had two young college graduates, S. M. Conger and L. L. Barnes; another, James H. Proffitt, was in practice at Wynnewood. J. M. Bond, Chickasha; Ira Malone, Sapulpa; G. R. Smith, Duncan; and J. H. Crockett, Durant, had already begun years of service in their communities that were to extend into the first fifty years of the state's existence. At Durant, too, practiced W. S. Williams, like Barnes a graduate of Vanderbilt University—a fiery, outspoken Kentuckian who could look back on a career as river pilot on the Mississippi and who was to serve on the State Board of Dental Examiners during the terms of seven governors of the state, longer than any other member. At Hugo, C. A. Thompson, graduate of Atlanta Dental College had begun a career of fifty years' service to the community. S. S. Mayfield, who alternated his practice at Enterprise, Quinton, and Stigler, later as state senator from Eufaula took a principal part in revising the dental law of the state.

Interest in the formation of an association was created over all the Territory through contacts and correspondence by Bonnell and Wright. On November 18, 1903, a group met at South McAlester with Dr. Wright presiding and Dr. Bonnell serving as secretary, and formed the Indian Territory Dental Association. Membership fee was set at two dollars; committees on jurisprudence, ethics, and constitution were appointed. Permanent organization resulted in the election of Dr. Wright, president; Dr. C. W. Day, Vinita, vice-president; Dr. J. G. Abernathy, Ardmore, secretary, and Dr. S. A. Long, South McAlester, treasurer. Present also were W. E. Busby, South McAlester; L. M. Doss, Ada; Francis M. Babcock, Ada; A. F. Griswold, Holdenville; C. R. Stevenson, Tulsa; C. O. Redman, Tahlequah; J. A. Ennis, Ada; F. A. Stickel, Jr., Muskogee; L. L. Patterson, South McAlester; M. W. Murray, Poteau; H. A. Weeks, Hartshorne; W. S. Pennell, Ardmore; L. S. Lyle, Tishomingo; J. H. Nicholson, Ardmore; and W. D. Kelly, Holdenville.

During the four years the Indian Territory Dental Association was in existence, annual meetings were held where national and local leaders in the profession read papers or conducted clinical demonstrations for the instruction and betterment of the members. Local societies were formed, too, which did much to stimulate fraternization and a better understanding of common problems.

— 4 —

WHEN THE Oklahoma Territorial Legislature convened in January, 1905, the Dental Association was confident remedial legislation in its behalf would be considered. Fred Sparks, president of the Board of Dental Examiners, and other leaders in the Association had worked as a legislative committee to draw up a bill to raise standards for those qualifying in the profession. Dentists had also contacted members of the legislature and informed them of the need for a better law. And when Sparks' fellow-townsman, Jesse B. Norton, was elected speaker of the House of Representatives, the dentists felt assured their weak and ineffective legislation would be revised.

On the ninth legislative day, Wednesday, January 18, Speaker Norton introduced House Bill 75, an act to regulate the practice of dentistry in the Territory of Oklahoma.[6] This was referred to the Committee on Ways and Means the following day, and on January 24 the chairman, Dyke Ballinger, Anadarko, made the favorable committee report. In Committee of the Whole, on February 4, the House passed the measure. Three days later the bill was read before the Council, then, the next day, referred to the Committee on Education of the upper chamber.

Here the Association received an unexpected setback. On February 10 the committee made an unfavorable report to the Council: Its recommendation was that the bill should not pass! The Association, however, was on guard against this possibility; friends in the Council forced consideration of the bill on the floor. Minor revisions were made. The bill passed the House of Representatives, March 3 by a vote of twenty-three to none, and the Council on the

[6] House Bill 75, in *Journal of the Proceedings of the Eighth Legislative Assembly of the Territory of Oklahoma*, beginning January 10, 1905, and ending March 10, 1905, pp. 90, 100, 116, 185, 193–94, 250, 300, 351, 401. Also, *Journal of the Council Proceedings of the Eighth Legislative Assembly of the Territory of Oklahoma*, pp. 106–107, 224, 234 (Guthrie, I. T., The State Capitol Co., 1905), and *Session Laws of 1905, Territory of Oklahoma*, Chapter XV, "Dentistry," pp. 210–16 (Guthrie, 1905).

ninth, nine to four. Governor Thomas B. Ferguson signed the measure the following day.

This legislative experience taught the Association valuable lessons which were profitably assimilated and passed on by experienced leaders to members in later years: Reforms in dental laws could be made only by concerted action of the Association, time-consuming detail work by a limited number of its leaders, ever recurring education of inexperienced legislators, and vigilant watchfulness over measures under consideration affecting the profession when a legislature was in session.

The dental act, effective June 1, 1905, incorporated many of the recommendations made by the Association. It required all applicants to be at least twenty-one years of age and, whether graduates or non-graduates, to be examined by the Board. If successful, the candidate was granted a certificate of registration to be recorded in the office of the county clerk where resident practice was established. Licensed dentists practicing in the Territory were required to register with the Board within sixty days. An annual license fee of one dollar was established.

The five-member Board, appointed by the governor, was to hold office for five years, and members could succeed themselves only once; at least quarterly meetings were required. The act provided that the Board could sue or be sued under its official name, the Board of Dental Examiners of the Territory of Oklahoma. The act also provided that legally authorized physicians and surgeons could extract teeth.

An event of greater political significance—the coming of statehood—now faced the associations. As early as 1891 movements were underway in the territories seeking single or double statehood; groups of territorial leaders met at various times in Oklahoma City, Purcell, Kingfisher, Shawnee, McAlester, and Muskogee and prepared petitions to Congress or sent delegations to Washington for political sovereignty. All agreed with the sentiment expressed by eloquent Thomas H. Doyle in a hearing before the Committee on Territories of the House of Representatives, January 20, 1904: "There, fanned by gentle zephyrs and clothed in the sheen of eternal spring, is a country where honest industry is sure to receive its just reward." Their persistence was finally rewarded. President Theodore Roosevelt approved on June 16, 1906 the Congressional act passed two days earlier to enable the people of the two territories to form a constitution and state government.

Celebrations were held in the principal cities; bonfires were lighted, parades were formed, speeches were made, and politicians began alignments for the coming struggle for choice of delegates to the constitutional convention. By November 20, when delegates convened in Guthrie, strong differences appeared between the Oklahoma Dental Association and the Indian Territory Dental Association in regard to constitutional provisions for their profession.

The Enabling Act provided that laws in force in the Territory of Oklahoma should apply in the proposed state until changed by the legislature. Dentists in Indian Territory interpreted the provision to mean they would be subject to examination in order to obtain a state license to practice, whereas licensed dentists in Oklahoma Territory would be exempt. Dentists in Muskogee consulted an attorney, who advised them of the improbability of such a provision inasmuch as it would be an attempt to discriminate in professional practice based upon geographical location. Their fears were not allayed, however, until the convention early in the session adopted the proposal that laws of a general nature should have uniform application.

Delegates to the convention, on and off the floor, were besieged by lobbyists and pressure groups offering guidance, seeking favors or consideration: organized labor, suffragettes, farm groups, bankers and railroad representatives, insurance companies and public utilities, the coal and oil industries, and educational leaders. Apparently every coterminous area of the state wanted to become a county and every town a county seat! Notables such as Coin Harvey and William Jennings Bryan appeared before the convention to offer suggestions for incorporation in the constitution.

To Guthrie came, too, Frank Jacobs. Although Indian Territory sent 55 of the 112 delegates to the convention—and leaders from the East Side assumed principal offices in its organization—members of the Indian Territory Dental Association thought it advisable to have a representative in Guthrie to watch proceedings. A group met in the office of the dental supply house, Murdoch-Hamlin Company, 417 West Okmulgee Avenue, Muskogee, and elected Dr. W. T. Jacobs, Muskogee, president, and Dr. A. L. Walters, Checotah, secretary-treasurer. Their principal interest was the raising of a fund to pay Jacobs to be their eyes and ears at the convention. Only two of the members present that evening were college graduates, A. E. Bonnell, Muskogee, and A. M. Bradley, Mounds. Bonnell bitterly opposed the purpose of the meeting; Bradley espoused it. At any rate, Jacobs was employed to represent their association and be on guard against any discriminatory measures that might be proposed for the constitution.

News of disquieting nature soon came from the convention city. In mid-March the Committee on Schedule, getting ready to consider provisions on dentistry and dental surgery, received a petition signed by dentists of Guthrie and Oklahoma City. Their resolution included recommendations that all dentists in Indian Territory who had practiced there three years before the Enabling Act (June 16, 1906) be entitled to license without further requirements. Dentists in practice at the time of the act who had diplomas from reputable colleges likewise were to be licensed; all others were to be examined. A spokesman for the group, Dr. C. L. White, maintained that the resolution, if adopted, would be "as nearly just to all as could be devised and as little as would guard the public welfare."

These demands were not unreasonable. From 1891–1905 ethical dentists working as the Board of Dental Examiners had decried a makeshift law which permitted charlatanism to go unpunished and quackery to flourish, and which created the greatest impediment to professional advancement. By tireless, unmitigating effort they and other members of the Association had written advancements into the law of 1905 that raised professional standards and protected the public. Secretary White of the Association had received inquiries from dentists throughout the country, many of whom indicated they sought admission to the dental profession of the state through the open door of Indian Territory. The resolution, therefore, was nothing more than an attempt on the part of a small group of members of the Oklahoma Territorial Dental Association to see that standards of their profession were not lowered.

— 5 —

WHILE THE constitutional convention was in session, leaders of the dental associations were formulating plans and a program for a joint session. The idea was first advanced in 1904 when the associations held successive meetings at Shawnee and Muskogee in May in order that guest speakers could appear on both programs. At Muskogee on May 6, last day of the session, the Muskogee Dental Association gave a banquet complimentary to the Indian Territory Dental Association which was attended by members of the profession from Oklahoma Territory.[7] Here, at the leading café, The Oxford, over "Mocha and Java" and cigars, with A. E. Bonnell acting as moderator, union of the associations was discussed and the general feeling expressed that it would be achieved before statehood.

The Fourth International Dental Congress, held at St. Louis, Missouri, August 29 to September 3, 1904, also helped point up mutual interests of the associations of the twin territories.[8] The first

[7] "Program and Menu" of the banquet, May 6, 1904, 9:00 P.M., The Oxford Café, Muskogee, Indian Territory. Mrs. C. W. Day enclosed a copy in a letter to Dr. H. H. Sorrels, June 1, 1954. Dr. Day began practice at Vinita in 1892; at this meeting he was advanced from the vice-presidency to the presidency of the Association.

The menu offered by The Oxford was:

Swiss Cheese Sandwiches

German Dill Pickles   Mixed Sweet Pickles

Queen Olives

Sliced Tomatoes

Chicken Salad

Hot Rolls   Raised Buns

Vanilla Ice Cream

Cocoanut and Chocolate Cake

Strawberries and Cream

Mocha and Java   Sweet Milk

Cigars

[8] *Transactions of the Fourth International Dental Congress held at St. Louis, August 29 to September 3, 1904*, (3 vols., The S. S. White Dental Manufacturing Company, Philadelphia, Press of the Dental Cosmos, 1905). Also, *The Dental Brief*, September, 1904 (L. D. Caulk, Philadelphia). This was a souvenir edition of the publication, distributed at the Fourth International Dental Congress. It includes pictures of chairmen of committees and sections at the Congress, including that of Dr. T. P. Bringhurst, Shawnee. The first article in the magazine, by Dr. M. I. Schamberg, Philadelphia, on "The Diagnostic Value of the X-rays in Dentistry and Oral Surgery" is a report of an illustrated lecture delivered before the Pennsylvania Associations of Dental Surgeons, May 10, 1904. The article, with forty-one illustrated radiographs, quite possibly was one of the first to call to the attention of territorial dentists the utilization of X ray by their profession.

These volumes were lent the Oklahoma State Dental Association in May, 1954, by Dr. T. P. Bringhurst, Shawnee.

The chronology for dates of international dental congresses appears in *A Century of Service to Dentistry 1844–1944*, published by the S. S. White Dental Manufacturing Company, Philadelphia, in commemoration of its one hundreth anniversary,

and third congresses had been held in Paris, 1889 and 1900, respectively; the second congress during the Columbian Exposition, Chicago, 1893, attended by Laura Davis, Henry Davis, W. J. Broadfoot, M. L. McConn, and D. A. Peoples, members of the Oklahoma Dental Association.

Delegates from thirty foreign countries or possessions, including Java, the Philippines, China, and Japan in the Far East, Syria, Egypt, major European countries, Peru, Brazil, Chile, the Argentine Republic, Guatemala, Nicaragua, and Mexico, attended the congress held in conjunction with the Louisiana Purchase Exposition. Although at this time the National Dental Association did not consider territory or state societies as subdivisions, state conference committees were provided for the congress. The chairman of the Oklahoma delegation was Dr. T. P. Bringhurst, Shawnee, secretary-treasurer of the Oklahoma Dental Association, who represented the twin territories at conferences called for state and local societies.

Indian Territory was represented at the congress by L. L. Barnes, Pauls Valley; B. C. Cunningham, Coalgate; C. W. Day, Vinita; F. E. Heflin, Tishomingo; S. A. Long, South McAlester; and J. H. Nicholson, Ardmore. From Oklahoma Territory came Bringhurst and J. A. Wells, Shawnee; F. H. Colter, J. W. Grant, and C. L. White, Oklahoma City; M. B. Furrow and R. O. Hirschi, Guthrie; Robert Wilson, Arapaho; D. M. Brenneman, Hobart; E. E. Miller, Geary; A. L. Nicholson, El Reno; L. P. Saunders, Pawnee; F. D. Sparks, Ponca City; E. C. Watkins, Jefferson City; and W. H. Connor, Stillwater. Not only did they meet and hear internationally known dentists, but they renewed acquaintance with leaders who had appeared on territorial programs and they renewed discussion on the advisability of the amalgamation of the territorial associations.

Dentists attending the annual meeting of the Oklahoma Dental Association in May, 1905, discussed the expediency of union, and the inevitable surge toward statehood hastened plans to merge the organizations. An official invitation for that purpose was extended to the Indian Territory Dental Association at its annual meeting at Ardmore in May, 1906. The invitation was accepted, and it was

1944. Names of delegates from Oklahoma Territory to the Columbian Dental Congress, 1893, appear in *The Western Dental Journal*, Vol. VI, p. 288 for the year 1892.

agreed the meeting for this purpose should be held in Oklahoma
City, June 17–20, 1907.

This was a busy and intense week for Oklahoma City.[9] Reduced

[9] See the *Daily Oklahoman* June 16–21, 1907. Also, for reference to Delmar
Garden at the time of 1903 convention, see the *Weekly Times Democrat*, Oklahoma
City, May 15, 1903. Issues of the *Daily Oklahoman*, the official program of the dental
associations, and the Oklahoma City *Directory for 1907* (Oklahoma City, Warden-
Ebright Printing Company, 1907) contain interesting advertisements of the period.
The *Western Dental Journal*, Vol. XXI for 1907, contains the following articles on
the joint convention in Oklahoma City: "The Oklahoma and Indian Territory—Legal
Conditions," by C. L. White, pp. 256–58; "The Organization of the New Oklahoma
State Dental Association, June 17–19, 1907," by C. L. White, pp. 690–713; "The
Oklahoma Dental Association" (author not listed), pp. 794–96; "The Indian Ter-
ritory Dental Association; Its Organization, History and Mission," by A. L. Walters,
pp. 804–809. This is a copy of the address delivered by Dr. Walters to the convention
Monday afternoon, June 17. A copy of the program, "Joint Meeting Oklahoma and
Indian Territory Dental Associations at Oklahoma City June 17–18–19, 1907," was
presented the Oklahoma State Dental Association by Dr. R. H. Pendleton, Norman
in July, 1953.

The program lists the following officers and committees:

INDIAN TERRITORY		*Executive Committee*
President	S. A. Long	L. G. Mitchell; F. H. Colter;
Vice-President	A. E. Adams	W. A. Weir
Secretary	F. A. Stickel, Jr.	*Membership Committee*
Treasurer	A. L. Walters	F. D. Sparks; A. C. Hixon;
Executive Committee		T. P. Bringhurst
S. A. Long; F. A. Stickel, Jr.; A. E.		*Publication Committee*
Adams; J. E. Wright; W. S. Williams		S. S. Swihart; R. S. Parsons
Supervisor of Clinics		*Clinical Arrangements*
C. W. Day		A. J. Beatty; T. A. Myers
OKLAHOMA TERRITORY		*Reception Committee*
President	A. A. Doughty	*Oklahoma City Dental Society*
Vice-President	A. O. Cromer	E. E. Kirkpatrick President
Secretary and Treasurer	C. L. White	W. A. Weir Vice-President
		A. J. Beatty Secretary and Treasurer

Clinicians and speakers from outside the territories were: Walter M. Bartlet, St.
Louis; W. J. Brady, Kansas City; D. D. Campbell, Ozark, Mo.; Clyde Davis, Lincoln,
Neb.; L. O. Green, Chicago; F. B. Lawrence, Eldorado, Kansas; N. D. N. Moore,
Chicago; Harry McMillen, Kansas City; J. H. Prothero, Chicago; A. W. Starbuck,
Iowa City, Iowa; F. G. Worthley, Kansas City.

Dentists from the territories who appeared on the program were: A. E. Bonnell,
Muskogee; S. A. Long, South McAlester; A. A. Doughty, Oklahoma City; Fred D.
Sparks, Ponca City; J. A. Wells, Shawnee; R. S. Parsons, Oklahoma City; A. L. Walters,
Checotah; E. P. R. Ryan, Muskogee; F. A. Stickel, Jr., Muskogee; H. R. Watkins,
Oklahoma City; F. E. Sims, Weatherford; D. W. Brenneman, Hobart; Roy V. Wool-
wine, Waukomis; Earl H. Westenhaver, Enid; J. H. Sims, Watonga; L. G. Mitchell,
Oklahoma City; C. A. Furrow, Perkins; A. C. Seids, Snyder; F. H. Colter, Oklahoma

railroad rates had been granted dentists, as well as delegates to a rally of the Christian Endeavor Society. The Lee, Grand Avenue, North Side, Windsor, Arcade, the Planters, The Saddle Rock, Hobson, the Waverly hotels, rooming houses, and many private homes were filled with out-of-town visitors. William Jennings Bryan appeared to deliver the keynote speech before Democrats assembled in convention from over the territories. Lord Bryce, former British ambassador, made a brief address at the Overholser Theater. In his party were Governor Francis of Missouri, President Davidson of the Frisco Railroad system, and Judge Alton B. Parker, Democratic candidate for the presidency in 1904, traveling by private coach on the way to Cache to visit Quanah Parker, leader of the Comanche Indians. Thick red headlines in the Wednesday morning edition of the leading newspaper proclaimed that Cruce was leading Haskell in the Democratic nomination for governor held the day before. But Friday the victorious Haskell appeared to receive a tumultuous welcome from his party convention. In the Lee Hotel, center of convention activity since it opened in 1900 and described by Col. W. F. Cody as the most perfectly appointed hotel in any city of like size in America, members of the two dental associations were going about the serious business of attending clinics, listening to visiting lecturers, engaging in general discussions, and perfecting a single organization.

Early on the program appeared the subject, "The Indian Territory Dental Association: Its Organization, History and Mission" by A. L. Walters, Checotah, with the discussion to follow to be opened by E. P. R. Ryan, Muskogee. Both men were leaders in the movement to protect the interests of dentists of Indian Territory; both were men of influence with delegates to the constitutional convention from their districts. Ryan had publicized their point of view in the *Western Dental Journal*. If knuckles were to be rapped or heads cracked at the joint session, these two were ready for battle.

Young, personable, and an able speaker, Walters began his presentation by tracing reasons why dentists settled in Indian Territory. He admitted that many dentists were practicing in the Ter-

City; J. M. Staples, Atoka; J. H. Proffitt, Oklahoma City; George Shimoon, Muskogee; W. S. Dardis, Ft. Cobb; R. O. Hirschi, Guthrie; L. L. Barnes, Pauls Valley; J. Q. Waddell, Kingfisher; C. W. Day, Vinita; G. A. Nichols, Oklahoma City.

ritory who had failed examinations before state boards, that the only requirements to practice among the Indian nations was the payment of a fee, that standards had been forced downward, "and with his circus posters the 'Painless Dentist' in all his glory traveled from town to town." He recounted some of the difficulties faced by dentists in Indian Territory, practicing among a people many of whom knew nothing of dental work except extractions. He mentioned accomplishments of the Association and benefits that it had brought him, a non-graduate.

Aware that he held every delegate's attention, Walters suddenly attacked: "The failure of those who drafted and submitted Article XIV to the Constitutional Convention," he shouted, "shows their lack of foresight. They should have known that a measure so unjust and unfair would not be tolerated!"

Voice vibrating with intensity of feeling and surcharged with emotion from the response engendered, he continued: "I may incur the displeasure of some when I state that I did all in my power to defeat that measure but under the same circumstances I would do it again and yet again, for the reason that it was too sweeping in its character, protecting one class only. There was no protection or provision for an ethical non-graduate, against the unethical graduate. No exemption as to time, yet the worst class of quacks we have today are those that have come within the last few years and many of these are graduates. No consideration at all was shown the ethical man who had spent the best years of his life in building up a practice, remained a true follower of the code through all the campaigns of the 'Painless Dentist,' putting forth his best efforts for the development of his town and state, who not only had severed his relationship with all other states, but had invested his money here and looked upon it as his future home. No consideration was shown him and because he might not be able to pass a technical examination, have to step down and out and turn over all to a man who had done nothing along the lines mentioned but who happened to be the fortunate possessor of a diploma. Why, that is preposterous! . . . If any guarantee had been given as to a practical, sensible examination with a reasonable fee, before honorable, ethical dentists elected by the Association, not one word would have been uttered and it would have had the sanction of ninety per cent of the dentists, where this was not even approved by ninety per cent of

68

the graduates! Examine all men, graduates or non-graduates, coming in less than three years previous, or go even further—examine all dentists now practicing in Indian Territory regardless of time or college, give them a square deal and graduates ought to be able to stand this if non-graduates must."

Walters' speech won approval from the assembly, and its timeliness was reflected in the schedule approved July 16 with the state constitution by the delegates at Guthrie. Section 14 of the schedule provided that dentists residing in Indian Territory before June 16, 1906, were eligible for a license to practice in Oklahoma without an examination. But the schedule also provided that laws in force in the Territory of Oklahoma at the time of the admission of the state into the Union should remain in force until altered or repealed by legislative action. Dentists who established their practice in Indian Territory after June 16, 1906, therefore, were subject to the law of 1905 which provided for examination. And, Article V, section 39 of the Constitution provided for the legislature to create a Board of Dentistry and prescribed its duties.

After three days and two nights of intense, serious, professional study, most of the dentists looked forward to the final entry on the program: "Wednesday, June 19th, 8:00 P.M. The Oklahoma City Dental Society will entertain the members of the association and the visitors by an informal theatre party at Delmar Garden."

The local society formed in 1905 had fostered through social and professional meetings cordial relations unique among the professional groups of the growing city. At stated meetings papers were read, new and improved methods discussed, and clinics held, while social gatherings brought individual understanding and lasting friendships. The reception committee, composed of E. E. Kirkpatrick, W. A. Weir, and A. J. Beatty, had planned well the finale to this epochal session as dentists of the host city knew the annealing influence of Oklahoma's most popular entertainment spot.

Delmar Garden! No better place in the territories could be selected to develop a spirit of camaraderie and to cement ties for the new association. Members of the Oklahoma Dental Association as early as the May, 1903, convention had included a trip to the amusement park as the closing feature of the annual program. The *Weekly Times Democrat* for May 15 of that year announced: "One of the largest crowds ever seen in Oklahoma City attended the opening of the summer theatre at Delmar Garden yesterday afternoon. When the curtain rose, the house was packed and nearly all the chairs and tables were occupied. The vaudeville was of the high class order. Everyone fortunate enough to obtain seats were well entertained.

"All during the vaudeville the crowds enjoyed sitting under the shade of the big trees and the management was well paid for the room used, as all refreshment stands did a splendid business. The street cars came in for their full share of business as they were crowded to their utmost capacity, both going and coming, until a late hour last evening. The business done by the system was estimated by some to be as large as that of circus day. One of the cars had to be taken off the University run and placed in service between Main and Broadway and the park."

Here, big foaming glasses of cold beer or iced soft drinks could be purchased for a nickel; the band concert was free, chairs and tables were conveniently arranged in the grove to afford a ready view of the stage, admission was only a quarter, and many of the dentists sat at the tables that warm Wednesday evening, June 19, enjoying Teal's Merry Minstrels, Mazey and Mazette "flying in the air," applauding sweet Lillian Southland and the comical antics of the four Banta brothers. Amid such surroundings and good fellowship the young Association closed its inaugural meeting and with high hopes and many plans looked forward to statehood.

CHAPTER THREE

After Statehood

— I —

STATEHOOD, in the fall of 1907, brought new problems to the Dental Association. Oklahoma Territory dentists read with unease how on Saturday night, December 3, Bill Murray had left the Democratic caucus at Guthrie which was to assure him the speakership of the First Legislature to attend a banquet at the Royal Hotel. The dinner was given by dentists of Indian Territory, who also presented the designated speaker a pair of gold-mounted meerschaum pipes in honor of his influence in protecting their interests while he presided over the constitutional convention.

The legislature which convened the following Monday continued in session until May 26. Although revisions of the dental act of 1905 were introduced, none passed and the territorial law was to continue in effect until March 28, 1913. Meantime, members of the Oklahoma County Dental Society became interested in a grand project: a dental college for the state.

Shortly after 1900, as Oklahoma City assumed leadership in the trade of the Territory, civic leaders became interested in its cultural growth. In 1901 the Commercial Club through its president, A. H. Classen, prominent layman of the Methodist Episcopal church, and C. B. Ames of the Methodist Episcopal church, South, presented to the Indian Mission Conference and the Conference of the Methodist Episcopal church a proposal for the founding of a university under joint sponsorship of the two churches.[1]

The city offered 240 acres of land, about 50 of which were to be set aside as a campus, the remainder to be platted and sold. Funds

[1] H. E. Brill, *Story of Oklahoma City University and Its Predecessors*, 32-34, (Oklahoma City, University Press, 1938).

raised by the sale of the town lots were to be used in constructing buildings; any reserve was to be applied to an endowment fund.

With characteristic enterprise shown by the growing city, members of the Commercial Club formed the University Development Company and won acceptance from the two branches of Methodism for the project. The first building of brick and sandstone was completed in September, 1903. It cost $40,000 and contained thirty-five rooms, including library, auditorium, and laboratory facilities. This building, which now houses the Epworth Methodist Church, 1901 North Douglas, is immediately west of the present Classen High School. The following year a Girls' Hall, located a few yards north of the main building, was completed. This was a two-story frame structure which had thirty-two resident rooms, baths, and a large dining hall. A power house was also erected in 1904, just west of the main building, to furnish heat, hot and cold water to the Administration Building, and Girls' Hall. In the summer of 1904 a two-story brick building to house the Weather Bureau was erected by the United States Department of Agriculture. This is located at the southwest corner of West Nineteenth Street and Classen Boulevard and marked the northeast boundary of the campus. Since it was located on a lot donated by the university, its facilities were available to the students. Meantime the traction company extended its streetcar line into the "College Heights" addition.

Epworth University officially opened on September 7, 1904. George L. Harrell, one of the instructors, wrote the following description three years later: "The main building was then back in the middle of what appeared to be a fifty-two acre weed patch, and could be reached by climbing steep wooden steps from the street and then circling round to the north near where the Weather Bureau now stands and following a path made either by the farm wagons from the northwest or by the cattlemen as they drove their herds across the plains. Not a tree was there on the campus, no flowers except the wild ones that grew in great quantities on the front, and the alfalfa blossoms on the back campus. Nothing was there to be seen except one big, lonesome looking building, the present main one, and the powerhouse, which was then under construction."[2]

Harrell described how members of the faculty were recruited to visit incoming trains and to wave pennants on which were let-

[2] *Ibid.*, 35.

tered "Epworth University" and to cry out, to attract the attention of those lonely ones, the prospective students, "Right this way for Epworth University."

"The day for the opening arrived and the faculty, some members of the board of trustees, some friends both from the city and a distance, and all the students assembled in the chapel for the first exercises of Epworth University. After the devotional exercise the work of classifying the students began and the first classes were met on the next day after the opening. The highest class in the college was the Freshman; thus it is seen that the material out of which to make a college was scarcely above the high school grade. The material equipment of the University was rapidly being installed. There were very few books in the library and until they came, the various professors made loans from their private libraries. Thus the machinery of an educational institution was set in motion."

One hundred and seventy students enrolled for the first term, but by 1907 the student body had grown to approximately four hundred. Increased enrollment prompted the addition of other schools and colleges: Colleges of Liberal Arts and Medicine and the School of Fine Arts were added in 1906; the next year the Schools of Pharmacy and Commerce and the Department of Law were added, and in 1908 a College of Dentistry.

Before statehood, members of the dental profession in Oklahoma City had considered the establishment of a proprietary college.[3] They incorporated the enterprise as the Oklahoma City Dental Surgery College and proposed to issue capital stock in the amount of $150,000. The money panic of 1907, however, resulted in the sale of only $30,000 worth of stock, and the following year Oklahoma City Dental Surgery College became a part of Epworth University and its name was changed to Epworth College of Dentistry.

Faculty members were: Dr. A. A. Doughty, dean, Operative Dentistry; Dr. R. S. Parsons, secretary, Special Anatomy; Dr. Elmer E. Kirkpatrick, Metallurgy; Dr. F. H. Colter, Operative Dentistry; Dr. L. G. Mitchell, Dentistry and Oral Surgery; Drs. W. A. Weir, C. L. White, and G. A. Nichols, Prosthetic Dentistry,

---

[3] Oklahoma City *Times Journal*, June 14, 1907. The *Almanac and Industrial Record of 1908* published by the *Oklahoman* included the following advertisement: "Epworth College of Dentistry. This college is located at Oklahoma City. Sec'y.— R. S. Parsons."

Crown and Bidgework; Dr. T. A. Myers, Dental Materia Medica; Dr. A. J. Beatty, Comparative Dental Anatomy, Histology, and Bacteriology; Dr. T. P. Bringhurst, Dental Pathology; Dr. S. S. Swihart, Anaesthesia and Ethics; Dr. W. L. Dutcher, Dental Physics.[4] Physicians of the College of Medicine faculty offered associate courses while young, brilliant C. B. Ames, dean of the Department of Law, taught a course in dental jurisprudence.

This college, more a prospect than a reality, was doomed to failure. The university itself, torn between the bickerings of the two branches of Methodism and experiencing financial difficulties, became a victim of the promotional schemes that led to overexpansion. During the period of financial doldrums that settled upon Oklahoma City shortly after it won the Capitol from Guthrie, the university was transferred from the city and its land-holdings reverted to the original donors.

Thus perished the dream of some Oklahoma County Dental Society members for a professional school. The Law School, School of Medicine, and College of Pharmacy were absorbed into the state-supported University of Oklahoma. In April, 1908, Senator Richard A. Billups, Cordell, included provisions for a School of Dentistry for the state institution in the appropriation bill, but, on third reading of the bill, this provision was deleted. Possibly if the dentists had conducted a better-organized campaign, the school would have been established for their profession.

— 2 —

DESPITE the disappointment of the Oklahoma County Dental Society members to make the Epworth College of Dentistry a success and, later, to have the University of Oklahoma establish a Dental School in conjunction with the Medical School, members were active in improvement of their profession. In March, 1908, the County Society, with Dr. A. M. Detrick, president, and Dr. T. A. Myers, secretary-treasurer, scheduled a meeting in Oklahoma City at which demonstrators from Kansas City showed the use of various machines in making pressure castings. Clinics were held under the supervision of Drs. A. A. Doughty, L. G. Mitchell, and E. E. Kirkpatrick.[5]

4 Brill, *op. cit.*, 41–42.

This year marked, too, the introduction of the use of X ray in Oklahoma dentistry. A German professor, William Conrad Röntgen, director of the laboratory at the University of Würtzburg, while conducting experiments in 1895 on the passage of high-voltage electric current through vacuum tubes, accidentally discovered the X ray. Röntgen isolated himself completely in his laboratory for the next two months, experimenting with materials that would resist penetration and found that lead and platinum could stop the rays completely. "Röntgen was the first to behold what no human eye had ever seen before, a perfectly clear outline of the bones in his hand, visible through the flesh. This was X ray, which ranks in importance with anaesthesia and has revolutionized medical and dental practice.

"Dr. C. Edmund Kells, of New Orleans, was perhaps the first dentist in the United States to attempt the use of the X-ray machine in connection with the teeth. Several others followed his example, but the profession at large remained uninterested. In 1906, almost ten years after he began his experiments, Kells was obliged to transport his entire equipment to Asheville, North Carolina, in order to give a demonstration before the Southern Dental Society, for there was no X-ray machine in Asheville at that time. Dr. Kells' contribution to the development of X ray in dentistry finally cost him his life. Nothing was then known about the hidden dangers lurking in the strange penetrating ray, and many of the pioneers, using the early crude apparatus, were badly burned or maimed. Dr. Kells first lost three fingers; later his whole hand had to be removed; later still his arm had to be amputed. Even this did not help. Preferring death to long and continuous suffering, Kells committed suicide—another unsung hero who gave his life for humanity."[6]

When the annals of the Oklahoma Medical Association are

[5] Dr. A. A. Doughty to Dr. R. H. Pendleton, February 17, 1908. The opening paragraph of the letter states: "The first meeting of the Oklahoma County Dental Society, auxiliary to the Oklahoma State Dental Association, will be held at Oklahoma City, March 10th, at which time Pressure Castings will be demonstrated by numerous clinics and will be the subject of several excellent papers. Able demonstrators from Kansas City are expected, and a variety of machines will be exhibited." The letter was presented to the Dental Association by Dr. Pendleton, July, 1953.

[6] M. D. K. Bremner, *The Story of Dentistry*, second edition (Brooklyn, Dental Items of Interest Publishing Company, 1946), 239–40, 241.

written, honored should be those pioneer physicians of the state who suffered broken health and the destruction of living tissue in the personally dangerous operation of the crude X-ray machines of the period. Fortunately Dr. Everett S. Lain, Oklahoma City, nationally known dermatologist and still active in his profession, graciously consented to co-operate with the Oklahoma Dental Association in placing in proper sequence his interest in X ray and its first use by the dental profession of the state. Below are excerpts from an interview in July, 1953, with Dr. Lain:

"My interest in X ray began during my senior year at Vanderbilt University in 1900 when I was privileged to look through a fluoroscope at bullets which had been fired into a laboratory dog. This new induction-coil machine had only recently been added to the laboratory equipment of the medical school.

"Looking at the mysterious greenish glow of rays set up by the passing of a high-voltage current through a vacuum glass tube, I was thrilled with wonder at its future possibilities in the field of medicine. During my move in August, 1902, from Bolivar, Texas— my first practice—to Weatherford, Oklahoma, I paid a visit to Dr. John A. Renck of Oklahoma City, who, several months previously, had installed in his office on the southeast corner of Main and Robinson streets, a new static X-ray machine. This machine had already become the wonder of Oklahoma City.

"After leaving medical college this, the most exciting experience of my senior year, continued to linger with me almost day and night until in January, 1903, I dared to consult my banker friend, J. W. Walters of Weatherford, about helping me to finance one of the marvelous machines for my office. An order was immediately sent to Chicago, where X-ray machines were being built. Within a few days a static machine had been shipped, cash upon delivery, in care of the First National Bank of Weatherford, Oklahoma.

"A few days after the installation of my new machine over the Exchange National Bank, an exciting incident occurred which proved to be the first fortunate boost for this doctor in his new location. Late one evening the cashier of the bank, O. H. Cafky, while putting on his topcoat dropped from his pocket a 45-caliber revolver which discharged a bullet directly through his ankle joint, taking with it pieces of trouser, shoe, sock, and also leaving in its path a clearly visible line of lead fragments. With the aid of friends, he was hastily carried to the office of Drs. Lain and Ballard where many fluoroscopic examinations were made in our endeavor to clear this wound insofar as possible of a mass of infectious debris. . . .

"My first X-ray machine was a static, consisting of sixteen round revolving plates which served as a step-up transformer of voltage and gave off a unidirectional current. This machine was a most emotional creature, influenced and governed by many factors, such as moisture, accumulated dust, carbon niozene, the contact brushes. The drying out of the cabinet was accomplished by means of placing inside a bowl of fresh chloride of lime, then carefully wiping the dust from the plates and cleaning and adjusting the fine-wire contact brushes.

"During those territorial days there was no source of electrical supply in Weatherford with which to operate a motor to spin the bevy of plates. The labor of cranking up and continuing this elbow exercise throughout each treatment was no small task. It was often done by obliging volunteers who happened to be visiting in the office. Drs. Fred and Everett Sims, dentists, who shared a common reception room with me, were always most gracious volunteers when they were not busy foot-pedaling their drilling machine or engaged in other professional work. These two good friends, even to this day, do not hesitate to remind me occasionally that they too contributed to the early development of X-ray work in Oklahoma Territory.

"In April, 1907, I was invited by Dr. Fred H. Clark, secretary of the Territorial Medical Association, to prepare and read a paper at the annual meeting at Sulphur. I illustrated by X-ray pictures some of the inestimable aids in diagnosis of fractures and in therapy of certain diseases by means of the X ray. The paper was so well received that a physician friend, after the meeting, suggested that Oklahoma City was in need of just such an X-ray specialist. After full counsel with Mrs. Lain, we were soon on our way to Chicago in order to take special training offered in dermatology, X ray, and electrotherapy.

"When we moved to Oklahoma City in September, 1908, I found static machines already in the offices of Dr. John A. Renck and Dr. Thomas A. Buchanan, and an induction-coil machine in the office of Dr. J. M. Postelle. These physicians very graciously welcomed me and later each offered to cease attempting to do X-ray work if I would aid them in disposing of their machines. Fortunately I found many other physicians in this fast-growing city ready to welcome me, and soon they began to call me for aid in X-ray diagnosis as well as occasionally referring to me certain skin diseases. . . .

"Early in November, 1908, while sitting in my office in the Buxton Building, on the northeast corner of First and Robinson streets, hopefully meditating about the many patients who had not yet arrived, I received a telephone call from Dr. John R. Caughron, dentist, asking if I was prepared to take X-ray pictures of infected teeth. I was momentarily perplexed because the smallest X-ray plate then available was a glass plate 8x10 inches. He announced he would bring to my office a patient and a dental journal containing an article written by an Indianapolis dentist, Howard R. Raper, in which there were illustrations of X-ray pictures of the teeth.

"After the arrival of Dr. Caughron and the patient, we examined the illustrations and read the article, which did not mention the size or character of the X-ray plates or films used. After a few moments' thought, I dashed out of my office and purchased a glass cutter. We then went into my dark room, cut small pieces from a glass plate, wrapped them in black paper (light proof) and made several exposures in the mouth of the patient holding these rough, uncomfortable objects in his mouth. Lady Luck was with us when we developed fairly good negatives that clearly showed evidence of infection at the apices of several teeth.

"This, insofar as I am aware, was the first attempt at X-ray pictures of teeth within our state. Lantern slides were made from these negatives and were often shown by Dr. Caughron at state and other dental meetings before his untimely death. Sons of Dr. Caughron, Sherill and Jack, now in dental practice here, have promised to try to find the original glass-plate dental films made by their father and me. I continued to do diagnostic X ray for dentists for many years thereafter or until the dentists began, one by one, to install specially built individual X-ray machines within their own offices."

Dr. Caughron never surrendered his enthusiasm for the diagnostic value of the X ray. As a member of the Executive Council of the state association, 1911–14, he never lost an opportunity to talk up its advantages and use. Each year found him winning more converts as he appeared before state and local meetings.

Progressive dentists, too, at this time became aware of the relationship between oral infections and systemic disorders. Although scientific investigations pointed to the relationship early in the 1890's, members of the profession were not generally aware of the implications, not until William Hunter, an English physician, stated that "American dentistry" was contributing to the ill health of its patients.

Dr. M. D. K. Bremner, in his *Story of Dentistry,* has related the impact upon the profession of Dr. Hunter's observations in regard to focal infection:

"After recording a number of such observations, Hunter read a paper before the Faculty of Medicine of McGill University at Montreal in 1911 roundly criticizing 'American Dentistry,' and referring to the ingeniously constructed dental bridges as 'mausoleums of gold over a mass of sepsis.' According to Hunter, cases of anemia, colitis, arthritis, kidney disease, and many other ailments could be traced to infection around the teeth and he cited a number of case histories of patients who had been ill, some even bedridden for months and years, who had recovered entirely, or had been very much improved as a result of the removal of the artificial restorations and the teeth which carried them."[7]

Hunter's report, widely circulated in the medical and dental professions, was timely fuel for renewed enthusiasm by Caughron on his presentations to the Oklahoma fraternity. Though interest created in the state by Drs. Lain and Caughron and, later, the appearance of national authorities on programs at annual conventions of the Association, dentists were apprised of positive benefits in diagnostic work from use of the X-ray machine.

Dr. A. J. T. Beatty was the first dentist in Oklahoma City to follow Dr. Caughron's example and install a machine in his office. When L. L. Barnes, Pauls Valley, joined W. A. Weir in practice in Oklahoma City, they installed a machine. In 1917, the Oklahoma X-ray Laboratory, with J. S. Rose as technician, was established in the capital city and offered its services to dentists. A former Edmond dentist, Dr. H. R. Watkins, periodontist, opened offices in

[7] Bremner, *op. cit.,* 238.

Guthrie and Oklahoma City, specializing in X-ray diagnosis. Dr. T. W. Sorrels, who established practice in Oklahoma City in 1915 as the state's first orthodontist, installed a Coolidge tube machine in 1919. That same year Drs. Bonnell and Pfeiffer of Muskogee installed a similar machine, and by the mid-twenties every well-appointed dental office included one.

The impact of the use of X ray cannot be overestimated. This was emphasized in December, 1953, when Dr. Harry Sorrels, Oklahoma City, historian for the Society, queried fifty of the veteran practitioners of the state in regard to five of the greatest advances made in dentistry during their careers. The majority listed the use of X ray as the most important.

— 3 —

THE DIAGNOSTIC use of X ray, the development of the focal-infection theory, conductive anaesthesia, improved castings, and the general educational advance of the dental profession in Oklahoma were brought to the attention of members of the Association at annual meetings.

Muskogee was selected as the site of the first annual convention after statehood of the Oklahoma State Dental Association. This city, Indian capital of the state, underwent its years of most phenomenal growth during the period 1907–10. Population increased from 14,418 to 25,278. Grant Foreman has recorded the importance of the location here of the Union Agency for the Five Civilized Tribes: "Congress again stimulated business when on May 27, 1908, restrictions were removed from an additional class of Indian allottees so that more millions of acres of land in Oklahoma were sold and made taxable. This was followed by another resurgence of buying and prosperity. Discovery of rich oil fields on lands of restricted Indians in remote parts of the Territory brought oil leases, money, and operators by the thousands to the Indian offices in Muskogee."[8]

By the time dentists gathered for their convention, streets were paved, utility lines extended into developing residential areas, and streetcar tracks spread to Hyde Park, on the Arkansas River near

[8] Grant Foreman, *Muskogee: The Biography Of An Oklahoma Town* (Norman, University of Oklahoma Press, 1943), 140.

the Three Forks area. Beautiful Hyde Park had been developed as an amusement center, and, through the influence of Governor C. N. Haskell, the first Oklahoma legislature officially established it as the site of the Oklahoma Free State Fair. Here, too, from the river boat *Mary D* and, later, the *City of Muskogee,* freight was unloaded that led to a reduction in railroad freight rates to Muskogee.

Convention headquarters were established in the Turner Hotel. Three years earlier delegates from Indian Territory had assembled here for the Sequoyah Convention held across the street in the Hinton Theatre. But in 1907 Muskogee opened its block-long convention-hall building between Main and South Second streets, the most commodious auditorium in the state. An open driveway through the building permitted carriages, surreys, and other horse-drawn vehicles to deposit passengers near the broad center stairway leading to the assembly room on the second floor. Here, two weeks earlier, Madam Schumann-Heink sang, one of the galaxy of famous artists whose visits to Muskogee marked it a cultural center of gracious living.

Drs. A. E. Bonnell and E. P. R. Ryan, in charge of arrangements, had busied themselves for weeks with plans for the convention. Dr. A. A. Pfeiffer, who had come to Muskogee from Mexico to enter practice in partnership with Dr. Bonnell a few weeks before the annual convention, has recently recalled the hearty co-operation by members of the Muskogee Dental Society in assuring the success of the meeting: Chairs were arranged in the convention hall, janitor service performed, decorations hung, reservations made, the assignment of exhibit space completed. All contributed to the success of this, the first state-wide meeting of the Association.

A friendly press helped build enthusiasm for the meeting. Beginning a week before the association convened, news stories appeared daily in the local papers, all stressing the fact that members of the Oklahoma State Dental Association were to be guests of Muskogee. Subscribers to the Muskogee *Times-Democrat,* students of foreign affairs, probably read with interest on June 2 the account under a Paris date line that an attempt had been made to assassinate Major Dreyfus while he was leading a parade to the Pantheon in memory of Émile Zola. Republicans and Democrats noticed that the nation's outstanding exponent of the strenuous life, President Theodore Roosevelt, had a narrow escape when the horse he was riding in Rock Creek Park reared and fell backward into the creek; followers of the "great commoner," William Jennings Bryan, were furnished ammunition for curbstone opinions on the new currency law by remarks made by him during the second week of his Nebraska tour. Teen-agers probably debated the advisability of spending a nickel at the Hinton Theatre to see the feature picture, Tennyson's song poem *Enoch Arden* and other films, or matching it with another to witness Virginia Jeffries and Company present a military drama, *Under Two Flags* at the Olympic Airdome. Doubtlessly small boys had a harder decision to make: whether to take their parents to "the biggest and best carnival company on earth, the Great Parker Shows," or postpone until tomorrow an afternoon with them at Miller Brothers 101 Ranch Wild West Show.

A few young ladies probably scrubbed and dressed to answer an advertisement in the "Too Late to Classify" section: "Wanted —Girls 16 years or older to learn cigar trade. Wages from the start. Cuban Cigar Factory, 317 West Broadway." The New Phoenix Clothing Company called to the attention of men its "new corn shades in shirts, coat style, cuffs attached, sizes 14 to 18" and to Hart, Schaffner & Marx suits of serge or fancy weaves for eighteen dollars. Housewives were attracted downtown to the Street Furniture Company for its continuation of a shirtwaist box sale. "A few were sold, but the disagreeable weather kept many away who we know want the boxes." But the Pioneer Telephone and Telegraph Company was trying to educate them to stay at home: "An exceptional opportunity to save time and trips is by installing an extension telephone in your residence . . . . The extension and present telephone are on the same line, so you call or answer from either telephone—less than 2¢ a day for residences."

Business must have been good for Madam Stanley, Clairvoyant and Medium with forty years' experience, who "helps, advises you truthfully on all affairs of life. Locates mines and buried treasure". . . . It should have picked up considerably after grafters and speculators read, then read again, a release with a Washington date line: "Assistant Secretary of the Interior Wilson and Judge Woodruff will leave this afternoon for Muskogee to begin the prosecution against land grafters who have been clouding the titles to Indian lands in the Five Nations."[9]

[9] Muskogee *Times-Democrat*, June 3, 1908. Issues of this newspaper, May 20–

Dentists, however, were more interested in the column-long account of the forthcoming "first meeting of the new organization." The article mentioned that visitors were to be royally entertained by city officials, the local dentists, and the Commercial Club. "Fifty prominent dentists from New York, Chicago, St. Louis, Kansas City, Denver, Nashville and other cities will help swell the throng when the convention opens here and prospects are for a most enthusiastic and successful meeting."

Next day the following notice appeared in the newspaper under the heading "Free Dentistry," signed by Dr. A. E. Bonnell, chairman, Executive Committee: "The Oklahoma State Dental Association meets in Muskogee June 8, 9, 10 at Convention Hall. I need a number of patients for crowns, gold fillings, gold and porcelain inlays and amalgam fillings; also one patient for full lower plate. The work will be done by experienced men and free of all cost to the patient. This is an opportunity for a limited amount of high class work, absolutely free . . . ."

The disagreeable weather, however, which kept many housewives wanting shirtwaist boxes away from downtown Muskogee spread throughout the state and Middle West. Front-page headlines in state papers were devoted to news of the weather; by Thursday the Muskogee area was preparing for one of the worst floods in its history. Channeling down the Verdigris, Grand, and Arkansas rivers converging on the Three Forks area surged a devastating flood tide. All railroad traffic was blocked toward the northern, northwestern, and western portions of the state. Before Sunday the flood had crested, but all railway lines were not open. Dr. T. H. Williams, Chickasha, recently recalled that the flood, which disrupted railway schedules, caused him to miss the only annual session of the state association that he has failed to attend; Dr. A. B. Walker, then in practice at Fairview, remembered the following experience, which he related in an interview at his home in Norman, June 2, 1953: "That was the spring when we had high water and we got only as far as Sapulpa by train. Couldn't get any farther that way and they sent us down to Kiefer by hack and then across to Muskogee on a freight caboose. I well remember that

June 8, contain news of the convention, local and national events. Madam Schumann-Heink appeared in Convention Hall, May 21.

Charley White wrote his president's address between Kiefer and Okmulgee in the caboose."

Notwithstanding the high water and poor traveling facilities, approximately two hundred members of the organization appeared for the informal reception and luncheon tendered by the Commercial Club. They were present in Convention Hall when the opening session was called to order by Dr. Bonnell. The complete program follows:

MONDAY, JUNE 8, 1908
Informal Reception at Auditorium at 11 A.M.
2:30 P.M.
Meeting Called to Order.
Invocation, Rev. A. N. Hall.
Address of Welcome, Hon. Leo E. Bennett, Mayor.
Response, A. C. Hixon, Guthrie.
President's Address, C. L. White.
Reading of Minutes of Preceding Meeting.
Paper, N. C. Wood, Ardmore,
"Advantage of Co-Ad Fillings Over Fillings of Any Other Character."
Discussion Opened by Fred D. Sparks, Ponca City.
Appointment of Committees.
Receiving Applications for Membership.

TABLE CLINICS

1. "Plaster Model Preparation in Prosthetic Work," W. S. Williams, Durant.
2. "Hollow Gold Inlay," A. A. Pfeiffer, Muskogee.
3. "Rubber and Gold Bridge," F. C. Holmes, Mangum.
4. "Some Points in Setting Up Full Artificial Dentures," J. P. Fann, Ardmore.
5. "An Accurate Method of Obtaining Articulation in Bridge Work," L. G. Mitchell, Oklahoma City.

CHAIR CLINICS

1. "The Restoration of Badly Broken Down Six Year Molars With Amalgam—Those Cases Where Many Dentists Crown," E. J. Woodward, Ardmore.
2. "Contour Gold Fillings, Using Nelms Gold," Wm. G. Bristol, Altus.

84

Vulcanizing in 1910—Dr. L. L. Barnes at work

California Street, Oklahoma City, August 7, 1912

3. "Porcelain Faced Gold, Bicuspid Crown," A. L. Walters, Checotah.
4. (Subject not given) A. L. Nicholson, El Reno.
5. "Pyorrhoea," L. G. Mitchell, Oklahoma City.

8:00 P.M.

6. "Practical Points in Prosthetic Dentistry," (Stereopticon Lecture) Walter M. Bartlett, St. Louis.

TUESDAY, JUNE 9, 9:00 A. M.

TABLE CLINICS

1. "New Anchorage for Removable Plate Bridges," C. W. Day, Vinita.
2. "New Anchorage for Fractured Bridges of Where One Abutment Has Given Away," C. W. Day, Vinita.
3. "Cast Inlay," F. E. L. Thomas, Muskogee.
4. "Metoline Compound" (Demonstration).
5. "Partial Lower Stationary Plate—Cast Work Gold and Acolite," J. A. Wells, Shawnee.
6. "Fitting Porcelain Crowns With DeTrey Porcelain Enamel," R. E. Morris, Tulsa.
7. "Accurate Joints of Porcelain Crowns," D. M. Brenneman, Hobart.
8. "Preparation of Cavities for Inlays," C. L. White, Oklahoma City.
9. "Seamless Gold Crowns," Robert O. Hirschi, Guthrie.
10. "Upper and Lower Artificial Teeth, Proper Occlusion, etc.," C. Clarence Perry, Chant.
11. "Cast Inlays," R. H. Pendleton, Norman.
12. (Subject to be Announced) C. C. Allen, Kansas City, Mo.
13. "Something in Plate Casting," A. C. Hixon, Guthrie.
14. "Amalgam Filling," J. R. Caughron, Oklahoma City.
15. "A Means of Preventing a Sore Tooth After Arsenical Application," J. D. Ratliff, Oklahoma City.
16. "Amalgam Filling," Givergus Shimoon, Muskogee.

CHAIR CLINICS

1. "Canal Filling," N. C. Wood, Ardmore.
2. "Administration and Instruction in Somnoform Anaesthesia," W. H. DeFord, Des Moines, Iowa.

3. "Pressure Inlay Casting, Inlay for Distal Approximal Bicuspid, Slight Contour," A. A. Doughty, Oklahoma City.
4. "Cast Inlay for Incisor Cavity," C. L. White, Oklahoma City.
5. "Large Gold Cast Inlay, in Molar Tooth Compound Cavity, Using Ashley Inlay Outfit," K. P. Ashley, Kansas City, Mo.
6. "Richmond Crown," A. E. Gossard, Kansas City, Mo.
7. "Porcelain Inlay," A. W. Starbuck, Denver, Colo.
8. (Subject to be Announced), D. R. Stubblefield, Nashville, Tenn.

1:30 P.M.

READING AND DISCUSSION OF PAPERS

1. "Civic Improvement," R. E. Morris, Tulsa. Discussion Opened by E. E. Overmyer, Muskogee.
2. "Dental Invention an Art," J. E. Wright, South McAlester. Discussion Opened by J. M. Staples, Atoka.
3. "Benefits of City, County and District Societies," G. C. Wallace, Shawnee. Discussion Opened by E. E. Kirkpatrick, Oklahoma City.

4:00 P.M.

Muskogee Dental Society Will Entertain Members With A Visit To Hyde Park.

8:00 P.M.

Stereopticon Lecture.

WEDNESDAY, JUNE 10, 1908
9:00 A.M.—TABLE CLINICS

1. "The Preparation of Inlay Cavities," C. L. White, Oklahoma City.
2. "Casting Bridges," J. B. Herring, Sulphur.
3. (Subject to be Announced) D. J. McMillen, Kansas City, Mo.
4. "Orthodontia," Harry McMillen, Kansas City, Mo.
5. "Chair Clinic Porcelain Crown," A. E. Bonnell, Muskogee.

CHAIR CLINICS

1. "Casting Lower Denture In A Cow Bell," D. D. Campbell, Kansas City, Mo.

86

2. "Small Contour of Anterior Tooth, Using Translux," S. A. Long, South McAlester.
3. "Pyorrhoea," F. H. Colter, Oklahoma City.
4. "Grinding Gum Section Teeth and Some Points in Prosthetic Work," F. G. Worthley, Kansas City, Mo.
5. "Repairing Fractured Roots for Crowns," K. P. Ashley, Kansas City, Mo.
6. "Silicate Cement Filling," A. E. Gossard, Kansas City, Mo.
7. "Non-Cohesive Gold Filling," D. J. McMillen, Kansas City, Mo.
8. "Cast Inlay," W. V. Ryan, Chicago, Ill.
9. "Mounting Logan Crown," A. M. Detrick, Oklahoma City.
10. "Patient With Upper Mandible Entirely Missing and Appliance for Same," E. C. Watkins, Pond Creek.

PAPERS

1. "Some Forms of Gingivitis and Their Treatment," F. H. Colter, Oklahoma City.

In the election of officers that fine balance was maintained which existed through the first ten years of the state association's existence, a period when the office of president alternated between representatives of the East and West sides of the state.[10] Dr. A. L. Walters, Checotah, was elected president; Dr. G. C. Wallace of Shawnee,

[10] Minutes of the Oklahoma State Dental Association, June 8, 9, 10, 1908. These appear in a bound volume on file in the Central Office, Oklahoma State Dental Association, Oklahoma City. The minutes include proceedings of the General Assembly and the Executive Council of the Association from the joint session of the territorial organizations held in Oklahoma City, June 17–19, 1907, through December 15, 1935. The volume also includes a copy of the constitution adopted in 1907 and the revised constitution adopted April 1, 1914, which changed the name of the organization to the Oklahoma State Dental Society.

The Executive Council was recognized as the principal governing body. The nine members were elected in 1907 for staggered terms as follows: three years, A. E. Bonnell, Muskogee; A. L. Walters, Checotah; J. E. Wright, McAlester. Two years, S. A. Long, McAlester; Fred Sims, Weatherford; T. P. Bringhurst, Shawnee. One year, A. E. Adams, Ardmore; G. A. Hughes, Guthrie; A. A. Doughty, Oklahoma City. Thereafter, members were chosen for a term of three years. At the Muskogee meeting in 1908, Adams, Hughes, and Doughty were replaced by C. W. Day, Vinita; E. J. Mills, Poteau; W. E. Flesher, Frederick. The unexpired term of Dr. A. L. Walters, promoted to the presidency of the Association, was filled by the election of Dr. H. A. Weeks, Hartshorne. The president, secretary, and treasurer of the Association were ex-officio members of the Council.

first vice-president. Following the business session Tuesday morning, delegates were guests of the Commercial Club. Among other things, before the luncheon, they took a trolley ride over the city.

— 4 —

GUTHRIE bid for the 1909 convention site, but the dentists voted to meet in Oklahoma City. Rivalry between the political capital and commercial center of the state continued unabated into the next year, when suddenly, dramatically, on Sunday, June 12, Governor C. N. Haskell, at the Lee Huckins Hotel, proclaimed that henceforth Oklahoma City was to be the seat of state government. The day before, the people of Oklahoma, voting on Initiative Measure 7 for the location of the capital at Guthrie, Shawnee, or Oklahoma City, indicated preference for the last place and despite provisions of the Congressional act of June 16, 1906 that the capital should remain at Guthrie until 1913, Haskell acted summarily. The Governor acted on the premise, later sustained by the Supreme Court of the United States, that the selection of a capital site rested with the people of the state rather than with Congress.

The removal of the capital was a serious blow to Guthrie. Census data reveal how serious. The population in 1910 was 11,654; ten years later, 11,757. With the removal of the capital, industry also moved. The peak of industrial activity was reached in 1910 when eight railroads entered the city and the community was served by a street railway with six miles of track. Principal industries were a cotton mill, three cottonseed-oil mills, a compress, two flour mills, three grist mills, two ice plants, four cigar factories, three candy factories, three ice-cream plants, a boiler factory, a cannery, a manufacturer of furniture, a shoe factory, a foundry, and a wooden- and paper-box factory. These and minor industries and machine shops furnished employment for 2,500 men; the value of manufactured products shipped was $4,355,193; no other city or county in the state equaled this amount.

With removal of the capital, however, out of business went the Model Rollings Mills, the cannery, the shoe factory, the Southwest Iron Foundry, the furniture plant, three of the cigar factories, and the box factory.

On November 22, 1907, six days after the inaugural of state government under Governor Haskell, the Oklahoma State Board of Dental Examiners met in Guthrie. Dr. F. C. Seids, Perry, and Dr. A. C. Hixon of Guthrie, holdover members from the territorial board, with Dr. W. W. Bryan, Claremore, Dr. M. W. Murray, Poteau, and Dr. A. E. Bonnell, Muskogee, comprised the membership of the first state board. Since the three members from the East Side held no territorial licenses, they had the unique distinction of receiving licenses under the state seal that also bore their names as members of the licensing board. To these members was delegated the responsibility of dividing the East Side of the state into three districts for the purpose of compiling lists of practicing dentists in each town, eligible under provisions of the constitution for automatic licensing, upon the payment of a fee of one dollar required by the dental act of 1905.

The Board held its next meeting on January 2, 1908, at the Turner Hotel, Muskogee, where it considered each application separately, accepting most of them for registration, rejecting some because the applicants entered into practice in Indian Territory after June 16, 1906, and held up action on a few pending further examination. By mid-May the Board had approved applications received from 107 dentists practicing on the East Side who had met resident qualifications. An additional thirty candidates qualified by examination.

The Board held a special session at Convention Hall, Muskogee, on June 10, following the annual meeting of the Oklahoma State Dental Association. Twenty-eight applicants presented claims of eligibility to register. Seven were approved and granted licenses, and the others were postponed for further examination and proof. The Board resolved that all dentists eligible for licensing under the resident provision of the constitution who had not made application should so do before the next meeting of the Board. After that date they would be subject to an examination.

At the regular November 10 semiannual session held at the Lee Hotel, Oklahoma City, fourteen of twenty-seven applicants from Indian Territory side of the state proved their rights under the automatic licensing provision.

At this time there appeared in the *Western Dental Journal* a letter of October 30, 1908, from Dr. P. D. Coleman, Wilburton, concerning the practice of dentistry in Oklahoma.[11] He related that many men who had lived temporarily in Indian Territory from fifteen to twenty-five years before had written the Board in an attempt to obtain licenses under the resident-qualification clause because they were here "on or before June 16, 1906." "Some have tried very hard to secure certificates for their wives," he related, "while others have journeyed hundreds of miles with their families and endeavored to register their sons, many of whom are without the first rudiments of a dental education."

Coleman explained that population figures of 1907 indicated there was one dentist for every 1,714 inhabitants, "but when it is taken into account that many are Negroes and Indians who rarely patronize the profession, it will be seen that one dentist to each eight hundred people is about the correct average. Of this eight hundred whom the dentist has to look to for his livelihood, a large percentage are newcomers, and, like most emigrants, are possessed of very little money."

Coleman pointed out that the Board had been threatened with many kinds of legal proceedings, ranging from mandamus suits to suits for damages, by disappointed applicants who thought they qualified for licenses under the constitutional provisions. A few were successful. In December, 1909, Dr. William Flamm, Muskogee dentist with thirty years' experience in the profession, was granted a writ of mandamus against the Board to compel members to show why they refused him a license. Flamm claimed he was a resident of Indian Territory before June 16, 1906. An answer was filed ten days later by the Board in the Superior Court, Muskogee. The decision was in favor of Flamm; the Board granted the license. In 1912, Dr. A. A. Gill, Oklahoma City, filed a mandamus suit in Oklahoma County against the Board in which he demanded registration under provisions of the Schedule to the constitution. The Board paid seventy-five dollars to C. G. Hornor, attorney of Guthrie, to assist the Attorney General in representing the state. Judge J. J. Carney ruled that Dr. Gill was entitled to a license and issued a court order to that effect. The license was granted May 19, 1913.

Many dentists from other states wrote the Board in regard to its licensing provisions. Some visited the state to take an examina-

[11] P. D. Coleman, "Concerning the Practice of Dentistry In Oklahoma," *Western Dental Journal*, Vol. XXII (December, 1908), 848-49.

tion before changing their residence. On May 14, 1913, Dr. J. W. Jose, St. Louis, Missouri, was one of the thirty successful applicants; the following November the Board had under consideration a letter from Mrs. Jose, who stated that shortly after her husband took the examination he had died and had never practiced in Oklahoma. She asked the Board to return the examination fee of $25.00 paid by Dr. Jose, as she was in need of funds. Her request was granted.

Much time of the Board at its semiannual and special meetings was taken in examination of applicants, in passing upon qualifications submitted by practitioners of Indian Territory, and in establishing policies and procedures. Dentists wrote in for duplicate licenses, the originals destroyed from such causes as the fire in San Francisco or in local offices. Reciprocal licensing agreements with other states were canceled while the problem came under review.

A change in state administration brought changes in Board membership. G. W. Bowling, Lindsay, and E. E. Heflin, Oklahoma City, were appointed to the Board by Governor Lee Cruce in November, 1911, to replace Fred Seids and M. W. Murray.

When the Board met December 3, 1912, at the Skirvin Hotel, Oklahoma City, the following rules were adopted to govern future examinations:

1. All persons desiring to commence the practice of dentistry in the State of Oklahoma must apply to the State Board of Dental Examiners for license.

2. The written examinations shall be in the English language in the following subjects: Dental Jurisprudence, Physics, Dental Pathology, Crown and Bridge and Prosthetic Dentistry, Anatomy, Anaesthesia, Materia Medica and Therapeutics, Oral Surgery, Physiology, Operative Dentistry, Histology, Chemistry and Metallurgy, Orthodontia, Bacteriology.

3. An applicant must make a grade of not less than 75 per cent on the subjects of Operative Dentistry and Crown and Bridge Work and Prosthetic Dentistry, and must not make a grade less than 50 per cent on any other branch on which he is examined. A general average of 75 per cent is required for a passing grade for license.

4. All written examinations shall be on paper furnished by the Board, no other paper being allowed in the room.

5. At the opening of the examination, the applicant will be fur-

nished with an envelope containing a card with a number. The applicant will write his or her name upon this card, seal the envelope, and use this number on all examination papers. These sealed envelopes will be handed to the Secretary and not opened until all papers are graded, when they shall be opened and the official number be placed together with the final grades opposite the name of the applicant on grade sheet.

6. When papers are turned in questions must accompany answers and no papers will be accepted unless accompanied by the questions.

7. No one will be allowed to leave the room, without permission of the Examiner in charge, after receiving the questions, until said subject is finished and handed in.

8. After two-thirds of the applicants have finished a subject others will be required to hand in their papers within thirty minutes after the announcement.

9. There must be no assistance given or accepted. If anyone assists another, both will be barred from the examination and each will forfeit all legal rights in the examination.

10. There must be no communication between candidates. Any whispering or conversation between candidates without permission of the Examiner in charge will be considered assistance.

11. The Board of Examiners shall begin their inspection and grading of the answers submitted by the candidates after the close of the examination and shall complete same with promptness and dispatch and notify all applicants as soon as possible.

12. Write answers in order of questions. Do not copy questions. Do not give information that is not asked for.

13. No smoking will be allowed in the examing room.

14. All applications together with fee must be in the hands of the Secretary at least ten days before examination.

At this meeting, too, a motion made by Dr. Bonnell was adopted by the Board which provided that practical examinations be given applicants in addition to written examinations.

— 5 —

IN THE interval before the next regular meeting of the Board, a new dental act was passed by the state legislature. The Oklahoma

State Dental Association during the first three biennial sessions of the legislature had proposed measures for the betterment of dentistry. In each session these were introduced and sometimes advanced through one branch of the legislature but later were sidetracked and lost before consideration for final passage. Dentists, however, persisted in agitation for a better law. Interest in better legislation was stimulated and planned by dentists in professional gatherings at local and state meetings; usually when the Association's president or secretary visited local societies and the need for better legislation was stressed.

Interest in a better state dental law was more than local, however. Other states were adopting more stringent laws and the question of reciprocal licensing agreements devolved upon equal professional standards. The Board entered into a reciprocal interchange of licenses with Iowa, June 18, 1907; this was cancelled June 4, 1909. On May 15, 1911, the Board considered a request from the Kansas Board of Examiners to interchange licenses. The request was held over, but the Board drew up recommendations for a form of agreement with states having equal or higher standards of licensing. At the meeting of the Board the following November, interchange of licenses was granted California, Texas, Missouri, Kansas, Colorado, Arkansas, Oregon, and Washington, D. C. The agreements provided that in the event standards were raised under a revised Oklahoma law, reciprocal agreements with the states should be screened for possible cancellation.

The *Bulletin* of the Oklahoma State Dental Association, first issued in June, 1911, called the attention of members to the need for a better dental law. In the March, 1912, issue Dr. A. E. Bonnell summarized the need: "There is nothing good that is too good for the citizens of Oklahoma; laws or anything else, and if there are laws on the statute books of any other state superior to ours they are there not because of a more worthy citizenship, but because we have been so busy building a new state we have not had time to go after everything we needed that was good.

"The time has come for us to turn our attention to a dental law that is more nearly in keeping with the times and dignity of our great commonwealth.

"The law under which we are now operating was doubtless good for the time when it became a law, but, laws like clothes get out of date . . . ."

93

When the Executive Council of the Association met in Oklahoma City, November 18, 1911, it authorized the president to appoint a legislative committee to draft a new and up-to-date dental law. The committee that undertook this responsibility was composed of B. L. Shobe, Bartlesville; A. B. Potter, Oklahoma City; A. C. Hixon, Guthrie; B. L. Neville, Maud; and A. E. Bonnell, Muskogee. Hixon and Bonnell, members of the Board of Dental Examiners, had first-hand knowledge of the many instances when unfavorable court decisions were rendered against the Board because of inadequacies in the dental act of 1905. All members of the committee examined dental laws effective in older states in order to incorporate better provisions in the proposed measure.

Dr. C. R. Lawrence, Enid, stated in the December, 1911, issue of the *Bulletin:* "If the dentists of the state want a new law they will have to get back of it, support it and work hard for it as such a matter as this cannot be brought about by some three or four men. Do you want it? If so let it be known."

The repeated plea for co-operation brought results. The fourth session of the Oklahoma Legislature was to convene in January, 1913, and by the preceding November a draft of the proposed legislation had been sent to members of the Association for discussion before local and district societies. Summing up the attitude of members, A. L. Walters, secretary of the Association, wrote editorially in the November, 1912, *Bulletin:* "The copy submitted to your Secretary was read and re-read and he wishes to compliment the Committee upon its success. As the draft now stands, it would make a splendid law. It is fair and just, and has many features which show that broad-gauged men were responsible for its present form. It would work no hardship upon any dentist in this or any other state, but will protect [the public] from men who are incompetent to practice dentistry. . . . There is just one way to eliminate the charlatan and quack and that is by having a law which is sufficiently strong to keep him out."

Following the plea of Dr. Lawrence that if the dentists wanted a new law they would have to support the movement, Dr. Shobe, chairman of the Legislative Committee, called for voluntary contributions from members of the Association. He explained that members of his committee had paid their own expenses in attending meetings to draft the measure and in making appearance before district

94

societies to explain their work, and added: "The committee has done its utmost and it now rests with the dentists, as individuals, whether or not the work proceeds, for we will do nothing more unless you come to our aid. We wish just here to call your attention to the fact that if you fail to take advantage of this opportunity it will be Two Years Before We can Even Try Again.

"No state has ever secured a good dental law at a cost of less than $2,000.00. We are reliably informed that Illinois paid even more, but your committee feels sure that we can carry on our work at a cost of $1,000.00. To do so, however, will require the services of the dentists themselves—they will have to do their part and do it promptly when called upon."

Funds, of course, were to be used for lobbying purposes: A better dental law, a law for the public welfare, was dependent upon vigilance against crippling amendments and education of members of the legislature on its benefits. Telegrams had to be sent, long-distance telephone calls placed, a lobbyist maintained in Oklahoma City during the legislative session to cultivate legislative leaders and make certain that after the bill was introduced it was advanced toward final passage and not pigeonholed. By the time the legislature convened, dentists had responded to Shobe's plea and raised $350 for the "legislative fund."

Dr. S. A. Long, president of the Association, made a final plea for co-operation: "While good may be accomplished by calling the attention of your own senators and representatives to the deplorable condition (and every dentist in the state will be remiss in his duty if he fails to make personal appeal to the legislators), the history of the fight in every state is that only through a well-informed, fair, tactful, persistent legislative committee can intelligent action be secured. They must not only push positive legislation but must successfully oppose emasculating amendments suggested by ill-informed legislators or inspired by sinister influences. . . .

"Our cause is just. The legislation we seek will be of permanent public benefit. We can convince any open-minded legislator of this fact. The state Department of Charities and Corrections is actively on our side. The progressive schoolmen of the state are with us.

"But the movement must be intelligently directed and must be persistently pushed. Legislation will not enact itself."

Few legislative sessions in Oklahoma have witnessed as much

turmoil and clash of interests as that compounded by the Fourth Legislature. No other session has spent so much time in investigative work and impeachment proceedings. Much time was consumed in these legislative diversions, in consideration of a capitol building program, Congressional redistricting, and the elimination of state institutions—so much time that Governor Lee Cruce had to call a special session immediately after the adjournment of the regular session to consider appropriation bills.[12]

Association members were pleased with the selection of J. H. Maxey, Muskogee, as speaker of the House of Representatives. Bonnell had discussed the draft of the dental measure with his fellow townsman and received a favorable reaction.

On Friday, January 10, the fourth legislative day, J. E. Wyand, representative from Muskogee County, introduced House Bill 93, relating to the practice of dentistry in Oklahoma. Maxey referred the bill to the Committee on Dentistry, which, on January 17, recommended its passage. Finally, at third reading on March 3, it passed the House by a vote of sixty-nine to three. How well the dentists had drafted the bill is indicated by its progress through the lower house: All attempts to amend the measure were voted down, with one exception. Section 6 of the draft prepared by the dentists provided that the Board of Examiners could revoke a license for the commission of any crime involving moral turpitude. Representative E. P. Hill of Pittsburg County offered an amendment that was adopted which provided no license should be revoked by the Board "until after hearing and conviction in a court of competent jurisdiction."

House Bill 93 was received by the Senate on March 1 and, two days later, referred to its Committee on Public Health. Dentists again were alerted because the session was drawing to a close and apparently senators were more concerned with other legislative matters than a revised dental law. Just two days before the end of the session, the Senate took the measure under advisement. A provision was added that all laws or parts of laws in conflict with the act were to be repealed.

[12] Angie Debo's *Oklahoma: Foot-Loose and Fancy Free* (Norman, University of Oklahoma Press, 1949) is a remarkable synthesis of what Oklahoma is like. Miss Debo's chapter four, "A Seething Caldron of Politics," gives an accurate summary of politics after statehood.

On third reading that day, the measure passed the Senate thirty-three to four. Senator J. T. McIntosh, one of those who voted against the measure, explained: "I vote 'no' on the passage of House Bill 93 because it was rushed through the Senate on such a 'Hurrah' that I could not tell what the provisions of the bill were, and could not hear the bill read for the noise."

Because the measure had been amended by the Senate, it was necessary for the House to vote upon the amended bill. Time was running out, but the dentists had Speaker Maxey call up the measure in the closing moments of the last day of the session, March 17. On roll call the bill passed seventy-one to none. Since an emergency clause was attached to the measure, it took effect March 28, on approval by Governor Cruce.

The act continued in effect a five-member Board of Dental Examiners. Tenure was to be five years and terms of office were staggered to permit a new appointment each year. Power of appointment remained solely with the governor, who could remove an appointee for neglect of duty, incompetency, or unprofessional or dishonorable conduct.

The act provided that examinations for licensing should be practical demonstrations of proficiency before the Board as well as written or oral.

Section 6 of the act deserves special consideration. Dr. C. R. Lawrence, secretary of the Association, wrote in the *Bulletin*, June, 1913: "Section 6 is one of the strongest sections ever written in a dental law and should be read and re-read and finally committed to memory and after we get it firmly fixed in our minds see that we do not violate any of its provisions."

Provisions of the section were: "The Board of Examiners may revoke a license after hearing, for the commission of any crime involving moral turpitude after conviction in court; for the habitual use of intoxicants or drugs to such an extent as to render him or her unfit for the practice of dentistry; for fraud practiced in examination or in obtaining license; for employing unlicensed operators; for failure to employ aseptic practice in dental operations; for deceit or fraud practiced upon the public or upon individual patients, provided, that no license shall be revoked by the Board until after a hearing and conviction in a court of competent jurisdiction."

Sections 9 and 10 defined the practice of dentistry. Section 11 referred to unethical advertisers. It provided: "It shall be unlawful to publish or circulate fraudulent or misleading statements as to the skill and methods of any operator." Sections 14 and 15 set forth provisions for reciprocal licensing agreements with other states; section 17 granted exemption from jury service.

Because the new dental act provided for practical examinations of applicants, the Board established the following criteria, each worth 25 per cent:

FIRST—Neatness of operator generally.

SECOND—Handling of patient and materials.

THIRD—Preparation of cavity for filling or preparation of roots of teeth for crowns.

FOURTH—Manipulation and finished work.

The first practical examinations were given by the Board at the Lee Huckins Hotel in May, 1913. This method met with such success that additional dental chairs were purchased by the Board in order that the practical portion of the examination could proceed with greater rapidity.

Although other states approached the Board during 1913–14 in regard to license-exchange privileges, the first arrangement was made with Arkansas, as follows:

"This agreement made and entered into this 17th day of June in the year 1915 by and between the Board of Dental Examiners of the State of Oklahoma and the Board of Dental Examiners of the State of Arkansas, witnesseth:—

"That we do hereby agree to recognize the license to practice dentistry issued by our representative Boards in so far as the state laws governing same shall permit, under the following conditions, to wit:—

"Any applicant having a license in one state and having been in legal practice five (5) years or more, may be admitted to practice dentistry in the other state without any further theoretical examination, provided he has the endorsement and recommendation of the Board of his own state. Said application shall be subject to the practical examination of the respective Boards.

"This agreement shall be in force from the time of its being signed by the members of both Boards and may be terminated at any time by either party, by said party giving to the other party sixty (60) days' notice."

Before reciprocal agreements under the dental act were made with other states, however, before the dental act was passed, the Association had inaugurated a plan for conducting annual meetings which is considered one of the great achievements of dentistry in Oklahoma, one that brought nation-wide recognition in the dental profession.

CHAPTER FOUR

The Oklahoma Way

— I —

THE CONSTITUTION adopted by the Oklahoma State Dental Association in 1907 provided for the organization of district or county societies where local groups could meet, fraternize, conduct clinics, and read and discuss papers. The formation of district groups, from two or more counties, was stressed by Dr. A. L. Walters, Checotah, during his administration, and in March, 1909, a series of meetings throughout the state resulted in district organization.

The first group of dentists to form a district organization were those in northwestern Oklahoma. They met at the Loewen Hotel, Enid, March 4, and formed the Northwestern Oklahoma Dental Society and elected E. H. Westenhaver, Enid, president; F. P. Hulen, Pond Creek, vice-president; C. R. Lawrence, Enid, secretary; I. E. McCarty, Enid, Treasurer; and Roy Woolwine, Hennessey, librarian. Others in attendance were T. J. Tourtellot, H. B. Shields, H. L. Entriken, L. R. Richardson, and O. H. McCarty, Enid; A. F. Merrill, Hennessey; E. C. Watkins, Pond Creek; J. A. Morrow, Carmen; C. W. Lyon, Medford; A. T. Watkins, Shattuck. After a banquet, "a motion was carried extending thanks to Dr. A. L. Walters for his paper, and to Clay Jewett for cigars."[1]

The meeting at the Robinson Hotel, Tulsa, March 11, to form the Northern Dental Association of Oklahoma, typifies organizational work under way in other areas of the state. In attendance were C. R. Woolomes, M. L. Ingram, B. L. Shobe, R. F. Stilwell and F. N. Buck, Bartlesville; Ira Malone and W. H. Pelky,

[1] Minutes of the Northwestern Oklahoma Dental Society, March 4, 1909, Central Office, Oklahoma State Dental Association.

Sapulpa; William Harrison, L. P. Owens, O. A. Stewart, William Wilson, G. E. Stevenson, J. M. Temples, C. S. Ferner, P. H. Ramsey, G. S. Defoe, and W. H. Gregg, Tulsa; H. H. Kaho, Claremore; L. J. Sizer and C. E. Clark, Broken Arrow; H. H. Messimer, Nowata; C. L. Hayes, Pawhuska; and H. L. McAdoo, Dewey.[2]

Dr. J. M. Temples was elected temporary chairman and Dr. W. H. Pelky, secretary. A committee consisting of Drs. Buck, Shobe, and Stewart was appointed to draft by-laws and constitution for the new organization. Members reported: "We the committee recommend the adoption of the by-laws and constitution of the state association with the modifications necessary to make same practical for a society which convenes oftener and one which is more limited in its membership."

The committee recommended the adoption of the following by-laws:

Article I (Meetings)

Section 1. The conventions of this association shall be quarterly and called meetings.

Section 2. Meetings shall be held at such place and at such time as the Executive Council shall determine.

Section 3. The Executive Council may call a special meeting whenever in their judgment extreme urgency shall render such a meeting necessary, provided that no business except that required to meet the emergency shall be transacted at such meeting.

Article II (Duties of Officers)

Section 1. The President shall be the presiding officer of the association, shall have general supervision over its affairs, and shall be a member ex-officio of all committees.

Section 2. The Vice-President shall take cognizance of the general interests of the association, advise with the President and pre-

[2] A paper-bound notebook, on file in the Central Office, Oklahoma State Dental Association, contains the minutes and proceedings of the Northern Dental Association of Oklahoma, March 11, 1909, to November 20, 1917. These records, handwritten with pencil or pen, vary in legibility and brevity with the yearly personnel changes of recording secretaries.

side in his absence. In event of death or disqualification of the President, the Vice-President shall succeed to the presidency.

Section 3. The Secretary shall conduct the correspondence of the association under its official seal, record its proceedings, collect all moneys due the association, keep an accurate account thereof, turn them over to the treasurer and take his receipt therefor and carefully preserve the archives of the association.

Section 4. The Treasurer shall receive all monies from the secretary, give his receipt therefor, pay them out on the order of the secretary (signed by the president) as directed by the executive council, take proper vouchers for such payments, and give a bond in such an amount as the executive council may deem sufficient.

Section 5. The Executive Council shall manage the affairs of the association, conduct its business, audit its accounts, annually report its finances.

Article III (Membership)

Section 1. Application for membership shall be made in writing, signed by the applicant and addressed to the secretary of the association, and recommended by two members of the association and accompanied by the fee of $2.00.

Article IV (Quorum)

Section 1. Six or more qualified voters shall constitute a quorum.

Article V (Code of Ethics)

Section 1. The state code of ethics shall govern, and are adopted by this association.

The committee offered the following constitution to the association:

Article I

This organization shall be known as the Northern Dental Association of Oklahoma.

Article II

The purpose of the association shall be to cultivate the science, art, and ethics of dentistry, to promote a cordial friendship among its members, to take cognizance of the common interests of the profession and collectively act thereon.

ARTICLE III

Section 1. This association shall be comprised of active members residing within the district.

Section 2. Any ethical dentist of good moral character residing and practicing within the jurisdiction of this association, is eligible for membership.

ARTICLE IV

Section 1. The officers of the Northern Dental Association of Oklahoma shall consist of president, vice-president, secretary, treasurer, and executive council.

Section 2. The president and vice-president shall be elected annually by the association and shall serve until their successors qualify.

Section 3. The secretary and the treasurer shall be elected annually and shall serve until their successors shall qualify.

Section 4. The executive council shall consist of the president, secretary, and treasurer as members ex-officio, and three other members who shall be elected annually and serve until their successors shall qualify.

ARTICLE V

This constitution may be amended at any meeting by three fourths of the entire membership.

After the by-laws and the constitution were adopted, the following officers were elected: Dr. B. L. Shobe, Bartlesville, president; Dr. L. J. Sizer, Broken Arrow, vice-president; Dr. J. M. Temples, Tulsa, secretary; Dr. Ira Malone, Sapulpa, treasurer. Members selected for the executive council were Dr. W. H. Pelky, Sapulpa; Dr. C. E. Clark, Broken Arrow; and Dr. G. E. Stevenson, Tulsa.

Minutes of successive meetings reveal the seriousness with

which associate members of the profession worked with improved techniques toward their betterment. On November 13, 1909, for example, the third meeting of the Association took place in the Tulsa offices of Drs. Wilson and Gregg to witness the following clinics:

Dr. Woolomes—Casting a porcelain-faced crown with improved adaptation to the root.

Dr. Ferner—Replacing a broken tooth on a rubber denture by using a low-fusing metal for the attachment.

Dr. Owens—Replacing a crown where the post remains in root without removing the post.

Dr. Stevenson—A cohesive foil filling.

Dr. Day—A bicuspid porcelain-faced shell crown.

Dr. Ingram—Swaging a shell crown.

Later, Dr. W. H. Pelky read a paper on "devitalized teeth." After discussion, the dentists adjourned to another building to enjoy a "light repast prepared under the skillful supervision of Dr. Wm. Harrison."

On Saturday, January 15, 1910, the Northern Dental Association met in Bartlesville. During the afternoon, clinics were held in the offices of Drs. Shobe and Woolomes. An evening session was held in the Masonic Lodge room. Dr. F. N. Buck read a paper on the advertising dentist and his influence on ethical dentistry. Dr. Fred Sparks, Ponca City, president of the state association, was a guest at the meeting. He delivered an address on "How to Elevate Dentistry by Elevating Ourselves." A discussion which led into an experience meeting followed, and "all present partook and seemed much benefitted."

At the first general meeting held by the Oklahoma State Dental Association at Muskogee in June, 1908, Sparks had offered the resolution adopted by the convention which resulted in dividing the state into district societies. His argument on the floor was that such divisions would engender leadership throughout the state. At this district meeting eighteen months later he pointed out how well the plan had spread: from early beginnings with local societies in Oklahoma City, Ardmore, and Muskogee to quarterly meetings attracting district-wide attendance in eastern, central, northern, and northwestern Oklahoma.

As much as any dentist in active practice, Sparks felt the need to improve his profession. His service on the Board of Dental Examiners and the dental act of 1905 which he helped fashion were only incidents in his program for professional advancement. He persistently taught that members of the profession should better themselves by studying new techniques and developments.

At the Muskogee meeting Sparks successfully blocked the resolution to pay the expense of a delegate to the annual convention of the National Dental Association. His contention was that it would be better to spend the money to pay the expenses of an expert clinician to come to Oklahoma and demonstrate advanced techniques to the dentists in annual assembly.

This idea was advanced by Walters during his presidency of the Association at meetings of the district societies. Sparks, the next year, stressed the need for better-trained dentists. Dr. Fred Sims, member of the executive board at that time, has recently recalled that Sparks appointed Dr. B. L. Shobe, Bartlesville, as program chairman with the intent to work toward stimulating interest in a locally held postgraduate course.

Shobe succeeded Sparks as president of the state association in June, 1910. Like his predecessors, Walters and Sparks, he visited district and local societies, stimulating interest in the postgraduate idea. Records of the Northern Dental Association for the district meeting at Tulsa, February 11, 1911, reveal Shobe's activity.

The evening session, held in the Robinson Hotel, was called to order by Dr. J. M. Temples, president. After the minutes of the previous meeting were approved, Dr. Temples gave a short address in which he reviewed the work of the organization during the past year. Following this, Dr. C. L. Hayes, Pawhuska, read a paper on "The Advantages of Cocaine and Pressure over Arsenic in Pulp Removal." Discussion followed; then Dr. A. C. Hixon, Guthrie, delivered an address on the subject, "Better Dental Legislation." A committee was appointed to present recommendations in June to the state association before the annual meeting at Enid.

The secretary has recorded in the minutes this important event: "Dr. B. L. Shobe, President of the State Association, then addressed the Association on the subject of a post-graduate course to be given by the state society.

"Discussed by Drs. Hope, Hayes, Bradley, Moore and Hawkins.

"Moved and seconded that N. D. A. endorse the propositions suggested by Dr. Shobe relative to post-graduate course. Carried."

At the annual meeting of the Oklahoma State Dental Association held in Enid, June 1–3, 1911, members approved the proposal advanced by leaders for a postgraduate course. The organization made plans to employ three nationally known dentists to deliver a series of lectures and clinical demonstrations during the next annual meeting. The association appointed a committee composed of B. L. Shobe, Bartlesville; F. D. Sparks, Ponca City; W. L. Dutcher, Oklahoma City; and A. L. Walters, Checotah, to make arrangements for this new and untried method of conducting an annual meeting.

Working through the national association the committee immediately began making inquiries that were to lead to the selection of outstanding technicians and teachers who would present postgraduate courses at Oklahoma City March 25–30. Lecturers' expenses were to be borne by the Association, and it was hoped that two hundred Oklahoma dentists would be willing to attend and pay a fee of five dollars each in order to finance the undertaking.

In December the committee was able to report arrangements had been completed with three prominent dentists to conduct the courses. Dr. J. P. Buckley, professor and head of the Department of Materia Medica, Pharmacology, and Therapeutics of the Chicago College of Dental Surgery; Dr. Hart J. Goslee, professor of Prosthetic Dentistry, Crown and Bridge Work of the Chicago College of Dental Surgery, and Dr. G. Walter Ditmar, professor of Operative Dentistry of the University of Illinois, were to comprise the faculty.

Through meetings of the auxiliary societies of the Association at Oklahoma City, Ardmore, Shawnee, Muskogee, Enid, and Tulsa, the postgraduate idea was presented by Shobe, Sparks, Walters, Dutcher, and other officials, either by personal appearance at group meetings or by correspondence. Dr. C. R. Lawrence of Enid, using the pages of the *Bulletin*, kept the program before its readers; he urged those who contemplated attending the courses to read standard textbooks by the lecturers: *Materia-Medica and Therapeutics*, by Buckley; *Crown and Bridge Work*, by Goslee; and the two-volume *Operative Dentistry*, by Black.

— 2 —

RAILROADS granted reduced fares to and from Oklahoma City for the 1912 meeting. The Lee Huckins Hotel, selected as headquarters for the convention, reserved its entire second floor for exhibits, clinics, and lectures of the Association. The large ballroom was arranged as a lecture hall, while different parlors on the floor were used as clinic and exhibit rooms. Special room rates, beginning at one dollar, were given dentists who stayed at the hotel during the session.

Dentists who had not visited Oklahoma City since the joint session of the territorial organizations in June, 1907, were amazed at the growth of the city. The Colcord Building, the state's first skyscraper and million-dollar office building, placed under construction in 1910, now housed dental and medical and other professional offices. The new Skirvin Hotel was one block north on Broadway from the Lee Huckins and rivaled it in size, accommodations, and grandeur. While the Skirvin became a center of Republican party activity and unofficial headquarters of the party, a rival of the Lee Huckins for convention headquarters, the latter remained the unofficial capitol of the state, the gathering place and residence of governors, the Democratic faithful, senators, and representatives. The thrust of railroads had made the city a transcontinental crossroads, and interurban lines radiated out to Edmond, Guthrie, Yukon, El Reno, Moore, and Norman. Gridirons of streets had been paved beyond residential fringes approaching Northwest Twenty-third. Bridges across the North Canadian River served as links for the paved streets of Walker and Robinson connecting Capitol Hill with the city, while propaganda was underway for a city-wide bond issue to convert a cornfield to the northeast into capitol grounds for an imposing statehouse. Along North Broadway, too, daring entrepreneurs were converting blocks into "automobile row," where the latest models of the Krit, Paige, Maxwell, Chalmers Henderson, Ford, Buick, and electric cars were on display.[3]

Possibly some of the out-of-town dentists who arrived in the

[3] See files of the *Daily Oklahoman*, advertisements as well as news stories, for the month of March, 1912.

city Sunday, March 24, were guests on the first automobile excursion, or "sociability jaunt" as it was designated March 22 by a reporter for the *Daily Oklahoman:* "It was arranged at a meeting of the Dealer's Committee of the Oklahoma City Club of the State Automobile Association to have Sunday the first of a series of sociability runs, the course being to El Reno and return.

"The run will be open to all and every man in the city who owns a car has been notified. It is estimated there will be more than 100 cars in the tour as this is the first run of its kind that has ever been pulled off in Oklahoma City.

"The cars will congregate in front of the *Oklahoman* building at 10 o'clock Sunday morning, beginning the trip to El Reno shortly afterward. An easy pace will be the rule all the time, and a stop will probably be made in Yukon. El Reno will be reached early in the afternoon and after a short stay there, the return run will be started. Roads between here and El Reno are in the best of condition now and the run promises to be very agreeable."

B. L. Neville, dentist from Stonewall, slipped away from the Monday morning session of the Association long enough to call upon W. H. Hampton, water commissioner, to suggest that Oklahoma City get its water supply from Boggy Creek, three miles below his city.

The six lady members of the profession in attendance for the session, as well as wives of dentists who came to the city Sunday, March 24, probably were attracted to North Robinson, street of churches, for the dedicatory service of the First Baptist Church. Constructed at a cost of $150,000, with a main auditorium "pronounced by visiting ministers and architects as the most beautiful and tastefully designed in the country," the church had a seating capacity of 2,000, choir accommodations for 100, and more "than 400 lights in the auditorium." More wives than usual had accompanied their husbands to the city, attracted by the week-long cooking school sponsored by the *Daily Oklahoman* at the Armory, 1011 North Broadway, where "one of the most expert culinary artists in the country" taught "the art of preparing various dishes and viands and preparing them in such an appetizing manner" they were a revelation to the best-informed cooks: proper recipes for broiled bacon, hominy crescents, spiced clovers, steamed chocolate pudding, cerise sauce, etc. As they window-shopped along Main

Street, shivering in a final wintry blast that had blanketed Kansas City under eighteen inches of snow, the ladies were attracted by the "sparkling Easter fashions" offered by Kerr's, and Brock's Easter millinery, a "replete, authentic showing of every new idea, every correct fashion forecaster for Spring and Summer."

Those who attended the cooking school on Monday were enthralled by thirty minutes of Pianola and Victrola selections preceding the school, courtesy of J. W. Jenkins Sons Music Company. And doubtless a few were attracted to the music store by a newspaper advertisement which showed an "active business man" pumping the Pianola piano, which "supplies just the kind of mental diversion that overtaxed business men ought to have in their leisure hours. . . . Business men who find the cares of a strenuous life bearing heavily upon them should investigate the Pianola Piano."

Certainly some of the ladies had their husbands pick up reservations for the Thursday night performance of Gilbert and Sullivan's *Pinafore*, with augmented orchestra and ensemble of seventy-five, at the Overholser Theatre. On other nights they attended this theater to see William Hodge in "the success of the century," *The Man from Home*, or on to the Met (any seat twenty-five cents) where the North Brothers Stock Company offered the "best society drama of the last twenty years"—*A Little Brother of the Rich*. But Friday night was to be reserved for a return to the First Baptist Church, where Clarence Eddy, admittedly "the world's greatest living organist, will formally inaugurate the new organ with a recital." The organ was rated second only to the one in the Salt Lake City Tabernacle.

These civic and cultural events available to visiting dentists and their wives represented the exciting advancements of the day. Yet no event in the dental history of Oklahoma contributed more to the advancement of the profession than the series of postgraduate courses which began the next day at the Lee Huckins Hotel. This series, and those that followed in successive years, became nationally known as the "Oklahoma Way," and dental associations everywhere recognized the forward step taken by the Oklahoma State Dental Association. C. R. Lawrence, Enid, president; C. W. Day, Vinita, first vice-president; Ira Malone, Sapulpa, second vice-president; A. L. Walters, Checotah, secretary; N. C. Wood, Ardmore, treasurer; and members of the Executive Council of the Association were called to other states at various times to explain the program and germinate the idea. Arkansas, Kansas, Texas, and other states adopted the plan. Dentistry, particularly throughout the Southwest, was improved by the missionary efforts of a few Oklahoma dentists who spread the story of the Oklahoma Way.

More important to Oklahoma, however, was the technical and professional advancement of dentistry in the state. Dr. Walters, while recently discussing the leadership of Dr. Shobe in projecting the program, has summed up reasons why Shobe advocated the presentation of postgraduate courses at the annual meeting: "Knowing that most of the dentists were poor, he decided it would be infinitely better to bring outstanding leaders of the profession to our state, which could be done for a nominal sum, rather than to expect the men to go elsewhere to school to take postgraduate work."

Dr. Shobe, at this time, was not an executive officer of the Association. He had served the organization as president the previous year, worked tirelessly and unselfishly to advance the postgraduate idea, and taken much time from his practice to visit every section of the state, every component society of the Association, to create interest in this move toward the betterment of state dentistry. Shobe, according to Walters, his close friend and associate, "was past fifty, of rather nervous temperament with definite opinions and yet considerate of others' viewpoints, but always demanding a reason for any disagreement with his point of view. Studious and sincere, he could forcefully summarize his thoughts, usually adding, 'Have you a better idea or plan?' " Others remember him as "a fine business and professional man, a splendid companion and the soul of generosity." Fellow-practitioners of Oklahoma have honored him as the outstanding member of the profession during its first half-century; the Shobe Memorial in the lobby of the Medical and Dental Arts Building, Tulsa, is another mark of the esteem in which he is held by the profession. No finer delineation of his character, the faith Association members had in him, can be expressed than to illustrate a trait he showed during the first postgraduate course. On Thursday, March 28, members of the Association assembled in the ballroom of the hotel to elect officers for the following term. Shobe was not present. Among the three names presented for the office of president was Shobe's. On the first ballot, he lacked a few votes of having a majority; unquestionably he would have been chosen on the next ballot. Before balloting could take place, however, he appeared in the room, was informed of what was transpiring, and immediately took the floor to withdraw his name and plead that the office should always draw upon members for new leadership. This precedent has remained unbroken in the history of the Association.

At this annual meeting members from over the state had first-hand evidence of the organizational ability of Dr. C. R. Lawrence. He came to Enid in 1908 from Illinois where he had been active in association work, and he remained a lifelong member of the Illinois State Dental Association. Shortly after his arrival in Enid, Dr. H. L. Entriken of that city was asked by Dr. Walters, president of the Association, to set in motion a movement for a district organization. Entriken informed Walters that the recent arrival, Lawrence, was the strongest believer in concerted action through Association support in the area, that he was young, capable, and experienced. The recommendation was most fortunate: Lawrence quickly assumed leadership for the Association in that part of the state. With the exception of local societies established at Ardmore, Oklahoma City, and Muskogee during the territorial period which became affiliated with the Oklahoma State Dental Association, the Northwestern Dental Society was the first organized component society in the state.

It is significant that Lawrence was chosen secretary of the district organization. Seven years later he wrote in the *Bulletin:* "Show me a progressive dental organization, be it National, State or City, and I will show you in that organization a man acting as secretary who is striving hard at all times toward the upbuilding of the organization." This was his creed, and his devotion to the duties of the office earned respect and emulation of members.

It is interesting that during the decade 1909–19, when component district societies of the Association were established and the postgraduate courses were bringing national recognition to Oklahoma, there were eleven presidents of the state association, but only three secretaries, each of whom succeeded to the more arduous office after a term in the president's chair: A. L. Walters, 1909–13; C. R. Lawrence, 1913–16; W. E. Flesher, 1916–19.

Before he gave up his secretarial duties, Dr. Lawrence wrote the following message in the February, 1916, issue of the *Bulletin:* "It has been my privilege to serve in almost every capacity in the

Oklahoma State Dental Society, from a private up to the presidency, and on to the secretaryship. Yes, I say on to the secretaryship, for I believe no member has served his dental society in its most important office, until he has acted as secretary. The presidency is an honor, but it does not afford the opportunity of being of real service to the society that the office of secretary gives. The work of the secretary is never spectacular, but it is constant, and he must be on duty at all times. His work consists of something more than recording a few minutes and collecting dues. The secretary is in touch with dental affairs of the state, more than any other man. . . . Mistakes can be made in the selection of a president without any serious results, but not so with the secretary, and this applies equally to all dental organizations, be they large or small."

Lawrence launched the *Bulletin of the Oklahoma State Dental Association* in June, 1911, shortly after his election as state president. This is one of the earliest publications of a state dental organization that has had an uninterrupted existence; it antedates the *Journal* of the American Dental Association by two years. The *Bulletin,* renamed the *Journal* in 1951, with interesting news items on the Association and component societies and personalities in dentistry, includes learned articles by members of the profession. The format has changed in the intervening years, but it retains that high fidelity of conscientious effort established by Lawrence.

This industrious, hard-working individual, who devoted his professional life to the improvement of dentistry and public welfare, was to win greater recognition in work devoted to tri-state programs held at Kansas City, in service to the national organization as a trustee of the Twelfth Dental District, and from appearances on national programs and before meetings of twenty-four other state associations. The Oklahoma Way gained international recognition in 1917, when an article by him, "The Post Graduate Dental Meeting," was reprinted and distributed by the National Dental Association. In 1933 he served as vice-president of the American Dental Association, an honor accorded only two other Oklahomans: Dr. A. E. Bonnell, Muskogee, in 1929, and Dr. H. O. Warrick, Enid, in 1953.

Lawrence came closer than any other Oklahoman to the presidency of the American Dental Association. At the 1939 national convention a spontaneous movement arose among the delegates that almost gave him this coveted honor. He lost the election by only four votes after friends from the Southwest who knew his qualities entered his name as a "dark horse." Had an organizational effort been made and groundwork laid before the convention, Oklahoma probably would have received this honor. Perhaps if Lawrence had been a better "mixer" and less the perfectionist in detail work, the honor would have been accorded him.

Issues of the *Bulletin*s during his editorship reveal these qualities and his lack of compromise with mediocrity. Dr. A. L. Walters, Tulsa, who was closely associated with other leaders of the Association during this period, has described Lawrence as the "reserved, thinking type. He seldom gave an opinion until all the evidence was in and then, let the chips fall where they may, he took his position. He was always calm, logical, not governed by sentiment. Though close friends, a guest in his home, I don't remember that I ever heard him laugh out loud a half dozen times throughout the years of our association."

The first series of postgraduate courses offered in 1912 set the pattern for successive meetings, and an examination of the program shows the technical and professional advancements brought Oklahoma dentists by professional leaders. Registration was completed Monday morning, March 25, with more than two hundred dentists from Oklahoma and others from surrounding states in attendance. At 10:00 A.M. the meeting was called to order in the ballroom of the Lee Huckins Hotel to listen to a welcome address by W. B. Moore of the Chamber of Commerce and the response by Dr. A. E. Bonnell. After necessary announcements, members were dismissed and given an opportunity to visit booths of exhibitors set up on the mezzanine floor.

The afternoon session was conducted by Dr. F. E. Roach, eminent dentist of Chicago, who replaced Dr. Goslee when the latter, through unavoidable circumstances, was unable to attend. For three hours Dr. Roach held the attention of dentists during his presentation of the use of dental instruments, while he explained modern techniques in making dentures. During the afternoon he gave an illustrated lecture, and manually presented modern crown technique as well as root preparation for various forms of crowns, the classification and discrimination in the selection of crowns, and detailed technique of constructing crowns.

Dr. Dittmar on Tuesday morning delivered a lecture on fundamental subjects relative to operative dentistry, and in the afternoon Dr. Buckley discussed the diagnosis and treatment of diseases of the dental pulp. Wednesday, Dr. Roach lectured on castings as applied in crown and bridgework and demonstrated detailed techniques of various forms and use. Dr. Dittmar called attention to various classes of cavities, the atrophy and erosion of teeth; Dr. Buckley called attention to the diagnosis and treatment of dentoalveolar abscesses, and illustrated the surgery of chronic abscesses by means of slides. That evening chartered interurban cars left the Terminal Building with a delegation of dentists for Edmond, where Dr. Buckley addressed assembled students, faculty, and guests of the Normal School on the importance of oral hygiene. A similar public lecture had been given by Dr. Buckley the previous evening at the high school auditorium, Oklahoma City. On Thursday and Friday, Dr. Buckley gave illustrated lectures on the filling of root canals and the diagnosis and treatment of pyorrhea alveolaris, and Dr. Dittmar lectured and gave demonstrations on various practical phases of operative dentistry.

During the annual banquet on Thursday evening there was discussion relative to the Taggart process. Dr. William H. Taggart, Chicago, had perfected a system for casting perfectly fitting inlays, considered by many to be the greatest contribution made to dental progress by an individual. It revolutionized nearly every phase of dental prosthesis. Since his announcement of his process in 1907, however, Taggart had become involved in a series of disputes with members of the profession concerning the use of his process without purchasing one of his casting machines or paying royalty on his patent.

At the banquet Dr. Dittmar was called upon to explain conditions pertaining to the Taggart patent. Dittmar explained the background of the controversy between Taggart and members of the profession and presented the plan of compromise worked out by the U. S. Dental Protective Association under the guidance of Dr. J. N. Crouse. Drs. Renz, White, and Buckley took part in the discussion. Buckley, incidentally, was one of the Chicago group who had worked out the compromise agreement. Both Chicago leaders expressed the hope that members of the Association would consider adopting the Crouse compromise.

Dr. Shobe then made a motion, which was adopted, "that a committee be appointed to investigate the Taggart patent and that the committee report to the society on the following day." Dr. Lawrence appointed A. E. Bonnell, Muskogee; N. C. Wood, Ardmore; and F. D. Sparks, Ponca City, who made the following report:

"We your committee appointed to investigate the contract entered into between the Dental Protective Association and Dr. W. H. Taggart, beg leave to submit the following:

"After conferring with Drs. Dittmar, Roach, Buckley and others who are thoroughly conversant with the case, we find three courses open to the profession.

"First. If you are not a member of the Dental Protective Association, upon the payment of $25.00 you may become one. Fifteen dollars of this amount goes to Dr. Taggart, and $10.00 to the Dental Protective Association. This gives you the protection of the Association and the right to use the Taggart casting process with any machine that you now or may hereafter possess. This includes the right to use any of the Taggart inventions or preparations. Second. The Taggart machine may be purchased for $99.00 cash or $110.00 on time. This gives all the privileges before mentioned except membership in the Dental Protective Association. Third. You may ignore the whole thing and take your chance.

"In view of the foregoing we present the following resolution and move its adoption.

" 'Recognizing the great service Dr. Taggart has rendered the profession and the public in giving us the casting methods as applied to dentistry and believing he is entitled to a just return for same, we wish to express our appreciation to him for his great service and to the Dental Protective Association for the fair and liberal contract they have secured with him.' "

On motion of Dr. Walters the report and resolution were accepted by the Association. Individuals made their own choice in regard to joining or staying out of the Dental Protective Association, in paying or refraining from paying for use of the Taggart process. Dr. Taggart finally wore himself out in litigation concerning his invention, and in 1923 his patents were declared invalid by federal court action.

— 3 —

THE MEETING of the Dental Association in Oklahoma City, March, 1912, was epochal in another sense: George W. Bowling, member of the State Board of Dental Examiners, was expelled from the Association.[4]

During the first year of the Cruce administration, Dr. W. W. Bryan, Claremore, was reappointed to the Board for a second term, to expire November 16, 1914. Dr. G. W. Bowling, Lindsay, was appointed to a term ending November 16, 1913, and Dr. E. E. Heflin, Oklahoma City, for a term ending November 16, 1915. Bowling and Heflin succeeded Dr. F. C. Seids, Perry, and Dr. M. W. Murray, Poteau. Dr. A. E. Bonnell, Muskogee, and Dr. A. C. Hixon, Guthrie, were holdover members.

Assembling dentists who opened their early morning *Daily Oklahoman* Monday, March 25 were struck by a two-column six-inch advertisement carrying a cut of Dr. Bowling and the announcement that he was organizing what "will be known as The Oral Hygiene Movement of Oklahoma."

Dentists, who condoned only card announcements in the way of public advertising, read further:

"The purpose of this society will be to teach the public prophylaxis. This subject will be taught through the press of the state, also by a system of lectures at public schools and colleges throughout the state."

This did not seem unworthy and expressed generally the aim of the Association in educating the public on the importance of oral hygiene. But members versed in the National Code of Ethics read and read again the next paragraph of the announcement:

"There are men in the dental profession like all other professions who are afraid to open their mouths for fear they will go beyond the bounds of ethics. These men are so narrow-minded that they need to be educated themselves not only along the line of ethics but along the fundamental principles of education."

The Executive Council of the Association met Friday noon. A motion immediately considered and passed called for the expulsion of Dr. Bowling from membership in the Association for "unethical

[4] Minutes of the Oklahoma State Dental Association, March 29, 1912.

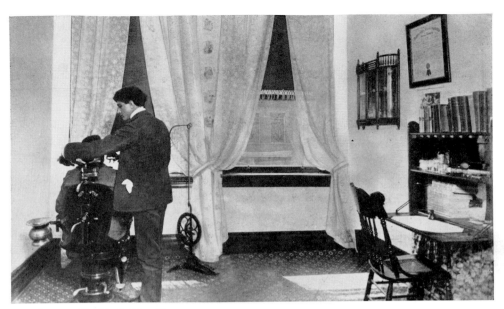

Courtesy Dr. R. G. Hirschi

Above: Operating Room of Dr. R. O. Hirschi,
Guthrie, Oklahoma Territory, 1900

Below: L. M. Doss "Dental Parlors," Ada, Indian Territory, 1902

The "New Look" in Dental Office Buildings
Above: Bungalow office of Dr. John G. Gerard, Dewey

Below: Utica Square Medical Center, Tulsa

and unprofessional conduct." A committee was dispatched to inform Dr. Bowling of the action. At the 3:00 P.M. final general assembly Dr. Lawrence announced that Dr. Bowling had been suspended, and warned, "This is an example of what will follow unless the Code of Ethics is more universally observed."

When the Association convened for its annual meeting the next year, Dr. Bowling was still a member of the State Board of Dental Examiners. Three members of the Executive Council, I. E. Cordrey, Blackwell; H. A. Weeks, Hartshorne; and L. T. Wyllis, Clinton, were named members of a committee to contact Dr. Bowling, now a resident of Oklahoma City, to ascertain if the suspension from the Association should be removed. The committee, however, had to report to the Council that Dr. Bowling had been notified to meet them, "but had failed to come to prove or show reasons why he should not have been expelled from the Society at the previous meeting in 1912, and that the action of the Society stand."

The report was accepted by the Executive Council and, on proper motion, the suspension stood.

The teaching of oral hygiene had been sponsored by the Oklahoma State Dental Association since 1909. At the annual meeting in June that year Dr. J. M. Temples presented a paper on "Public Education and Dental Necessities." A special committee appointed to consider recommendations made by Temples reported the following day: "We your committee desire to report favorably and feel that every effort should be made to get the matter before all the school boards of the state . . . ."

This campaign led to the preparation of news items on oral hygiene that appeared in newspapers of the state, to the preparation of material on the subject to be presented by teachers in the public schools, to talks by dentists before public groups. At the Enid meeting in 1911 the Education Committee reported effective work underway in the Tulsa, Muskogee, and Checotah schools. Dentists were urged to make examinations of school children in their communities and furnish the Education Committee, on specially prepared blanks printed by the Association, the following information: the number of school children in each room with sound teeth, with carious teeth, with teeth showing they receive dental services, and the number of children suffering from malocclusion.

This was a comprehensive program successful only in communities where dentists had the full co-operation of school boards and teachers. Examples set by Bonnell at Muskogee, Walters at Checotah, and Temples at Tulsa, with assistance from other members of the profession in those cities, inspired public and professional interest.

The Bowling affair at the 1912 meeting prompted renewed interest in the movement. J. P. Battenberg, superintendent of Oklahoma City schools, appeared at the annual banquet and pledged the full co-operation of the public school system. Through the interest of Dr. L. G. Mitchell, the local society secured other dentists to work with him in making dental examinations and conducting free dental clinics in the public schools.

The Society organized a special Oral Hygiene Committee in 1913 under the chairmanship of Dr. H. R. Watkins, Edmond. Other members included Drs. J. M. Temples, Tulsa; L. G. Mitchell, Oklahoma City; T. P. Bringhurst, Shawnee; I. E. McCarty, Enid; J. W. Potter, Ardmore; A. E. Bonnell, Muskogee. The following year, when component district societies were established, the Oral Hygiene Committee of the state society was composed of Drs. L. G. Mitchell, H. R. Watkins, A. E. Bonnell; N. C. Wood, Ardmore; R. M. Van Duzer, Bartlesville; A. W. Clark, Alva; R. H. Pendleton, Norman; George Ruddell, Weatherford; J. C. Devin, Cherokee; and W. J. Scruton, Oklahoma City. District committees included D. M. Brenneman, Hobart; C. A. D. Beer, Thomas; L. H. Lanier, Cordell; F. C. Holmes, Mangum; G. E. Roland, Elk City; B. B. Bell, Hollis; H. H. Eaton, Altus; C. B. Ball, Frederick; W. H. Bell, Cheyenne; T. W. McKinley, Stigler; F. E. Fisher, Muskogee; C. E. Berkshire, Fairview; F. C. Moore, Perry; E. A. Hodges, Newkirk; H. Jacobi, Tonkawa; J. R. Gossett, Temple; R. Anderson, Lindsay; C. D. Chandler, Anadarko; W. S. Williams, Durant; and E. J. Woodward, Ardmore.

In this period dentists received assistance and co-operation from the physicians of the state in promoting public attention to mouth hygiene; joint meetings of local groups discussed common problems of health and preventive medicine and thus developed a better understanding of mutual health aids.

The public, too, responded to the educational program. The State Department of Education incorporated in the Course of Study for Common Schools a book on *The Why of Mouth Hygiene* for use by teachers in the first four grades; essays were written by students in the upper grades on the subject, "Care of the Teeth." The winner received fifty dollars from the Oklahoma State Dental Association; the runner-up, a gold medal from the Dry Farming Congress, an agricultural organization of the period. The *New Education*, a bi-monthly publication of the A. and M. college of that period, *Progress*, the teacher magazine, and The *Farmer-Stockman* and the *Dry Farming Rural Homes*, magazines directed at rural readers, featured articles on oral hygiene. Miss Irma E. Matthews of the Oklahoma State Board of Agriculture appeared before meetings in rural communities and spoke on the subject. Her message was important enough to be delivered before the annual meeting of the National Dental Association in Kansas City in June, 1913. On May 19 of that year Dr. L. G. Mitchell addressed the county superintendents in convention at the Lee Huckins Hotel on the subject, while a week-long showing of the motion picture *Tooth-Ache* was featured in the theaters of Oklahoma City, sponsored by the Women's Auxiliary clubs. Other dentists lectured before county teacher institutes, where the film was also shown. R. H. Wilson, superintendent of public instruction, recommended to the county superintendents that the following credit be given upon all monthly and final grades of children in the public schools:

> *1st*—3 per cent on Mouth Hygiene.
> *2nd*—2 per cent on Personal Hygiene.

Lecturers who appeared to present the annual postgraduate courses were invited to appear before luncheon groups and at other public forums to discuss the subject of oral hygiene. Speakers visited the normal schools of the state to impress prospective teachers with the importance of oral hygiene. In the spring of 1914, Dr. J. C. Mahr, state commissioner of health, conducted a statewide campaign on the importance of health. Included was an exhibit which featured oral hygiene. Dr. Bonnell reported the effect of the week-long display and program at Muskogee: "On Sunday night all the churches joined in a big union meeting at Convention Hall: 1,500 to 2,000 people were present, with the mayor presiding. Dr. Thompson, one of the pastors, made the principal address, followed by Dr. Mahr, whose address was excellent. The meeting was a decided success. Each day for the week addresses were given in the afternoon and evening touching various phases of the health problem.

"On Wednesday Dr. Thomas spoke on Oral Hygiene; Thursday, Dr. Bonnell spoke on the subject of 'Care of Children's Teeth.' All those present were deeply interested."

This interest, the co-operation of state health officials, professional men, school officials, and members of the Federated Clubs, advanced the cause of mouth hygiene and contributed greatly to the general education of the public on care of teeth. In 1912, "toothbrush" drills were a novelty in Oklahoma schools; before the end of the decade oral hygiene became a part of the school curriculum. Smaller communities of the state inaugurated periodic mouth examinations of school children. This work was done without charge by local members of the Association. In larger communities members likewise conducted periodic examinations of school children. Near the end of the decade some of the schools were able to supplement this service by the employment of school nurses to make health check-ups at fixed intervals. T. H. Williams gave the Association a slogan used with telling effect in 1918: "You musn't let your teeth ache; ask your dentist why." Out of this movement came better care of teeth and better general health.

At the annual convention of the Oklahoma State Dental Association held at the Skirvin Hotel, Oklahoma City, during March of 1913, Dr. Frank O. Hetrick, president of the National Dental Association, addressed the assembly. The national society was undergoing reorganization and the president gave reasons for affiliation by state groups. His address was favorably received; on motion by Dr. C. W. Day, the state association voted to join the national organization. The secretary was instructed to collect an additional dollar from each member for national dues. When the National Dental Association met in Kansas City the following July, several Oklahoma dentists were in attendance. The constitution adopted at the meeting by the Association provided that dues should be collected from members of state societies at least thirty days before annual conventions. Only the District of Columbia and Oklahoma societies had complied with these provision by the time of the Kansas City meeting. Oklahoma has had continuous membership as a component society in the national organization since that time. Dr. C. L. White was elected to the Board of Trustees of the National

Dental Association at the 1913 meeting. Members of the profession in Oklahoma appreciated the honor accorded their former president, but they were more concerned with internal problems relating to the organization of the State Board of Dental Examiners, and further development of the annual postgraduate plan of instruction.

CHAPTER FIVE

The Oklahoma Way (Continued)

— I —

AFTER THE Dental Act of 1913 passed the legislature, Governor Lee Cruce requested the Association to submit names of members for his consideration for appointment to the Board of Dental Examiners. The act provided that present members should continue in office until their terms expired. At the general assembly of the Association on March 25 several motions were considered for the presentation of names. The approved motion provided that a list of five Republican and five Democratic party members of the Association should be submitted to the Governor. Balloting on the floor resulted in the selection of the following roster: C. R. Lawrence, Enid; G. C. Wallace, Shawnee; A. C. Hixon, Guthrie; D. M. Brenneman, Hobart; W. E. Flesher, Frederick; A. L. Walters, Checotah; I. E. Cordrey, Blackwell; C. L. White, Oklahoma City; T. H. Williams, Chickasha; and C. W. Day, Vinita.

Governor Cruce, although not confining his selections to the list submitted by the Association, made appointments from its membership acceptable to Dental Association officials. Dr. A. C. Hixon, whose term of service on the Board under territorial and state organization extending from 1901 to 1914 had been the longest in the history of the agency, was succeeded by Dr. H. Overbey of Ryan. When G. W. Bowling's term expired November 16, 1913, he was replaced by G. C. Wallace, vice-president of the Association in 1912, member of the Executive Council, and one of the Republicans on the roster submitted to the Governor.

It was during this period that the Association took disciplinary action against Dr. W. W. Bryan, veteran member of the Board of

Dental Examiners. During the official meeting of the Board in May, 1913, Bryan became involved in a controversial discussion which led to an altercation. This was reported in the September issue of the *Bulletin* as follows: "Oklahoma is known as a state that does things in a way that is a departure from the beaten paths, and not to be outdone, two members of the Oklahoma State Board of Dental Examiners put on, at the last state board examination meeting a 'Clinical Stunt' in gymnastics mixed with a pyrotechnic display of language not suitable for print, that is probably unheard of in dental history. The first step in this clinic, as shown by the clinicians, consists in the use of a lot of language that is unfamiliar to most persons; supposedly to gain the admiration (?) of your victim. The use of this language must be in a very emphatic way and manner, for without that, you will fail to gain the confidence of your victim; if your manner and actions are such you impress your victim, that you know what you are doing, it is not long until you have him partially hypnotized, and he begins to pass into the analgesic stage.

"It was then shown that this must immediately be followed by a short right uppercut on the jaw, and if the victim then shows any signs of reaching the excitement stage, to follow it very quickly with a long forceful swing on the other jaw.

"Now much of the success of this operation will depend upon your rapidity in getting in this long forceful swing, for in the excitement stage a slow operator is liable to lose control of his patient and the whole operation prove a failure.

"According to the clinicians, it is absolutely necessary to have a lady present, as in this case. She seems to inspire a flow of language you cannot command without her presence.

"Your success with these methods will probably not be so marked at first, but will become greater with experience and you will become very proficient after you are an appointee of some public political office, such as the Oklahoma State Board of Dental Examiners.

"This 'Clinical Stunt', while entirely new and unheard of, smacks much of quackery, and the unethical, and I am sure will not meet with the approval of the Oklahoma State Dental Association."

Dr. Lawrence, the writer, employed the medium of exaggeration to record an incident that occurred during the heat of contro-

versy, an act that certainly did not smack of quackery. He pointed
out that the new dental act had been passed despite reported opposition from some of the members of the Board, that "the time should
be past when a man is required to know more about the political
game than he does about dentistry, in order to receive an appointment to the Oklahoma State Board of Dental Examiners."

The Oklahoma State Dental Association took cognizance of
the controversy on the opening day of the annual session at the Lee
Huckins Hotel, Oklahoma City, March 30, 1914. Dr. Charles L.
White offered a motion, adopted by the convention, that a committee be appointed to call upon Governor Cruce and ascertain if he
would consider appointing to the Board, as successor to Dr. Bryan,
a member recommended by the Association. Committee members
were A. B. Walker, Fairview; W. E. Flesher, Frederick; and F. D.
Sparks, Ponca City. The following evening a letter of apology from
Dr. Bryan was read to the assembly:

Gentlemen:

At the meeting of the State Board of Dental Examiners held in
Oklahoma City in May, 1913, a very unpleasant occurrence occurred between another member of the Board and myself. This
affair has been a source of very great regret to me, and being a
member of the State Board of Dental Examiners, I feel an apology
is due the profession of the state, and I hereby present this my
apology and ask you to accept it in the spirit of sincerity in which
it is given.

Very Truly,
W. W. BRYAN

This letter prompted much discussion on the floor, motions and
counter motions. Finally, a motion prevailed and passed. N. C.
Wood, Ardmore, and C. R. Lawrence, Enid, were appointed to a
committee to call upon Dr. Bryan and ask him to sign a document
which stated that, under no circumstances, would he accept reappointment to the state board. They invited him to appear before
the convention and make his apology, as the Association had voted
not to accept his written apology.

At the night session April 2, Wood and Lawrence reported that
Dr. Bryan would not consent to appear before the Association and

make a public apology for his conduct. He also refused to sign any document stating that he would not accept reappointment to the Board, "but gave his word of honor to the committee that he would not accept any such reappointment."

The Association then adopted a motion that unless Dr. Bryan appeared before the convention prior to the following afternoon, charges would be preferred against him and presented to the Governor requesting that Bryan be removed from the Board. Dr. Bryan then appeared before the Association "with Dr. J. E. Wright who acted as his spokesman, and made the public apology asked for. A motion was then put and carried that in view of the fact Dr. Bryan had made the public apology asked for and had given his promise to not accept reappointment to the State Board of Dental Examiners that all charges against him be dropped."[1]

The committee appointed Monday to call upon the Governor made its report to the assembly Wednesday, April 1. Governor Cruce told the committee he would not bind himself to appoint a member of the Association to fill the forthcoming vacancy on the Board of Dental Examiners. The governor promised, however, that if he did appoint a member of the Association to fill the vacancy, he would make the appointment from a list of names recommended by the organization.[2]

Bryan's term was scheduled to end November 16, 1914, near the close of the Cruce administration. Dentists in annual convention March 30–April 4 foresaw the importance of keeping a prospective governor informed of their standards, ideals, and aspirations. The minutes of the Association record an interesting story: "April 1, 2 P.M., Judge Williams [since statehood, a member of the Supreme Court who had resigned and announced his candidacy for the democratic nomination for chief executive] was then introduced as the next Governor of Oklahoma and gave an interesting address.

"April 1, 8 P.M., Mr. Al Jennings [territorial county attorney of Canadian County, reformed train robber, lecturer, and evangelist] was introduced as the next Governor of Oklahoma, and addressed the Association."

Out of deference to the incoming governor, Robert L. Wil-

[1] Minutes of the Oklahoma State Dental Society, March 30–April 2, 1914.
[2] *Daily Oklahoman*, April 1, 1914.

liams, Cruce failed to make an appointment to the Board during the intervening two months of his term. Dr. Bryan, therefore, continued to serve as a member. Since the Board met semiannually, in June and December, and Bryan was still a member at the time of the June 14–17 meeting in 1915, members of the dental society began to fear that Governor Williams might continue him in office. The Executive Council of the Association met in Oklahoma City on June 20. On motion by Dr. Lawrence it was decided that Governor Williams should be apprised of Bryan's promise not to seek reappointment, that affidavits in regard to the promise be presented the Governor, and that an official protest be entered by the Oklahoma State Dental Association against the retention of Bryan on the Board. W. E. Flesher, president of the Association and former presidents J. M. Temples and C. R. Lawrence were selected to present the motion to Governor Williams.

Williams, never one to act too hastily on anyone's advice, waited until shortly before the December meeting of the Board to make an appointment. His choice proved most acceptable to the Association and marked an element in his character that made his an able administration. The Governor knew that Dr. Bryan was not interested in reappointment; he had served on the Board since its organization at Guthrie, November 22, 1907; he had done as much as any man could do to apologize for the flare-up at the Board meeting in May, 1913. On the other hand, Williams knew that members of the Oklahoma State Dental Association were motivated only by the thought of recognition in the growth of their profession.

F. D. Sparks, Ponca City, had introduced a motion at the annual meeting, April 2, 1914, "that the Association elect three of its members whose names are to be presented to Governor Cruce, recommending any of them be appointed to the State Board of Dental Examiners." H. R. Watkins, Guthrie; Roy V. Woolwine, Hennessey; and E. E. Sanger, Yukon, were recommended for the position. Governor Williams was tactfully reminded of the recommended list, and shortly after the December meeting of the Board, he appointed Dr. H. R. Watkins to the place held since statehood by Dr. Bryan.

The appointment of Watkins, an active member of the Committee on Oral Hygiene and the Executive Council of the Oklahoma State Dental Association, was considered suitable recognition of the high standards of service established by the organization. This struggle for recognition and the acceptance by the Governor of the right of the society to be consulted in regard to appointments made to the licensing agency marked an important advancement in the relationship between the profession and the chief executive. Already the Association was looking ahead toward legislation that would make consultation mandatory.

— 2 —

AT THE annual session in 1913 a committee of the Association was appointed which revised the constitution and by-laws of the organization. Submitted to the general assembly and adopted April 1, 1914, they incorporated the best features embodied in provisions of similar organizations in other states and the National Dental Association.[3]

The constitution provided that the organization should be called the Oklahoma State Dental Society, its object "to promote the public welfare by the advancement of the dental profession in education, science, mutual fellowship and good feeling, . . . by the advocacy of proper legislation and by co-operation with the medical profession in all matters of mutual interest and advantage to the people of the state."

Provisions were included for the selection of officers of the Society, standing committees, membership, and methods to amend the document. Two years later, after component societies had spread to every district of the state, the constitution was amended to revise membership of the Executive Council to include, in addition to the president and secretary, a member from each district society. And, at the annual meeting in 1917, an amendment was adopted that dropped the practice of choosing a vice-president. Thereafter, a president-elect was chosen, who, if he showed ability and took an active interest in the Society, was, if recommended by the Executive Council, promoted to the presidency at the next annual meeting. This practice continues to the present time.

[3] A copy of the constitution and by-laws appears in the Minutes; *Daily Oklahoman*, April 1, 1914.

The by-laws spelled out the duties of regular officers, the executive council, and standing committees. Included were specific instructions relating to component societies or district organizations. Annual dues were set at three dollars, one dollar of which was forwarded to the National Association for membership.

The by-laws also included a Code of Ethics, adapted from the national code.[4] This set a high standard of professional ethics which the majority of members scrupulously followed, and through preponderance of opinion brought the rare neglectful member into concurrence. The code provided:

Section 1. In his dealings with patients and with the profession, the conduct of the dentist should be in accordance with the Golden Rule, both in its letter and its spirit.

Section 2. It is unprofessional for a dentist to advertise by hand bills, posters, circulars, cards, signs, or in newspapers or other publications, calling attention to special methods of practice, or claiming excellence over other practitioners, or to use display advertisements of any kind. This does not exclude a practitioner from using professional cards of suitable size with name, titles, address and telephone number printed in modest type, nor having the same character of card in a newspaper. Neither does it prevent a practitioner who confines himself to a specialty from merely announcing his specialty on his professional card.

Section 3. It is unprofessional for dentists to pay or accept commissions on fees for professional services, or on prescriptions or other articles supplied to patients by pharmacists or others.

Section 4. One dentist should not disparage the services of another to a patient. Criticism of work which is apparently defective may be unjust through lack of knowledge of the conditions under which the work was performed. The duty of the dentist is to remedy any defect without comment.

Section 5. If a dentist is consulted in an emergency by the patient of another practitioner who is temporarily absent from his office, the duty of the dentist so consulted is to relieve the patient of any immediate disability by temporary services only, and then refer the patient back to the regular dentist.

Section 6. When a dentist is called in consultation by a fellow

4 Article Eleven, By-Laws, includes the Code of Ethics.

practitioner, he should hold the discussions in the consultation as confidential, and under no circumstances should he accept charge of the case without the request of the dentist who has been attending it.

Section 7. The dentist should be morally, mentally and physically clean, and honest in his dealings with his fellow men, as comports with the dignity of a cultured and professional gentleman.

In his annual address March 30, Dr. R. S. Parsons, president of the Society, recommended the formation of district societies. A committee composed of A. L. Walters, J. M. Temples, and L. G. Mitchell reported favorably on the recommendation, and the Society adopted a motion that district societies be established "after careful study of the centers of population." At a special session of the Executive Council January 24, 1915, seven component societies were officially established as follows:

Southwestern Oklahoma District Dental Society comprised Custer, Washita, Kiowa, Tillman, Jackson, Harmon, Greer, Beckham, and Roger Mills counties. Northwestern Oklahoma District Dental Society comprised Kay, Grant, Noble, Garfield, Kingfisher, Blaine, Major, Alfalfa, Woods, Dewey, Woodward, Ellis, Harper, and Panhandle counties. Northern Oklahoma District Dental Society comprised Ottawa, Delaware, Craig, Nowata, Washington, Tulsa, Creek, Pawnee, Payne, Osage, and Rogers counties. Eastern Oklahoma District Dental Society comprised Mayes, Cherokee, Adair, Wagoner, Sequoyah, Muskogee, Okmulgee, McIntosh, Okfuskee, Hughes, Pittsburg, Haskell, Latimer, Le Flore, Coal, Atoka, and Pushmataha counties. Southern Oklahoma District Dental Society comprised Murray, Johnston, Carter, Love, Marshall, Bryan, Choctaw, and McCurtain counties. South-Central Oklahoma District Dental Society comprised Caddo, Grady, Stephens, Jefferson, Cotton, Comanche, and Garvin counties. Central Oklahoma District Dental Society comprised Logan, Lincoln, Oklahoma, Canadian, Cleveland, McClain, Pottawatomie, Seminole, and Pontotoc counties.

Active district organizations gave an impetus to professional growth and understanding among the members. Here, where membership was small, individual leadership and initiative were developed midst the exchange of ideas. Discussions which followed clinical demonstrations and the reading of papers stimulated better clinics and better papers for future meetings. Improved techniques were shared and became apparent in better dentistry throughout the state. District societies, too, formed the best local contact with non-members and by creating high standards, by resolving technical difficulties inherent in scientific practice, attracted new members to the Society. The local district secretary was responsible for collecting dues from members for the district, state, and national organization. The district society became the solid base from which professional growth developed.

Under the revised constitution, the Southwestern Oklahoma District Dental Society was the first to organize. Since the report of the first meeting, made by Dr. J. N. Glass, Hobart, typifies work done in other districts, his account appears below:

"Twenty-one dentists from southwestern Oklahoma met in Hobart on December 5th, 1914, for the purpose of organizing the Southwestern Oklahoma District Dental Society. Dr. C. R. Lawrence of Enid, the secretary of the State Society, called the meeting to order and later a permanent organization was formed, officers elected, and everything started off in a business like manner. Much enthusiasm was shown, especially considering that this is the first real dental organization in this part of the state.

"A constitution and by-laws were adopted after which the afternoon was spent seeing a number of interesting clinics among which were Dr. C. R. Lawrence demonstrating the Hollingsworth system of filling in cement models, and attachments for removable bridgework. Dr. Brenneman demonstrated the cast joint for the bicuspid crown, and brought out a point that everyone should profit by. Dr. Holmes of Mangum gave some very interesting points on orthodontia. Dr. Byam of Carnegie gave a very interesting and practical method of making crowns with pliers only. Dr. G. E. Roland of Elk City gave some new things in cavity preparation and synthetic porcelain work. Dr. Coffin of Apache showed a beautiful bridge made from molar block teeth, and Dr. Flesher of Frederick showed some valuable points in cavity preparation for inlays.

"The members retired to the Campbell Hotel and enjoyed a banquet, after which Dr. Lawrence read a paper on 'The Dental Society—A Necessary Factor in Professional Growth,' which all present most earnestly approved. The paper read by Dr. W. E. Flesher on 'Conscientious Service—the Fee,' was strongly discussed. Every member present entered into the discussion.

"The members present were Drs. D. M. Brenneman, Hobart; W. S. Vaughan, Mangum; L. S. Lanier, Cordell; C. A. D. Beer, Thomas; W. H. Bell, Cheyenne; L. E. Duncanson, Hobart; W. G. Bristol, Altus; J. N. Glass, Hobart; F. E. Sims, Weatherford; W. S. Smith, Hobart; George Ruddell, Weatherford; W. E. Flesher, Frederick; F. C. Holmes, Mangum; R. J. Mansell, Cordell; D. E. Lamont, Gotebo; G. E. Roland, Elk City; R. P. Byam, Carnegie; E. F. Greer, Snyder; and A. B. Coffin, Apache.

"Almost every man in attendance paid his local, state, and national dues for 1915.

"The officers elected were W. E. Flesher, President; D. M. Brenneman, Vice-President, and J. N. Glass, Secretary-Treasurer.

"We want it to be a slogan that any and every dentist who is a member of this society is a good one and to bring this about shall be our aim. Plans are already well formed to get a closer contact between the members of this society, and to be affiliated in such a way that the profession in this section of the state will be greatly benefited, which in time means that the public at large will receive better dental service."[5]

The annual or semiannual meetings not only afforded local members an opportunity to read papers and make demonstrations, but other state and out-of-state leaders in the profession appeared before the societies as lecturers and demonstrators. The Executive Council of the state society, for example, approved dates for district meetings, November 20–23, 1916, held consecutively at Tulsa, Enid, Oklahoma City, and Lawton. The schedule was arranged in order to make it possible for Dr. Willis A. Coston, Topeka, Kansas, to appear before the local groups and repeat lectures and clinical demonstrations on dental operations. W. E. Flesher, editor of the *Bulletin* had this to say in the February number: "Judging from the reports from the different parts of the state, we are satisfied that more dental restorations have been made in Oklahoma by the indirect method since Dr. Coston's visit than in its previous history. He presented it to us in a way we could apply it. Dr. Coston's

[5] The report of J. N. Glass, secretary-treasurer is on file in the Central Office, Oklahoma State Dental Association.

method of constructing removable bridge work was new to most of us. He made the points of advantage over the fixed bridge very clear. No doubt he turned the minds of some of the strong advocates of the fixed bridge."

This type of program proved so successful, and techniques mastered by members so beneficial and practical in their dental practice, that another nationally known dentist, Dr. J. M. Prime, Omaha, Nebraska, was their invited guest the following year. Dr. T. H. Williams, president of the state society, met Dr. Prime at the annual convention of the National Dental Association in New York and arranged to accompany him to the meetings of the district societies, November 26–30, in Muskogee, Oklahoma City, Enid, Chickasha, and Hobart.

Presentations made by Dr. Prime, simple and thoroughly practical, proved so acceptable to the members in attendance that by popular demand he was selected to be one of the instructors at the annual meeting of the state society the following March. His professional career was an inspiration to all in attendance at the local meetings, particularly those practitioners from smaller communities where there were no competitors. Prime had practiced for several years as the only dentist in a small Nebraska town. In those early years, during long intervals between patients, he busied himself with amalgam fillings, with molds and matrices, and with the study of tooth-forms. He studied simple, everyday operations and tried to improve them.

At each district meeting local dentists provided an operating chair, dental engine, straight and contra-angle hand-pieces, table, blackboard, and chalk. Dr. Prime made practical demonstrations supplemented with lantern slides. Each member in attendance had an opportunity to interrupt with questions during the program and satisfy himself on every point covered. Although the scheduled meeting of the South-Central District Society at Chickasha was Thanksgiving Day, dentists gathered at the Geronimo Hotel, enthusiastic over the proceedings.

From the grass roots, from these district meetings where dentists could not only see and hear, but feel, touch, handle, and take part, then stow in their minds these learned techniques for use in their practice, came a movement that prompted the Executive Council to change procedures for the annual postgraduate plan.

Heretofore, nationally known leaders had presented lecture courses supplemented by demonstrations in large assembly halls to the full body of members. The Oklahoma Way had been adopted by dental societies in other states and gave Oklahoma a national reputation for progressive advancement.[6]

— 3 —

AFTER FOUR YEARS of the postgraduate arrangement for conducting annual meetings, plans were made for a tri-state meeting of members from Oklahoma, Kansas, and Missouri at Kansas City, March 20–26, 1916. Oklahoma members of the committee on arrangements were W. E. Flesher, president of the Society, and C. R. Lawrence, secretary.

Lawrence was chosen secretary-treasurer of the tri-state committee. The name of the state publication was changed temporarily to the *Tri-State Dental Bulletin* and issued by him from Enid. Complete coverage was given to the forthcoming convention in the three issues of the *Bulletin* preceding the meeting, while the fourth and final issue was devoted exclusively to the program.

In the June, 1915, issue, Lawrence presented the proposed plan for the meeting and the choice of location: "Another important factor in the success of a dental meeting is to convene in a city that can meet all the detailed requirements for the meeting, and in the selection of Kansas City the committee feels sure they have chosen the logical place for this meeting.

"Kansas City is centrally located, and is easily accessible to all

[6] Both the *Dental Cosmos* (S. S. White Dental Manufacturing Company, Philadelphia) and the *Journal of the National Dental Association* carried articles in issues published between 1913 and 1918 in reference to the "Oklahoma Way." The *Dental Cosmos*, a monthly publication devoted to dental science, was the leading trade journal of its kind in the country from the time of the first issue August, 1859, to the last, December, 1936. It was merged with the *Journal of the American Dental Association*, which carried the joint titles 1937–38. In January, 1939, the *Journal* dropped the dual titles. See *A Century of Service to Dentistry, 1844–1944*, pp. 102–105 (Philadelphia, S. S. White Dental Manufacturing Company, 1944). Scattered bound volumes of the *Dental Cosmos* for the years 1891–1925, formerly the property of Dr. C. R. Lawrence, Enid, are in the Medical Library, Oklahoma City.

In 1917, the *Journal of the National Dental Association* distributed to state and foreign societies reprints of an article, "The Post-Graduate Dental Meeting," by Dr. C. R. Lawrence.

sections in the middle west, and by the way, when you now land in Kansas City, you walk into one of the finest union depots in the United States. . . . No longer do you have to keep your hand on your pocket book the minute you enter the depot gates. . . . if you are one of the high toned silk hat dentists, you can have an attendant carry each one of your suit cases and be able to keep your eye on both of them at the same time. In fact the contrast between the old and new depots in Kansas City is as great as the contrast between the old and new style dental meetings.

"Here the hotel accommodations are ample to take care of the throngs who will take advantage of this dental educational event. A large percent of the dentists of this section of the country are from the Kansas City Colleges, and to go back there will be like a visit back home. Efforts are being made to have the alumni meetings of the different colleges postponed until this time, thus giving you an opportunity to meet old classmates from other states."

This was a period when the Interstate Commerce Commission had granted increased passenger fares on interstate travel; Lawrence advised dentists in Oklahoma to take advantage of Oklahoma's constitutional provision for a two-cent fare within its borders: "If your starting point is in Oklahoma, you may be able to get the benefit of a two-cent rate by getting your crowd together and buying tickets to the state line, send one of the boys ahead to the first station in Kansas, and have him purchase tickets for the whole crowd to Kansas City, Kansas." A streetcar fare from there to Kansas City, Missouri, would complete transportation charges and reflect savings over the interstate railroad rates.

Convention headquarters were established in the Muehlebach Hotel, where room accommodations were $2.50 a day. Enrollment fee for the six-day course was five dollars; Lawrence estimated any Oklahoma dentist could attend at maximum expense of fifty dollars.

This meeting, described May, 1916, by the *Dental Review* as the most important in the history of dentistry in the West, was conducted by leaders in the profession: Drs. Thomas P. Hinman, Atlanta, president of the National Dental Association, who had appeared before territorial meetings in 1904, and before the Oklahoma State Dental Society at both the 1913 and 1914 annual meetings; Forrest H. Orton, St. Paul; M. L. Rhein, New York; Richard H. Riethmuller, Philadelphia; Weston A. Price, Cleveland;

J. P. Buckley, Chicago, who gave the introductory lecture at the inaugural of the postgraduate course plan in Oklahoma in 1912; and C. N. Johnson, Chicago, who had lectured at the Shawnee meeting in 1904.

More than one thousand dentists representing eighteen states were in attendance; morning classes were held in the Gaiety Theatre; afternoon classes at the Muehlebach. Since the lecture room at the hotel seated no more than six hundred, afternoon classes were divided into two groups. This gave the alternate group an opportunity to visit near-by Convention Hall, where seventy-four exhibitors displayed dental products in booths and where attendants conducted clinics or demonstrations on improved dental office and laboratory supplies and equipment.

One hundred and sixty-three of the 255 members of the Oklahoma State Dental Society were in attendance at the meeting. This was a remarkable tribute to the earnest desire of associate members to improve in professional growth. The previous year, at the postgraduate courses offered in Oklahoma City, only one more dentist had been in attendance.

This was more remarkable when one considers the following statistics: the ten leading cities of Oklahoma were represented by 58 members; from the smaller towns and communities, therefore, came 105 dentists, an indication that improvement in professional technique and knowledge was spreading to all areas of the state. Through efforts of the Society, a reputation was being built statewide in the improvement of dental practices.

Dr. W. E. Flesher of Frederick, president of the Oklahoma Dental Society at the time of the meeting, later secretary, had this to say in regard to the meeting:

"From point of interest, this meeting could not be excelled. Every lecture was of vital interest, for the lecturers held the attention and interest of this body of dentists for three hours each morning without a recess throughout the entire week, and then they were eager to return for a one and one-half hour lecture in the afternoon, not just one day, but every day.

"I am satisfied that fully 99 percent of the dentists in attendance were present at every lecture. Do you get the significance of that? Every dentist went there to learn and what he learned he put into practice on his return to his office. . . .

"Dr. John P. Buckley opened the Post Graduate meeting in his usual impressive and characteristic manner. His first lecture dealt with the etiology and pathology of the diseases of the soft tissues of the mouth, not directly associated with the teeth. It was a masterful lecture and showed that Dr. Buckley was as much at home in this field as in his specialty, pyorrhoea alveolaris and materia medica and therapeutics, as we are accustomed to know him. He pointed out to the dentists that it is often their responsibility of recognizing and diagnosing certain symptoms that are in the mouth and referring the patient to the family physician. Otherwise the pathological condition might become greatly extended before the patient was aware of it. The importance of the co-operation of the dentist and the physician in all mouth manifestations was impressed on us. His lecture was profusely illustrated, showing mouth lesions and their differentiations.

"Dr. Buckley's second lecture was on 'Pyorrhea Alveolaris.' He took up this subject in all its phases. He impressed upon us the fact of thorough surgical treatment of the surfaces of the roots, eliminating pus pockets and the excision of denuded roots. . . .

"Dr. Thomas P. Hinman . . . lectures for this meeting were to deal with plastics (amalgams and cements). We knew he had been making some investigations along this line and that he would present his results. . . . He gave a splendid lecture on the manipulation of amalgams, the insertion into the cavity and the 'stepping' process, and the use made of the plastic mass of mercury alloy that works to the top while filling the cavity. He showed how amalgam fillings inserted by this method would stand the air pressure test, while by other methods they would not. Also that these fillings gave a hard contact point.

"In his lecture on cements he pointed out the necessity of great care in handling cements, how to keep cements so as not to lose their properties, how affected by atmospheric and climatic conditions, by spatulating, temperature of slab and spatula. His lectures were illustrated by both stereopticon slides and a motion picture, made especially for this meeting.

"Dr. M. L. Rhein, of New York City, presented in three great lectures one of the most important subjects before the dental profession today, as pertains to the health of the general public, 'Periapical Infections.' This had been a special work of his for a number of years, he being the first to make use of the Roentgenogram and to foresee its future use as a value in the correct filling of root canals. He has some decided views about the treatment of these periapical infections and filling root canals, which he proves in every sense. He tells you why you should go through the apical foramina with the root canal filling and he shows you.

"His method of opening to the apical foramen of roots was well received, though it seemed radical to the most of us. Still we see the necessity. Of what use is the coronol portion of a devitalized tooth unless it has a perfect root canal filling, when we are treating a case of periapical infection or trying to prevent same?

"His lectures were profusely illustrated, showing the infected apical regional in the different stages, the dental granuloma and the alveolar abscess. The regeneration around the apex, after the root had been filled, was clearly demonstrated. Every statement he made was well proven.

"Dr. Weston A. Price, head of the Research Institute of the National Dental Association and one of the greatest men in our profession today, presented two of the greatest lectures that have ever been delivered to a dental body. Dr. Buckley, in speaking of a lecture just delivered, said: 'That is the greatest lecture that has ever been delivered to a body of dentists by any man, on any subject, any time.' He simply held his audience spellbound. His lectures were the result of his research work in the Research Institute laboratories. Most of the subject matter he presented was given for the first time. He used the stereopticon and motion picture as a means of illustration. . . . The study of the struggle between cell life and the invading organisms, and the factors which determine which will prevail, as well as the principles determining the power of selectivity for certain tissue, as possessed by certain organisms, and the mechanisms of defense possessed by the tissue and fluids of the body, was of profound interest.

"Since the day is here when painless dentistry is a reality, we were very anxious to hear Dr. Riethmuller's lectures and we were not disappointed. Dr. Riethmuller has translated Dr. Guido Fischer's *Local Anaesthesia* and is one of the chief authorities on conductive anaesthesia. He gave a discussion on pain and then took up drugs for local anaesthesia. Parenthetically, he stated that soon novocain will be manufactured in America and we can procure it easily.

137

"He gave the complete technique of the preparation of the solution, method of injection and the sterilization of the instruments and the field of operation, asepsis being a great factor in a successful operation. He carefully considered the anatomy, nerve and blood supply of the mandible and maxillae and the landmarks used in conductive anaesthesia, as only by the proper location of these landmarks is it possible to deposit the solution in the proper region. He also considered general anaesthesia, its place in dentistry, choice of anaesthetic for the case in hand and the therapeutic and medico-legal precautions. The technique of conductive anaesthesia was nicely illustrated by a motion picture.

"After studying oral hygiene and the causes of pyorrhoea alveolaris, the gold banded crown ceases to be the bosom friend as of old. We looked to Dr. Orton to help us out of the 'rut' and he did not fail us. The subject was considered from the very beginning, giving us a good foundation for what was to follow. We studied tooth forms, principles involved in banded crowns, relation of banded crown to pathological conditions, importance of correct cusp relation and occlusion, importance of restoring the form of the tooth in all dimensions, preparations of root for banded crown, and the importance of the relation between the band and the soft tissues adjacent thereto.

"The last lecturer to arrive for the meeting and the one we have been trying to secure for several years for our post-graduate course, was Dr. C. N. Johnson. His lecture on 'The Inter-Proximal Space and the Contact Point' was, perhaps, the most practical delivered during the entire meeting. He presented to us the proper form of the inter-proximal space and contact point, the deleterious effects on the teeth and surrounding tissue because of faulty contact point and abnormal inter-proximal space, and the agencies which cause these faulty conditions. He then gave us methods of restoring the contact point and testing same, and methods of preventing foods from wedging between the teeth."

This meeting and the postgraduate courses offered made a lasting impression upon Oklahoma dentists in attendance. Thirty-seven years later, in the summer of 1953, Dr. E. E. Sanger recalled the vivid impression made by Dr. Riethmuller when he demonstrated the use of novocain in nerve blocks, one of the great advances in dentistry. Dr. T. H. Williams related: "One of the outstanding men was Dr. Weston E. Price, Cleveland, who so timely and fully brought home to us the seriousness of focal infection. Well do I recall how, with tears in his eyes, he gave us the case history of his son, noting that the operations of removing pulps and root canals of deciduous teeth developed root-end infection, caused arthritis, crippled him, and caused his passing prematurely." Dr. A. B. Walker, who closed his office December 2, 1953, fifty-one years after beginning practice in Oklahoma, wrote in a letter one week later: "The thing that gave dentistry its great boost here and over the whole country was the postgraduate course plan. Intangibles are often the things that count most in life. It was not altogether what we learned at the meetings but rather they set on fire our desire to learn more about our work. Dr. C. N. Johnson, who was a lecturer at the Tri-State meeting in Kansas City in 1916, marveled that we would sit for hours listening then yell for more."[7]

Twenty-five years later the veteran dentist, Dr. F. C. Holmes, Mangum, described in the *Bulletin* contrasting methods in operative dentistry before and after postgraduate courses: "Speaking of root fillings. We remember the time when methods of filling root canals were a matter of paramount importance. Much of the space in dental journals was devoted to that subject. It was our daily practice to treat nerves and abscessed teeth. We were taught to save teeth and attained a remarkable degree of proficiency in so doing.

"Many materials and medicinal agents were advocated and sold by the manufacturers for root-canal filling which we never hear of now. I remember discussing with Dr. C. L. White, about thirty-five years ago, the method of soaking hickory pegs in creosote and forcing them into root canals as a permanent filling. The two of us had tried the method and considered it of value at the time.

"My usual method was to roll out a wax point with my cement spatula on my slab, incorporating a little iodoform powder as it was formed. Then after drying out the canals with a hot smooth broach made from a tapered hair pin, place the wax points in the canals, then plunge the hot broach into the wax-filled canal and break it off quickly. The broach had previously been semi-cut for proper length, leaving the broach incorporated in melted wax with iodoform for the antiseptic value—a hermetically sealed root. I men-

[7] A. B. Walker to Harry Sorrels, December 9, 1953. The letter is on file in the Central Office, Oklahoma State Dental Association.

tion this method as a relic of bygone days. It was used for many years when we took our root fillings seriously.

"Then came Dr. M. L. Rhein from New York City to show us the way. His method was to force chlorapercha through the end of the root, previously enlarging the apical foramen, if necessary for that purpose, and thus encapsulating the root-end. He finished the filling with gutta-percha points. Dr. Rhein mentioned putting in eighteen hours work on one root-canal filling. . . .

"At the same meeting, Dr. Tom Hinman of Atlanta, Georgia, was with us showing on the screen, pictures of patients suffering from arthritis. Deplorable examples of the result of focal infections from root-ends, a brand new theory, and soon we ceased to wear ourselves out with tedious root-canal technique and began extracting instead, especially following the advent of novocain which rendered the operation less dreaded by both patient and operator."[8]

The social event of the tri-state meeting, still remembered by participants, was the banquet, held in the ballroom of the Muehlebach Hotel, Thursday night, March 23.

"The interest was very intense when Dr. Walters was called on, and after paying a high tribute to Dr. Lawrence, our Secretary, for his valued services to our Society, he, on behalf of the Society, presented Dr. Lawrence with a beautiful Howard, solid gold watch.

"On behalf of the Oklahoma Society, Dr. L. G. Mitchell presented to Mrs. Lawrence and Mrs. Flesher beautiful bouquets of roses, as tokens of the Society's appreciation of their interest in the organization and the assistance rendered their husbands."

— 4 —

LECTURE PROGRAMS gave members of the profession valuable theoretical training. The average dentist, upon his return to his office, however, realized his inadequacies in the general field of practice, but found he had not retained the technical knowledge presented. In order to supplement this need, the Executive Council proposed the following innovations for the annual meeting in 1918:

1. Divide the full attendance into special classes.

[8] F. C. Holmes, "Reminiscences of an Early Dental Practitioner in Western Oklahoma," in the *Bulletin*, Vol. XXIX, No. 3, (January, 1941), 90–92.

2. Have each class take up the study of one particular subject for a full week, under the direction of a competent teacher.

3. Instruction to consist of lectures and practical work.

4. Have special clinics organized for each class and require the students to do practical work.[9]

Dentists were limited to enrollment in only one class. For example, each member who enrolled in the nerve-blocking class, after the presentation of lectures and demonstrations by Dr. Arthur E. Smith, Chicago, was required to do every phase of the work, "from all preliminary preparation, seeing that the patient is properly seated in chair, and assured it 'won't hurt,' etc., down to the completed operation." Under the direction of Dr. Elmer S. Best, Minneapolis, the class in X ray, Root Canal Fillings, and Focal Infections, a continuous clinic was conducted. Every member of the class was required to use the X ray and instructed in oral examination and diagnosis. Dr. Prime instructed in the field of Operative Dentistry—Crown and Bridge Work; and Dr. F. E. Roach, Chicago, veteran instructor of previous postgraduate courses, returned to lecture and demonstrate casting processes on the subject, "Removable Partial Artificial Dentures." Dr. Rupert Hall, Chicago, made similar presentations relating to Full Dentures; Ida Mae Hover, Omaha, presented a special course on Lady Dental Assistants.

State leaders in the profession, including T. H. Williams, J. M. Temples, N. C. Wood, W. E. Flesher, C. R. Lawrence, the general manager for the postgraduate course, and A. L. Walters had articles in the February, 1918, issue of the *Bulletin* relative to the program. Walters, in his article, summarized reasons for departure from the original Oklahoma Way:

"In my opinion this plan of having a superior teacher and clinician combined, taking a small class, putting them to work, supervising at every stage and holding them down to the thing at hand, is why it is so superior to the plan of having someone simply lecture or do the work for them. In the latter we take notes, watch the clinics carefully, and try to get everything in a few days with the result that we return home and, when we attempt to put into practice the things we thought we had learned, we find ourselves short on important details and while we have had the inspiration of the

[9] Articles on the 1918 meeting appear in issues of the *Bulletin* for November, 1917, and February, April, and June, 1918.

meeting, the broadening influence and the many things of general interest, we have not accomplished much in the way of technique and ability to put into actual practice the things we listened to or witnessed. . . .

"There is no discussion as to the advantages of Conductive over all other forms of anaesthesia, in any part of the body, but especially in our particular field. There are few but who will agree that anaesthesia of the field under our care would be a splendid thing for both patient and operator. Then, why do we continue hurting our patients when there is a method which is safe, sure, and comparatively harmless, provided we are experts in all the details of its use? Simply because we do not KNOW how to use this most valuable method. Why do we not know how? Dr. Smith was with us last year and lectured; Dr. Logan, the previous year. Then why do we not put into practice the things that were given us in these lectures and demonstrations? Simply because we do not remember the things, or remembering them, we find ourselves fearful to use them because we realize we have not had the necessary training. What will be the result this year? Why we will come, join Dr. Smith's class and with him to inspire confidence we will, under his direction and supervision, prepare our solutions, inject them ourselves into patients and do actual operative work under the influence of this wonderful method of anesthetizing the nerve trunk. We will, after five or six days of continuous work, go home, and, with the confidence of knowledge and practice, continue the making of our solutions and the injecting of them into the different locations for the benefit of our patients and ourselves.

"Do I make anatomically occluded teeth? No, I do not. Why? Don't know how, do I? Had the work of these men, haven't I? Yes, but when I got home the old way was easier, and I managed to 'get by' and, since I was unable to put into practice the things I had learned, my trip in this respect was comparatively a failure. This year I'll go, join this particular class and under the supervision of an expert, I'll make impressions, casts, will set up and grind the teeth to occlusion and when I get home I'll continue to do it, for I am not lazy and want my patients to have the best they are able and willing to pay for.

"What about cavity preparation and the making of approximately perfect inlays either by the direct or indirect method, the difference in preparation for foil or amalgam fillings and the making of good restorations? . . . How should one clean and fill root canals? Well, here is the method; it is given in detail . . . ."

The Society met in annual convention at Tulsa Central High School, April 1–6, 1918. This building, the most imposing public school in Oklahoma, had recently been completed and epitomized the restless energy of Tulsa citizenry that made the young, bustling city outstanding in America for cleanliness, with beautiful forested residential sections, planned parkways, and a growing, symmetrical sky line.

The Society had held its annual convention in Tulsa in 1910, shortly after the city entered its period of phenomenal growth. While other towns and cities of Oklahoma in 1908 were taking a more sober look at the future after the financial panic, the Tulsa Commercial Club sponsored a daring innovation that attracted the nation's attention. The impetus given by the discovery of the Glenn Oil Pool in 1905 was rapidly dying out; real estate suffered a slump, home building was at a standstill; things were not going so well for Tulsa in the late winter of 1908. Its population was less than 10,-000; Enid, Shawnee, and near-by Sapulpa, with the Frisco shops, were as large, while Muskogee was twice as large.

Tulsa sought a publicity stunt, something no other town had undertaken.[10] In the early spring one hundred Tulsans, including Dr. W. M. Wilson, pioneer dentist, bought tickets at one hundred dollars each to help finance a special industrial train. On April 20, the train, supplied by the Frisco, with Pullmans, a baggage car equipped with printing press and type, and an exhibition coach, left Tulsa with a twenty-five-piece band and the town boosters for eastward points. Stops were made in fourteen cities; invited guests visited the exhibit car, which included samples of peaches about the size of walnuts on limbs cut from trees in the vicinity of Tulsa, alfalfa about a foot high, and photographs of spouting oil wells and the town's one refinery. Each day a paper was printed, the first page featuring entertainment at the last visited city, which served to spur additional activity at other points.

The high point of the trip was a visit to the White House to receive greetings from President Theodore Roosevelt. The wide publicity from the trip brought immediate results to Tulsa. Within

[10] See daily issues of the Tulsa *World*, April–July, 1908.

three months real estate transactions amounted to $2,000,000, and during the next decade Tulsa's sky line, broken only in 1908 by the five-story Central National Building erected the previous year and the three-story Robinson Hotel, was pierced by five other buildings eight to sixteen stories high, including the Tulsa Hotel, the Daniel, Cosden, Palace, and Mayo office buildings. In 1920 the population of Tulsa was 72,075. Proudly wearing the title "Oil Capital of the World," Tulsa had become a serious rival of Oklahoma City in the business and industrial development of the state.[11]

Typical of the type of co-operation that made a small town grow into a proud city were the arrangements made to accommodate the dental profession in its 1918 convention. The school board, principal, and teachers vacated rooms in the high school building; some of the rooms were rewired and others piped for gas to serve clinical purposes. The Tulsa Dental Society, with Drs. Ira E. McCarty, C. S. Ferner, and C. A. Furrow as officers, and the Commercial Club entertained the out-of-town guests at the Empress Theatre. Flowers, daily papers, both local and home, and other courtesies were furnished officers of the Society and visiting lecturers.

On the opening day, lectures were given by the visiting faculty, but the remainder of the week was devoted to classroom instruction and practice on patients. Dr. Smith's class in "Nerve Blocking and Anesthesia" treated more than two hundred patients, while other classes were equally busy in the actual treatment of subjects under the instructors' expert guidance and counsel. Tulsa dentists had advertised in newspapers for persons needing dental care, while other dentists brought patients from over the state to the meeting.

The new departure of the postgraduate plan was an outstanding sucesss. On Monday, April 1, W. E. Flesher, secretary, recorded in the official minutes of the Society: "This in reality was the opening program of the first post-graduate meeting of the class type held by any state dental society in the history of dentistry." The National Dental Association in its *Journal* gave recognition to the Oklahoma Way and the state society. It pointed out that, some years before, Oklahoma had established a precedent adopted by many states in offering postgraduate courses at annual meetings. The plan adopted in 1918, according to the *Journal*, "more thoroughly systematizes

[11] Tulsa *Tribune* (Silver Jubilee Edition), November 13, 1932.

or standardizes the teaching course, so that the individual member may receive, in one week's intensified study, the specific work he may need to better fit him for his particular work." The editor of the *Journal* urged other states to study the plan and adopt it for use at annual meetings. Oklahoma's precedent-making plan, heralded as the most progressive and profitable type of dental meeting in the United States, was adopted by fourteen other states the following year.

More important, active participation in use of techniques under the guidance of national authorities made Oklahoma dentists among the best in the country. And equally important, this knowledge was diffused into the smaller cities and communities of the state; because dentists from these areas year after year regularly enrolled in the postgraduate classes, took part in professional growth, and returned to their practice better able to serve the public. Communities, in turn, took pride in the advancement of their professional men. Outstanding leaders who normally might have been attracted to a metropolitan center remained in the smaller communities to render service as good as could be found anywhere in the nation.

Young men entering practice fresh from college, where the course of study covered four years' preparation, were abreast of modern techniques, but they likewise benefited from the intensive postgraduate courses. Older practitioners, however, were most enthusiastic about the contacts made with national leaders, the stimulation of improvements in practice. Their point of view was expressed by Dr. J. Q. Waddell, who was in continuous practice at Kingfisher from 1893. Dr. Waddell wrote, shortly after the Tulsa meeting of 1918:

"Unfortunately—in the minds of the laity, dentistry is associated with pain. The Advertiser who uses the phrase 'Painless Dentistry,' and does not 'deliver the goods,' only intensifies in the minds of the people, 'that it can't be did,' but Conductive Anaesthesia in dentistry assures us that it can.

"I had the pleasure of taking Dr. Arthur E. Smith's course and I would not give up what I learned for anything if I could not retake the course. Dr. Smith is not only conversant with the work but is an able instructor.

"Learn how to relieve pain in your operations and let it ad-

145

vertise you, and I can assure you it will be the biggest practice build-er you can associate yourself with."[12]

— 5 —

BEFORE THE Sixth Legislature convened in January, 1917, the Board of Dental Examiners had been reorganized to include Drs. G. C. Wallace, Shawnee; H. R. Watkins, Guthrie; L. M. Doss, Oklahoma City; H. Overbey, Ryan; and A. B. Potter, Oklahoma City. Dr. Potter was appointed the previous month by Governor Williams to replace Dr. A. E. Bonnell, the last of the original board set up by Governor Haskell at statehood almost ten years before.

It had been customary for the state society to submit a selected list of its members to the governor for consideration of appointment to a forthcoming vacancy on the Board. At the annual convention in March, 1916, however, the state society, reflecting the stature of Bonnell in its ranks, adopted the following resolution: "Motion carried that this Society give its unanimous support to Dr. A. E. Bonnell for reappointment to the State Board of Dental Examiners and that we refuse to support anyone else for this position."

However worthy the intentions of the Society were, they re-flected a poor understanding of the disposition of Governor Wil-liams never to yield to dictation or persuasion. Williams, as zealous in keeping prerogatives of the office of chief executive intact as any predecessor or successor, was impatient of advice from any source and not amenable to dictation. Under the dental act the power of appointment rested solely with him; his selection of Dr. Potter, active member and official of the Society, was to prove satisfactory to the dentists, but Bonnell had established a record of public serv-ice that was difficult to emulate.

The state society sponsored a bill introduced during the legis-lative session that would have made it mandatory for the governor to appoint to annual vacancies occurring on the Board of Dental Examiners a member from a list submitted by the Society; Gover-nor Williams had the measure killed.

Two revisions were made to the Dental Code, however; both passed with little opposition. Dentists were required to display, in their operating rooms, their official license issued by the Board of

[12] The *Bulletin*, February, 1919.

Dental Examiners. The other provision made it unlawful "for any person or persons to practice or offer to practice dentistry or dental surgery under the name of any company, association, or corporation except those who have been in actual business for fifteen years or more prior to the first day of January, 1917, and every person or persons practicing or offering to practice dentistry or dental surgery, shall practice under his or her own respective name or names, only."

Dr. W. E. Flesher, secretary of the Society at the time, recently explained the reason for the last-named provision:

"A condition had developed in some of the larger cities in which a number of dentists were operating under the name of companies, associations, or organizations, the owners of which did not need to be dentists. Dentists could be employed and dismissed by these organizations or companies without the knowledge of the Dental Board officials or of the public.

"Such practices offered a harbor for quacks and charlatans and an opportunity for graft, racketeering, and unprofessional conduct. A dentist could change locations and avoid responsibilities of any misconduct or obligation. It was difficult for the Dental Boards to keep in touch with dentists employed under such circumstances. These organizations used advertising as a method of attracting the public to their offices with names displayed in large letters or on billboards in places easily seen by the public.

"Practicing under one's own name places obligations and responsibilities where they belong. One knows the dentist delivering the service and that he can be reached for counsel in his office. Practicing in another's office, however, and under another name, a dentist can come and go and be relieved of his responsibility to the public for any low-grade service he has rendered."[13]

Dr. S. S. Mayfield, Eufaula, member of the House of Representatives from McIntosh County, was one of the co-sponsors of House Bill 208, which embodied these revisions. A measure of the esteem in which he was held by legislators is indicated by the vote accorded in the House of Representatives on the bill when it was up

[13] Dr. W. E. Flesher, Oklahoma City, in 1950 compiled for the Association a "History of Our Dental Laws." His manuscript has been invaluable; details of legislative consideration for proposed changes in the dental acts appear in official House and Senate journals of the legislatures.

for third reading and final passage: 108 to 0. At the annual convention of the Society, March 26, Dr. Mayfield was presented an engraved ring by the members for his work in securing the legislation.

The Sixth Legislature had adjourned in Oklahoma before the United States entered World War I in 1917. The Seventh Legislature did not convene until two months after the Armistice; therefore, Oklahoma's resources in the war effort were directed by Governor Robert L. Williams through state and local agencies working directly with national organizations and agencies of the federal government.

The State Council of Defense directed home-front activities during the war, and its great strength lay in county and local organizations. Williams made nonpartisan appointments: executive committees in counties usually included the leading banker, lawyer, editor, and the county agent. Farming groups and trade and professional associations co-operated in the crusade which President Woodrow Wilson described as one to make the world safe for democracy. The efforts of all citizens were enlisted. An enthusiasm, an earnestness, and a dramatic intensity of purpose and accomplishment were engendered that won Oklahoma national recognition.

Congress, on May 18, 1917, passed the first of a series of Selective Service acts as a means of raising an army in accordance with national need rather than individual enthusiasm and patriotism. Before the war ended, all males eighteen to forty-five years of age were registered for the draft. Through local boards Governor Williams quickly set in motion the mechanics of selective service, and Oklahoma again won national recognition.

In these programs the Oklahoma State Dental Society gave the Governor and the national government unstinted co-operation. When, early in June, 1917, a quota was assigned Oklahoma for dentists to enter the Dental Reserve Corps of the United States Army, the following dentists appeared before Dr. H. Overbey, secretary of the State Board of Dental Examiners, to take the preliminary examination: Otto Hine, Muskogee; E. F. Ammons, Tulsa; George Meredith Dott, Perry; Ed Granger, Ada; Harry B. Laird, Tecumseh; William D. Rush, Cleveland; Harvey N. Lewis, Carmen; Robert E. Keith, Ardmore; Harold R. Wolfe, Yale; John G. Peach, Lamont; George E. Roland, Elk City; Robert E. Henson, Shawnee; Edward F. Keyes, Guthrie; Robert

Dr. A. D. Black

Dr. C. N. Johnson

Dr. Howard R. Roper

Dr. J. P. Buckley

"The Oklahoma Way"—Postgraduate Course Lecturers

Photographs courtesy American Dental Association

Past Presidents of the Oklahoma State Dental Association in 1951
Left to right, front row: Drs. A. L. Walters, W. E. Flesher, T. H. Williams, A. B. Walker, A. F. Sebert, W. T. Jacobs, W. J. Scruton, Roy H. Ellis, C. A. D. Beer; *middle row:* Drs. J. A. Wells, C. B. Ball, A. B. Rivers, F. J. Reichmann, Harry H. Sorrels, Scott P. Bowyer, G. A. Roelke; *back row:* Drs. C. A. Hess, J. B. Ratliff, H. O. Warrick, Max G. Armstrong, David W. Matteson, Robert M Dunn, Fred O. Pitney.

E. Beattie, A. J. T. Beatty, F. H. Colter, James T. Hedges, L. G. Mitchell, L. M. Doss, A. A. Pollock, James P. Neal, and W. J. Scruton, Oklahoma City.

On October 6, President Wilson signed a Congressional act which offered commissions to members of the Dental Corps equal in rank to those assigned to physicians in the Medical Corps. This marked a triumph won after fifteen years of persistent effort on the part of the National Dental Association. Before 1904, dentists located near army posts won the consent of local commanders to practice for army personnel, who bore the expense. But in 1904 the Army Reorganization Bill provided for the creation of a corps of dental surgeons, the first step taken by any government to recognize the dental profession in military service.[14] Dentists served under contract, however; they were paid $150 a month and furnished quarters when serving with the troops. The dentist, under this act, was not a commissioned officer nor an enlisted man, but a civil employee. He had no military status, no opportunity for promotion, no inducement of increased pay for foreign service, or longevity pay, or retirement for disability or age. By the end of 1904 there were only thirty contract dental surgeons in the Army Dental Corps, the majority of whom were serving with troop units in the Philippines and Cuba. The legislation of 1917 was belated recognition of the dental profession, that members who entered the armed service were entitled to be commissioned as officers.

Members of the Oklahoma State Dental Society who were accepted for active service and commissioned in the Army Dental Corps or the Dental Reserve Corps included G. E. Roland, Elk City; Otto Hines and F. E. L. Thomas, Muskogee; E. F. Keyes, Guthrie; H. B. Laird, Tecumseh; Harvey N. Lewis, Carmen; C. A. Hanson, Chandler; Howard H. Eaton, Altus; A. C. Albert, Frederick; W. P. Morrison, El Reno; R. C. Kibler, Duncan; R. M. Titterington, Stroud; L. A. Patterson, Hennessey; D. A. McKellar and R. E. Keith, Ardmore; John T. Obert, Altus; A. B. Rivers, Stilwell; C. S. Jones, Pryor; C. L. Berry, Drumright; P. W.

---

[14] John R. Marshall, "Military Dental Practice," a reprint from the "Dental Brief," in *Polk's Dental Register* for 1904–1905, pp. 59–66; also, John R. Marshall, "The United States Army Dental Corps," with discussion by leading dentists, in *Transactions of the Fourth International Dental Congress*, (Philadelphia, Press of the Dental Cosmos, 1905), Vol. I, 39–56.

Schwartz, Medford; A. J. T. Beatty, R. E. Beatty, C. B. Shannon, J. E. Dean, James P. Neal, A. A. Pollock, L. G. Mitchell, W. J. Scruton, and T. W. Sorrels, Oklahoma City.

Other members who did not enlist or were not accepted for active service made direct contributions to the war effort on the home front. Dentists were placed on medical advisory boards and local selective service boards and the majority of the membership joined the Preparedness League of American Dentists.

The Preparedness League, organized in March, 1916, under the chairmanship of Dr. J. W. Beach, Buffalo, New York, was one of several patriotic societies that sprang into existence that year. When Congress, responsive to public opinion over continued violations of American neutrality by warring powers of Europe, passed the National Defense Act in June, the volunteer organizations helped convey to Americans the impending threat of war.

After war was declared, the Preparedness League directed its efforts toward the improvement of dental conditions of draftees. This work, performed free of charge, actually began in August, 1917; the following instructions were sent to all members of the League:

"All devitalized teeth, all teeth having a history of periodical abscess (even if without symptoms at the time of examination), all teeth actually afflicted with pyorrhoea as well as all crowded and inflamed third molars should be extracted.

"The only teeth which should be filled at this time are those which through having painful cavities are made useless for masticating purposes, and those having deep cavities which must be filled immediately to prevent involvement of the pulp.

"Whenever practicable amalgam fillings should be inserted in occlusal cavities; cement should be used as the filling material in all other cavities.

"Make no return appointments. See each man but one sitting."[15]

Work of the League was co-ordinated with the office of the Surgeon General, War Department. Dr. W. A. Heckard of that office was authorized to set up the voluntary organization. The country was divided into six regions; Dr. William D. McCarty of San An-

[15] See issues of the *Journal of the National Dental Association*, June, July, October, 1917, and February, March, 1918.

tonio was placed in charge of the Southwestern Department, which included Oklahoma.

Governor Williams appointed Dr. T. W. Sorrels, Oklahoma City, state director of the Preparedness League. Dr. N. C. Wood, Ardmore, and Dr. J. M. Temples, of Tulsa, were appointed state finance committeemen to accept membership fees of one dollar. Funds received were used for clerical assistance, printing of reporting forms, and postage. A director for the League was appointed in each county, and members were placed on call to perform necessary dental services for draftees called into service.

Dr. W. E. Flesher, county director of Tillman County, wrote in the *Bulletin*, July, 1918, his experiences with the local draft board and the Preparedness League: "The writer wishes to make mention of the assistance given him by the Local Board of his county, as an example of efficiency. It seems that the list [of draftees] is practically made out before the Board receives the call. Then all they seemingly have to do is check it over and hand it to the County Director, which usually gives him plenty of time to arrange for the boys' work. This has been done without any urging on the part of the County Director. . . . This county, since the work has been organized, has been able to send all the boys away dentally prepared.

"The Oklahoma dentists, as a whole, are very eager to take care of the work for the soldier boys. The following example represents the spirit of most of them—may it be all of them: A telephone call asks, 'Have you any time to give to the selective service men?' The reply comes, 'Why, yes, send them along. I may have to dismiss some of my patients but let them come, I'll take care of them.' "

Dr. Earl Williams, Dallas, recently recalled the time devoted to this activity by his father, W. S. Williams, Durant.[16] No boy entering military service from Bryan County left in need of fillings or other emergency work. Dr. Williams, senior, did the necessary dental work himself, "working nights and Sundays so that everyone who departed from Bryan County to the army or navy had his mouth in good condition, and without any cost." A similar spirit was manifested throughout the state.

Dr. Sorrels neglected his practice to make a success of the Preparedness League. How well he and fellow-members of the Okla-

[16] Dr. Phillip E. Williams to Harry Sorrels, June 14, 1954.

homa Dental Society succeeded was attested by Dr. McCarty, who wrote in July, 1918, that Oklahoma had made the best organization record in the United States. Major W. A. Heckard likewise reported, at that time, that Oklahoma was making an outstanding record.

The Executive Council of the Oklahoma State Dental Society met in Oklahoma City, July 14, 1918, and approved a motion made by Dr. C. L. White authorizing Dr. Sorrels to write "the Councils of Defense in counties where the dentists fail to respond to his call." Sorrels has recently recalled, however, that no member of the Society refused to donate his services to the draftees. Thousands of teeth were extracted or filled at no expense to the government or to the men entering service.

Dr. Sorrels, who had applied for a commission in the Dental Reserve Corps in 1917, was finally inducted into service September 15 of the following year. Dr. J. M. Temples, Tulsa, succeeded him as state director. Within less than two months, however, the Armistice was signed; two days later, November 13, the Preparedness League and its free dental care of inductees came to an end. Dentists and fellow-Americans were ready for the return to normalcy.

CHAPTER SIX

Between Two Wars

— I —

WHEN THE Seventh Legislature convened in January, 1919, the dental profession had already prepared a proposed bill for remedial legislation. As early as June, 1917 the Board of Dental Examiners called attention to the deletion from the dental act of 1913 of provisions for annual licensing fees, funds needed to prosecute illegal practitioners. The Board also passed a resolution that a law should be enacted to license oral hygienists for practice under the supervision of licensed dentists.

These recommendations were incorporated in the annual address of the president of the Society, Dr. T. H. Williams, at Tulsa, April 1, 1918. They were referred to the Legislative Committee, composed of Drs. G. G. Lowes, Lawton; L. M. Doss, Oklahoma City; F. H. Colter, Oklahoma City; and S. S. Mayfield, Eufaula. Dr. Colter was not in attendance, but the other committeemen approved the suggested revisions to the dental act and made additional recommendations. They added provisions for the addition of a course in oral hygiene to the curriculum of public schools; that it be mandatory for the governor to appoint members of the State Board of Dental Examiners from a list of professional members furnished by the Society; that a more stringent law be passed to provide for the revocation of licenses of unethical practitioners, drunkards, drug addicts, and those who advertised as painless dentists. These recommendations were ratified July 14 by the Executive Council of the Society at a meeting in Oklahoma City.

Dr. S. S. Mayfield, Eufaula, promoted to the state Senate by his constituency and appointed a member of the Board of Dental Examiners to succeed Dr. H. Overbey by Governor Williams in

December, 1918, introduced Senate Bill 95, "An Act regulating the practice of Dentistry in Oklahoma," on January 22.[1] This measure included provisions recommended by Dr. Lowes and other members of the Legislative Committee. The Dental Society had studied other state laws and used as a model a Kentucky statute of 1915 which had been found to be constitutionally sound when tested in the courts of that state.

The Mayfield bill also included provisions for the annual publication of a list of the licensed dentists and for raising the pay of members of the Board of Dental Examiners from five to ten dollars a day. A section was included to provide for the prosecution of violators of the act by the office of the Attorney General. It was thought this would eliminate much expense and fraternal and religious sympathy on the part of Board members, and assure speedier and more equitable justice.

Through Dr. Mayfield's influence the bill passed the senate February 21 by a vote of thirty-six to none. Only one amendment was added, with approval of the Board of Dental Examiners. This was a provision suggested by the Board to provide that a dentist should keep his official license in prominent display in his operating room. This strengthened provisions of the 1917 act.

The Dental Society, meeting in annual session at the Lee Huckins Hotel, Monday, March 3, was urged by Dr. C. W. Day to contact members of the House and urge them to support the Mayfield bill. On Wednesday the convention adjourned for the morning to permit the entire membership to visit the Capitol and throw its influence behind the proposed legislation.

Despite these efforts amendments were added to the measure by the House. The principal change reduced the proposed control of the Society over selection of personnel of the Board of Dental Examiners. After this and minor amendments were inserted, the House on March 17 passed the measure seventy-five to one. Upon its return to the upper chamber the amendments were accepted, and

[1] "An Act regulating the practice of dentistry in Oklahoma and declaring an emergency," Senate Bill 95, Chapter 41, pp. 63–69, *Session Laws 1919* (Oklahoma City, Harlow Publishing Company, 1919); also, *Journal of the Senate of the Seventh Legislature of the State of Oklahoma, Regular Session,* January 7 to March 29, 1919, pp. 408, 429, 573, 784, 818, 827, 829, 843, 863, 1443, 1574, 1581 (Oklahoma City, Warden Company, 1919); and *House Journal* (abbreviated title), pp. 956, 1009, 1077, 1542, 1661 (Oklahoma City, Harlow Publishing Company, 1919).

the bill passed unanimously. Governor J. B. A. Robertson signed the measure on March 22, and since an emergency provision was attached, it became a law immediately.

This act, which made important revisions and additions to former legislation, remained in effect until 1935. The biggest disappointment to the Society came from lack of control over appointments to the official board; however, the act provided that the governor should select three of the five members from lists submitted by the Society.

Educational standards of applicants to practice dentistry were raised to include submission to the Board of evidence of graduation from high school in addition to presentation of a diploma from a reputable dental college. Affidavits in regard to the character of the applicant were also required. Reciprocal licensing agreements with states that had equally stringent laws were permitted by the act.

An annual license fee of one dollar was reinstated; the secretary of the State Board was required to publish annually a list of all licensed dentists, the year licensed, and the address. A license could be revoked only after a proper hearing before the Board. Any person who had his license revoked could appeal to a review board consisting of the Attorney General and a justice of the Supreme Court.

The section pertaining to unethical advertising was strengthened by making it unlawful to publish or circulate misleading statements in regard to superior equipment, painless operations, or the use of drugs of unknown formula.

Section 16 provided: "Any registered or licensed dentist may employ women assistants who shall be known as dental hygienists. Such dental hygienists may remove lime deposits, accretions, and stains from exposed surfaces of the teeth, and directly beneath the free margin of the gum, but shall not perform any other operation on the teeth or mouth or any diseased tissue of the mouth. They may operate only in the office of any registered or licensed dentist under the general supervision of such dentist. The State Board of Dental Examiners may revoke the license of any registered or licensed dentist who shall permit any dental hygienist operating under his supervision to perform any operation other than that permitted under the provisions of this section."

Dental hygienists were required to be at least eighteen years of age, graduates of a reputable school for this newly recognized profession, of good moral character, and to pass an examination given by the State Board.

Defects in the loosely written law became apparent when it was subjected to tests in the courts. Definitions and requirements of dental hygienists proved to be vague. The law did not provide that witnesses before the State Dental Board were required to submit sworn testimony, and no provision was included in the act for the enforcement of orders of the State Board. The statutory provisions concerning fraudulent advertising and the advertising of painless dentistry were incomplete.

The Dental Society, too, in its zeal for translating ethics into law had provided for an appellate tribunal from decisions of the Board. The tribunal was composed of the Attorney General and one justice of the Supreme Court, whose duties were to review, when requested, an action of the Board of Dental Examiners which resulted in the cancellation of a license. In an opinion filed February 15, 1927, the Supreme Court raised a question concerning the judicial duty added to the office of Attorney General by the act:

"This provision, while not in conflict with any express limitation or provision, is at least inconsistent with the real philosophy and plan of our Constitution, which makes no provision for, nor even contemplates an appellate tribunal consisting partly of one member of the Supreme Court and the Attorney General, and is also inconsistent with the provision which constitutes the Attorney General the legal advisor of all state departments. . . . It is not consistent with our plan of government to vest the Attorney General with final judicial powers in determining the validity of an act of the Legislature and at the same time makes it his duty to represent the state in prosecuting violations of such acts."[2]

The Supreme Court recommended in the opinion that all doubt could be removed by vesting appellate jurisdiction from action by the Board of Dental Examiners in a regularly constituted judicial tribunal. When a "model law" was prepared by the Dental Society for submission to the legislature in 1935, it provided the Supreme Court should have jurisdiction over an appeal from the Board.

In the severest test of the constitutionality of the dental act of

[2] *State Board of Dental Examiners et al* v. *Pollock*, 125 *Oklahoma*, 170–72.

1919, the six Supreme Court judges who participated in the opinion unanimously affirmed its provisions.[3] One part of their opinion, however, merits examination because no finer tribute can be paid the Dental Society than considerations of the concessions it had won in the appointment of members of the Board of Dental Examiners. Oklahoma dentists, following the suggestion of Dr. A. E. Bonnell in 1912, had been striving for an autonomous Board; the eminent jurists, better versed in Oklahoma practical politics, were more concerned with limitations on the appointee power of the governor.

The Supreme Court questioned that section of the law which required the governor to appoint three of the five Board members from a list of ten members submitted by the Society. "This provision," the court ruled, "which in our opinion could not be binding on the governor, at least purports to make it obligatory upon the governor, or at least leaves the governor's power to appoint three such members conditioned upon their nomination by the State Dental Society, thus vesting a Society which constitutes no official part of the state government with power to limit the executive authority of the governor to appoint an official Board created by law for governmental purposes.

"While such provision does not render the creation of the Board clearly unconstitutional . . . yet we feel it is appropriate to suggest that all doubt as to the validity of such provision could be removed by an amendment giving the governor full power to appoint the entire Board, at least free of any limitations imposed by an organization which constitutes no part of the official machinery of state government."

The Court, while sustaining the constitutionality of the dental act, also upheld the action of the Board in revoking the license of Dr. L. L. Pollock for the employment of an unlicensed assistant as a dental hygienist. Dr. Pollock had appealed the action of the Board to the appellate tribunal. George F. Short, attorney general, and James I. Phelps, an associate justice of the Supreme Court, upheld the Board's action. Thereafter Dr. Pollock petitioned the district court for an injunction to keep the Board from enforcing the judgment to cancel his license; alleging that the dental act of 1919 was unconstitutional.

T. G. Chambers, district judge, Oklahoma City, sustained his

[3] *Ibid.*

petition and granted a permanent injunction against enforcement of the order to revoke the license. Thereupon the Board of Dental Examiners appealed Judge Chambers' decision to the Supreme Court. The Board, represented by Lee G. Gill, an assistant to the Attorney General, contended the act was valid and that it had power to cancel the license. In the opinion filed by the court February 15, 1927, written by Judge John B. Harrison and concurred in by Judges Fred P. Branson, James I. Phelps, E. F. Lester, Albert C. Hunt, and Robert A. Hefner, the district court was reversed and the act declared constitutional. Later the Board reinstated the license of Dr. Pollock.

— 2 —

DESPITE defects apparent to attorneys in the dental act of 1919 pertaining to dental hygienists, members of the Society employed and trained capable assistants interested in professional advancement. To the 1919 meeting the Society invited Dr. A. W. Starbuck, Denver, to give a special course relating to office and operational duties of assistants.

The following assistants enrolled in the course: Miss Hazel Doyle, from the office of Dr. G. W. Badgely, Tulsa; Miss Blanche Doyle, from the office of Drs. I. E. and O. H. McCarty, Tulsa; Miss Nettie Higgins, assistant to Dr. Robertson, Coffeyville, Kansas; Miss Eunice Magee, representing Dr. J. C. Devin, Cherokee; Mrs. W. C. Mitchell of the office of Dr. W. C. Mitchell, Elk City; Miss Flo Arnold, assistant to Drs. R. E. Beattie and J. T. Miller, Oklahoma City; Miss Marie Rust and Miss Lee Fretch, Cushing, assistants to Dr. C. A. Ruhlen; Miss Juanita Key, assistant to Dr. L. O. Render, Pauls Valley; Miss Viletta Williams, assistant to Dr. F. D. Sparks, Ponca City; Mrs. Grace Sallors and Miss Myrtle Johnson of the office of Dr. A. L. Walters, Tulsa; Miss Anna Hunt, assistant to Drs. A. E. Bonnell and A. A. Pfieffer, Muskogee; Mrs. Maude Wiles, representing Dr. C. A. Furrow, Tulsa; Miss Olga Phillips, assistant to Dr. F. C. Reisling, Tulsa; Mrs. J. A. Morrow, assistant to Dr. J. A. Morrow, Carmen; Miss Wanda Hodges, assistant to Drs. H. A. McKeown and F. A. Lenhart, Tulsa; Miss Hunter Jean Watson, assistant to Dr. T. C. Nichols, Oklahoma City; Miss Nicholson, from the office of Dr. W. W. Boyd, Purcell;

Miss Harris, from the office of Drs. L. M. Doss and Roy Daniel, Oklahoma City; Miss Gasaway, representing Dr. R. M. Van Duzer, Bartlesville; Mrs. Glen Morris, from the office of Dr. W. O. Talbot, Fort Worth, Texas; Miss Laura Lawes, assistant to Dr. W. A. Coston, Topeka, Kansas; Miss Lola Whittier, representing Drs. E. C. and A. T. Watkins, Enid; and Miss Mae Yancey, Enid, office assistant to Dr. C. R. Lawrence.

They received instruction from Dr. Starbuck on "The Business Side of the Dental Office," "Assisting at the Chair," "Dental Radiography," "Personality in the Handling of Patients," and kindred subjects on asepsis, anaesthesia, office appliances, and bookkeeping. As Dr. Lawrence stated: "A dental office without an assistant is like a businessman writing his letters in longhand. The time is past when any little sixteen-year-old girl, who can answer the door bell and chew gum between acts, will fill the bill. The present demands are for intelligent women who are willing to learn the duties of the office and here is where many of us have fallen down on the proposition." The course offered by Dr. Starbuck pointed up many economies in office management effected by capable, trained assistants.

At the tri-state meeting held in Kansas City in 1922, further recognition was given this new profession. Dr. C. N. Johnson, Chicago, gave a special course under the subject of "Office Efficiency and Dental Assistants," which stressed values of economical management. Miss Myrtle Johnson, Tulsa, appeared on the program; one afternoon those in attendance visited and made a systematic inspection of a number of the efficiently equipped downtown dental offices.

When the State Dental Society met in Tulsa in April, 1926, members helped organize the Oklahoma State Dental Assistants' Society. Dr. T. W. Sorrels, president-elect of the State Society, aided the assistants by drawing up a constitution and by-laws for the organization. Dr. A. E. Bonnell appeared on the first program, which featured table clinics by the assistants. At the organizational meeting, Miss Blanche Doyle, Tulsa, was elected president; Mrs. Nettie Higgins Turley, Oklahoma City, president-elect; Miss Retha Rogers, Tulsa, secretary; and Miss Alma Desmond, Oklahoma City, treasurer. The Dental Assistants' Society, now in its twenty-ninth year, has proved a useful adjunct to the state society; members have kept abreast of modern dental practices.

After the dental act was passed upon by the Supreme Court, the Board of Dental Examiners notified all practitioners that its provisions would be enforced. Members of the Board in 1929 were Dr. A. C. Seids, Oklahoma City; Dr. W. S. Williams, Durant; Dr. E. E. Sanger, Yukon; Dr. C. A. Hess, Idabel; and Dr. J. D. Moon, Mangum. In August Dr. Seids reported to the Society through the *Bulletin* on activities of the board:

"In November, 1928, complaint was made against one O. E. Black, of Lawton, for employing an unlicensed operator and for fraudulent conduct. The case was heard at the March term of court and both Mr. Black and his operator were found guilty and fined $100 and costs. However, Mr. Davidson, the operator, saw fit to jump his bond and being out of the jurisdiction of the court, Dr. Black chose to pay his fine rather than surrender the bond which was $2,000.

"This is a short story but it took lots of time and considerable expense. Doctors Sanger and Moon both put in many hours of time without pay. On July 29 Dr. Black was summoned before the Board in special session. After hearing evidence substantiating every charge, the Board unanimously voted to revoke Dr. Black's license. Dr. Black was called back before the Board and sentence pronounced: Forever prohibiting him from practicing dentistry in Oklahoma.

"In March complaint was made that one Dr. Bancroft was practicing in Tulsa on the strength of a dead cousin's license. Dr. Sanger investigated this case and Bancroft came before the County Attorney and surrendered the license. At the same time the Miller advertising office, Tulsa, was investigated and Dr. Miller's son was found in charge, Dr. Miller having died about the holiday time. When young Miller was face to face with prosecution, a deal was hurriedly consummated whereby the office was disposed of and young Miller passed out of the picture.

"At the October term of court at Hobart a case will be heard involving Mrs. Dr. Watson. At statehood Mrs. Watson, then Miss Black, was registered under provisions of the enabling act to practice dentistry. It is alleged her husband, an unlicensed man, has been practicing dentistry in her office. This case will be prosecuted by the Board and in case of conviction by the court she will be tried by the Board and if found guilty, her license will be revoked.

"This, I hope, will give the dentists of the state an idea as to steps the Board is taking to keep the state clean and make your license worth what it ought to be. Our sole support is derived from the two dollars you pay for your bi-ennial license, and let me say here and now, that it burns one up, to have remittance accompanied by a terse remark, 'I'll pay but you have no power to make me pay.' Personally, I think it is damn poor sportsmanship. Your State Board this year [1929] has spent over one thousand dollars on prosecutions in enforcing the dental law while it costs 15% of the gross income to collect the license fee, therefore you should see the Board is not wallowing in wealth.

"Today every city in Texas is being over-run by a bunch of fakers, doing 'painless extractions' on the streets. We defy that kind of stuff in Oklahoma and it is your two dollars that goes to keep the state as clean as it is. It is not a pleasant matter to sit in judgment and deprive a man of his means of livelihood, but so long as we hold our commissions we will continue to enforce the law to the best of our ability.

"If you know someone who is violating the law, it is your duty to make a complaint and I assure you that action will be taken. It is with pleasure that I can say that the Board is working in complete harmony and only what is good for the profession is ever considered."

As a result of further investigation, and conviction by the district court at Hobart, the Board canceled the license of Mrs. M. E. Watson.[4] Dr. J. D. Moon, member of the Board from Mangum, immediately became involved in a countersuit filed in district court by Dr. Black and his sister, Dr. Watson. They alleged he had committed perjury when he had testified he was in the office of Dr. Watson on October 23, 1928, and saw her husband grinding teeth. The state society came to the defense of Dr. Moon. The Executive Council met April 21, 1930, and acted favorably upon the motion of Dr. C. R. Lawrence to contribute $700 for his defense. Actually $791 were spent by the Society in behalf of Dr. Moon. He was cleared of all allegations; again, the Society had shown its willingness to test the effectiveness of the dental law in the state courts.

[4] J. D. Moon to E. E. Sanger, January 5, 1931, in the *Bulletin*, January, 1931, p. 10; also, Minutes of the Executive Council of the Oklahoma State Dental Society, October 4, 1931.

— 3 —

MEANTIME, with the rapid growth of cities throughout the country and the shift from a rural to an urban population, physicians and dentists began co-operative movements for the construction of office buildings for their professional use. Tulsa and Oklahoma City joined a succession of cities in this movement.

Dentists and physicians in Oklahoma City, cramped for office space in the growing city, joined forces early in 1923 to develop plans for a Medical Arts Building.[5] This plan had been discussed for months; in May an association of the professional men signed a 99-year lease on the old Lyric Theatre property at the southwest corner of Robinson Avenue and First Street. On this site, which belonged to the estate of the late J. K. Perrine, it was proposed to erect a nine-story building to include a medical library and auditorium, with office space to be occupied exclusively by dentists and physicians.

Financial and legal difficulties brought cancellation of the lease agreement. The dentists and physicians, determined to pursue their plan, finally settled upon the site of the Frisco depot near Harvey between First and Second streets. Since 1909 civic leaders had sought unsuccessfully to move the railroad tracks, the Rock Island depot near the Skirvin Hotel, and the Frisco depot. Streetcar, automobile, and pedestrian traffic on north-south streets several times each day came to a standstill because of the switching of freight cars and regular freight and passenger service. Already Oklahoma City was looking ahead to a bond issue to remove rail facilities from the downtown area. In 1927 a four-million-dollar bond issue was voted for this purpose and the purchase of the right of way, but not until 1930 was this accomplished.

In the summer of 1923, however, the dentists and physicians felt assured they could obtain the Frisco depot site. They decided to take one-half the space and the Y.W.C.A., for a proposed building, the remainder. Attorneys for the Society, nevertheless, decided against the title to the property, and again the professional groups had to seek another location.

[5] *Daily Oklahoman*, August 5, 1923; April 26, 1925; January 4, 1928; September 5, 1930. Oklahoma City *Times*, May 8, July 16, September 15, 1923; May 26, October 2, 1924.

The site finally selected for the building at the southwest corner of Broadway and Park Avenue (then First Street) was occupied by an old two-story building owned by the Security National Bank. The bank agreed to donate the site, estimated to be worth $225,000 and to contribute $125,000 toward the cost of erecting the building and furnishing quarters to be occupied by it. Members of the Physicians and Dentists Building Company agreed to contribute $250,-000, to be raised by selling stock at $1,000 a share. Professional men who invested in the building were to get a discount on their rent, which was to vary according to the amount of space; the maximum discount was to be 6 per cent. A ten-year loan of $450,000 was advanced to the company by the bank, making a total amount of $1,-050,000 available for the building.

The projected building was to be co-operatively owned by the Oklahoma City Physicians and Dentists Building Company and the Security National Bank. The bank planned to occupy the first two floors and the basement, the remaining ten stories were to be reserved for members of the two professions, laboratories, and supply-house representatives. A drugstore was to occupy a small space on the third floor. Under the contract the dentists and physicians also reserved a small portion of the basement and lobby and elevator space near the principal entrance to the building.

Construction work on the building began in February, 1924. In May, Dr. J. S. Pine, chairman of the building stockholders, announced that four hundred rooms had already been spoken for and that 130 professional members had subscribed $305,000 toward the project.

The interior of the building was specifically planned according to the wishes of the interested professional men and women. All the suites were finished with their needs in view, while stockholders personally studied and revised blueprints of suites they were to occupy. Special fittings were supplied for gas, electricity, compressed air, and other professional necessities not ordinarily found in commercial buildings. Special four-bulb daylight chandeliers were fitted over operating chairs and tables. Among other features of the building were an elaborate ladies' rest room, shower rooms for occupants, a medical and dental library, and a drugstore.

When, on April 1, 1925, the twelve-story structure was completed and ready for occupancy, it towered aloft at the pinnacle of the city's sky line. Five years later the Security National Bank discontinued operation when it joined resources with the First National Bank and Trust Company. Reconstruction operations provided additional offices for physicians and dentists on the second floor and retail shops on the ground floor. When the drugstore moved to more spacious quarters near the main entrance, additional space was released on the third floor. The Physicians and Dentists Building Company met all financial obligations, often with increased payments. The company on November 30, 1943, acquired the bank's interest in the building.

The facilities of the building have been kept up to date by repeated modernizing of operating equipment, including the elevator system. In March, 1954, a 750-foot well was completed that furnishes pure water adequate for the building's needs. Marble walls add distinction to the lobby, which offers entrance to the drugstore, a lunch room, and a ladies' shop. Street entrances give access to an art shop, a men's store, and a modern eating place. Plans have been projected to air-condition the entire building.

The Medical Arts Building was constructed at a time when similar ventures were launched by professional groups throughout the country; it is now the only one in operation under its original ownership and management.[6] Many of the original tenants are still occupants, including Leonard Reeves, founder and operator of the Reeves Dental Supply Company.

In 1930, when the Physicians and Dentists Building Company assumed control of the real estate and building, plans were announced for the construction of the sixteen-story Skirvin Tower Hotel across Park Avenue, the thirty-four-story First National Building at the west end of the block, and the thirty-two-story Ramsay Tower, now the Liberty National Bank Building, across the street from the First National. Already in operation was the Auto Hotel, standing next to the Medical Arts Building. The completion of these buildings within the block between Robinson and Broadway made the area the most important business block in Oklahoma City.

Tulsa, likewise, responded to the need for a special building to house offices for dentists and physicians. This movement was inspired, and financed, by Dr. Charles W. Day, veteran dentist and

[6] W. E. Flesher to J. S. Clark, March 3, 1954.

active member of the Society. Day was a lifelong friend of Drs. A. L. Walters and A. E. Bonnell and, like them, served the dental organization faithfully. He was elected president of the Indian Territorial Dental Association in 1904, first vice-president of the state association in 1907, member of the committee that wrote the constitution adopted in joint session of the territorial associations in June, 1907, first vice-president of the state association in 1910, 1911, and 1915; nominated for the presidency in 1912 and elected to the office in 1920. In each instance his name was placed in nomination by Bonnell. He served as a member of the Executive Council from 1908 until 1911 and was chairman of the important Oral Hygiene Committee from 1920 until 1924. He appeared as a clinician on many district and state programs. As one of many instances that could be cited of his generosity toward his profession, in 1920, when he found the oral-hygiene movement in need of funds for printing, and other purposes, he made a personal donation of five hundred dollars.

Dr. Walters, who moved to Tulsa from Checotah in 1918, has recently written: "Charles W. Day was a pioneer and a builder, a hard worker. He was a fine dentist, a truly religious character, and of the fibre that starts with little and ends with much or nothing. Not a gambler, other than in the sense all men who believe in the future of a village, town, city, or state are gamblers when they invest and reinvest. His investments were in lead and zinc mines in the Joplin area, and Tulsa real estate.

"He loved our profession and gave generously of himself and his money to advance any and every phase of it.

"The night after I moved to Tulsa a banquet was held in my honor and Day took me home.

" 'I could have sold my mining interests today for a million dollars,' said he.

" 'Why didn't you?' I asked.

" 'Want two million.' "[7]

Day added lots at the corner of Sixth and Boulder to his holdings in 1925. The only other building that had occupied the site was a two-story frame residence erected by Flowers Nelson in 1905. Nelson, pioneer Tulsa attorney, represented District 68 in the constitutional convention which convened the following year. Legend

[7] A. L. Walters to J. S. Clark, September 24, 1953.

165

has it that after delegates to the convention, busy with the problem of creating counties for the new state, carved Tulsa County in the form of a cross, Nelson found himself so unpopular at home that he soon left the city. Nevertheless, the Nelson site was a valuable location in downtown Tulsa, where expanding demands of major oil companies had created one of the most beautiful sky lines in America.

In January, 1926, Dr. Day approached members of the medical and dental professions in Tulsa in regard to a building for joint occupancy, and in April he called a meeting in the City Hall Auditorium. This was attended by physicians and dentists interested in his project for a Medical and Dental Arts Building on the site of the Nelson property. A committee was formed, including two representatives of the Tulsa Dental Society, Dr. Oren McCarty and Dr. E. F. Woodring. The professional men accepted Day's proposal and early the next year construction began on the eleven-story building. Day underwrote the venture; professional men who became interested planned their own suites and took a personal interest in making possible for Tulsa a modern building to house offices for 150 members of Tulsa's growing medical and dental professions. The building was ready for occupancy in 1929.[8]

— 4 —

THE TYPE of postgraduate instruction inaugurated in 1918, that is, specific classroom instruction by nationally known teachers with student participation in clinical demonstrations, was unanimously adopted for the 1919 meeting of the Society in Oklahoma City. Dr. Lawrence again was selected to manage the program; fees were set at thirty dollars.

This was called the "Victory Post-Graduate Course" in the official program mailed to members of the Society as the February copy of the *Bulletin*. Members were returning from the armed services, while younger dentists, members of the Student Army Training Corps in college, had graduated and "passed" the Board. Drs. Rhein, Smith, and Roach again were selected to offer courses: Rhein in X ray and pulp surgery, Smith in nerve blocking, and Roach in

[8] Tulsa *World*, January 29, April 3, 1926; August 29, 1946; Walters to Clark, January 12, 1954.

partial removable dentures. Dr. M. M. House, Indianapolis, taught those enrolled in the class in full dentures; Dr. W. A. Coston of Topeka, operative dentistry; Dr. Thomas B. Hartzell of Minneapolis, pyorrhea. Dr. A. W. Starbuck of Denver conducted a course for lady dental assistants.

Dr. Howard R. Raper recently wrote of an incident in the professional career of Dr. M. M. House which illustrates the high standard of ethics maintained by the faculty of that period.[9] Dr. Raper, member of the faculty of Indiana Dental College, was the first teacher to introduce dental radiography into the college curriculum. It was his writings on the subject that attracted the interest of Dr. J. R. Caughron and Dr. Everett Lain. Dr. Raper recalled that in 1915, although still a member of the college faculty, he opened an office devoted exclusively to dental radiography. Forward-looking dentists of the state sent their patients to him. He relates: "All in all, the dentists of Indianapolis and the state took the 'exposure' splendidly. I had occasion to watch them under very trying circumstances. I recall a case of 'reconstruction of the mouth' from Dr. M. M. House. It had taken weeks of hard labor to complete. X-ray examination revealed the dismaying fact that the 're-construction' was built on septic teeth. I placed the negatives on the viewbox, which hung on the wall, and Dr. House stood looking at them. Dr. House did not say much. Neither did I. The negatives were doing the talking. Beads of sweat stood out on Dr. House's forehead. He shook his head, finally took the mounted negatives from the viewbox, tucked them in their envelope, turned toward the door, and said, 'I'll have to start over again, from scratch.' It took nerve not to offer alibis. Dr. House had the nerve." And indeed it did take courage of the highest order to admit that the new medium had exposed mistakes and to start over again, "from scratch." The dental profession has reason to be proud of such an attitude on the part of its members.

Classes of the 1919 postgraduate course were limited in number in order that the instructors could give personal attention to problems faced by each enrollee. The school of instruction was limited to two hundred members; dues for the postgraduate course brought the Society $6,000. After salaries to the instructors in the

[9] Howard R. Raper, "Notes on the Early History of Radiodontia," in *Oral Surgery, Oral Medicine, and Oral Hygiene*, Vol. VI, No. 1, (January, 1953), 70–81.

amount of $3,300 and other incidental expenses were paid, the Society voted to pay Dr. Lawrence $500 for serving as general manager. Approximately $1,250 remained in the Society's treasury after all expenses were met. Thus the meeting was not only a professional success but a financial success as well.

At the general session, March 7, Dr. Lawrence received special recognition from his associates for his organizational ability. A spontaneous movement that had started in the Northern District to propose his name for president-elect of the National Dental Association gained the blessing of the Society. After Dr. Bonnell proposed Lawrence's name for the candidacy and Dr. C. L. White seconded the nomination, Dr. Willis A. Coston, Topeka, promised the support of the Kansas Society; Dr. A. E. Smith gave Chicago's endorsement. This was supplemented by speeches of approval by Dr. F. E. Roach, Chicago; Dr. G. P. Robertson, San Antonio; Dr. M. M. House, Indianapolis; some of the thirty-five dentists in attendance from six neighboring states; and members of the state organization. An unanimity of opinion prevailed that Oklahoma through Dr. Lawrence deserved recognition for the introduction of the progressive postgraduate plan of conducting annual meetings.

In the following year fourteen states adopted the Oklahoma Way. Texas, Oklahoma, Kansas, and South Dakota dental societies arranged their weekly meetings in sequence for the convenience of teachers contracted for the series and in order to cut down overhead expense. Fees in each state were set at fifty dollars.

The Oklahoma meeting was held in Tulsa, March 16–20. Drs. Smith, Roach, and Hartzell returned to teach block anesthesia and oral surgery, removable partial denture prosthesis, pyorrhea and prophylaxis, respectively. Dr. Dayton Dunbar Campbell, Kansas City, who had taught many members of the Society when they were students in the Kansas City Dental College or the Western Dental College, conducted a course in full dentures. Dr. Clyde McClelland, Kansas City, assisted Campbell and instructed in laboratory techniques. Dr. T. W. Maves, Minneapolis, completed the corps of teaching experts. He conducted classes in crown and bridge and inlay technique.

After five and one-half days of expert teaching instruction a general clinic under the direction of Dr. W. E. Flesher was held by members of the state society. Dentists who appeared on the program were C. A. Furrow, Tulsa; R. C. Daniel, Oklahoma City; A. F. Sebert, Clinton; A. L. Walters, Tulsa; L. L. Barnes, Oklahoma City; J. M. Temples, Tulsa; J. B. Jenkins, Edmond; F. C. Reisling, Tulsa; I. E. McCarty, Tulsa; T. W. Sorrels, Oklahoma City; E. F. Woodring, Tulsa; E. K. Mabry, Oklahoma City; C. L. White, Oklahoma City; G. W. Badgely, Tulsa; B. N. Hope, Pawnee; C. W. Day, Tulsa; L. H. Johnston, Vinita; G. E. Roland, Pawhuska; and A. B. Walker, Fairview.

An unvoiced advantage of state gatherings was the opportunity to renew associations with friends from other communities; younger members of the Society were always particularly grateful for being recognized and remembered by the dental veterans. To this convention, welcomed by all, came the pioneer leader, Dr. F. H. Colter, Oklahoma City, after an enforced absence from serious illness that caused him to miss the 1918 and 1919 meetings. Colter was a charter member of the Oklahoma County Dental Society, which he had served twice as president; in 1903 he was chosen president of the Oklahoma Dental Association; he had represented the Dental Society as a member of the House of Delegates to the National Dental Association; he had been one of those who organized the College of Dentistry for Epworth University. Always a hard worker, he was a princely, dignified gentleman. Though not fully recovered from a lengthy illness, he had looked forward to the Tulsa meeting; early arrivals at convention headquarters, Ketchum Hotel, were pleased to find him in attendance.

Under provisions of the constitution of the Society, the president-elect assumed the office of chief executive, if found acceptable, at the close of the annual convention. A choice for the office of the presidency, therefore, was always designated a year in advance of assuming the office. At the Tulsa meeting Dr. A. E. Bonnell was completing his term as president, an office he had assumed on the last day of the March, 1919, meeting. On the final day of this meeting Dr. C. W. Day became president, promoted from the office of president-elect, to which he was elected in March, 1919. It was necessary to choose a president-elect who would be promoted to the presidency in March, 1921.

The intense gratification that members of the profession felt at the return of Dr. Colter to active participation in affairs of the Society are reflected in the official minutes prepared by Dr. J. A. Morrow, secretary. Morrow, from Carmen, was president of the Society for the 1918–19 term, the only member from a small town to be so honored. Like his predecessors in office—Walters, Lawrence, and Flesher—he had assumed the more exacting secretarial duties after serving as president. Morrow recorded for the official minutes March 18, 8:00 P.M.:

"Society met in general session for the purpose of electing officers. President Bonnell presiding. Proceed to nominate by informal ballot for President-elect.

"Dr. Colter received the highest number of votes cast in the informal ballot. Motion made by Flesher and seconded by White that the informal ballot be made formal and that the secretary be instructed to cast the entire vote of the Society for Dr. Colter for President-elect.

"Dr. Colter in a very few well-chosen words expressed his appreciation of the honor conferred upon him."[10]

Thus Dr. Colter was designated to become one of a small group honored by the presidency of the state organization who, before statehood, had been similarly honored by territorial organizations. Dr. S. A. Long, McAlester, president of the state association for the term 1912–13; Dr. A. E. Bonnell, Muskogee, 1919–20; Dr. C. W. Day, Tulsa, 1920–21, had served as presidents of the Indian Territory Dental Association. Dr. R. S. Parsons, Oklahoma City, president of the State Dental Society 1913–14, and Dr. J. A. Wells, Shawnee, who was to be president for the term 1934–35 were the only other members who had presided over the Oklahoma Dental Association, the organization composed of dentists practicing in Oklahoma Territory.

The following night, Dr. Colter, surrounded by intimate friends and associates who had honored him by selecting him for the highest office in the Society, had his career brought to a dramatic close. "March 19, 7:30 P.M.:

"President Bonnell in chair. A letter was read from Mrs. Shobe. Memorial discussion by Drs. Reisling and White.

"At this moment Dr. F. H. Colter, President-elect of the Society, entered the hall and walked up the center aisle to a front seat

[10] Minutes of the Oklahoma State Dental Society, March 18, 1920.

where he fell to the floor. His friends rushed to his aid but in spite of their efforts he passed away in a few minutes.

"With heavy hearts we watched his body removed from the hall and after appointing a resolutions committee, composed of Drs. White, Scruton, and Walker, the meeting adjourned."[11]

It became necessary the following morning to convene the Society in order to select a successor to Dr. Colter. Dr. L. M. Doss and Dr. W. J. Scruton of Oklahoma City, each of whom later was to serve the Society as president, were considered for the position, but Dr. A. B. Walker, Fairview, was unanimously elected.

— 5 —

Dr. Lawrence, who through the years had been manager of the post graduate courses, resigned in October, and Dr. Bonnell was appointed by the Executive Council to take his place. Bonnell secured for the annual meeting in Oklahoma City, March 14–19, 1921, the return of Drs. Roach, Smith, Coston, Maves, Campbell, and McClelland. Two Oklahomans, Dr. J. M. Temples and Dr. A. L. Walters of Tulsa, were selected to teach courses in pyorrhea, prophylaxis and root canal work. Dr. Wallace Seccombe, superintendent of the Royal College of Dental Surgery of Toronto, Canada, gave lectures on "Preventive Dentistry" and "Diet in Relation to Dental Diseases."

The following year the second tri-state meeting was held at Kansas City, April 10–14, 1922. Dr. Lawrence again was placed in charge of arrangements as secretary-treasurer of the organization committee. In November, 1921, and in February and March, 1922, from his office in Enid he edited the *Tri-State Dental Bulletin*, published by the Missouri, Kansas, and Oklahoma state dental societies in lieu of their regular quarterlies. The issues were devoted to promoting the meeting; the number issued in March included the official program. General lecturers included Drs. Smith, Seccombe, and House, who had appeared on recent programs in Oklahoma. Dr. Arthur D. Black, Dr. C. N. Johnson, and Dr. Frederick B. Noyes, Chicago; Dr. Howard R. Raper, Indianapolis, and Dr. Marcus L. Ward, Ann Arbor, Michigan, also presented lectures.

[11] Minutes, March 19, 1920.

Twelve sectional departments with detailed instruction in special phases of dentistry also were on the program, as well as general clinics by representative dentists in attendance.

Sectional directors included A. L. Walters, Tulsa, "Preventive Dentistry and Dietetics"; Charles A. Furrow, Tulsa, "Anchor Dentures"; J. M. Temples, Tulsa, "Pyorrhea and Prophylaxis"; and F. C. Reisling, Tulsa, "Block Anesthesia." Dr. Furrow was assisted by Dr. Fred D. Sparks, Ponca City, who demonstrated various techniques in porcelain saddle, gold, and vulcanite construction, and by Dr. A. F. Sebert, Clinton, who demonstrated simplified techniques in handling materials for castings. Dr. Warren L. Dutcher, Oklahoma City, assisted Dayton Dunbar Campbell, sectional director of "Full Dentures," each afternoon by casting one or more aluminum bases. Drs. C. L. White, Oklahoma City, and Frank H. Dougherty, Tulsa, appeared on the program directed by Dr. Temples, and Dr. I. E. McCarty, Tulsa, on the one directed by Dr. F. C. Reisling. Miss A. M. Johnson, Tulsa, read a paper "Dental Assistants Of All Kinds" in the section on office efficiency and assistants directed by Dr. C. A. Martin, Winfield, Kansas.

Friday, April 14, was devoted to general clinics. Dr. C. A. Ruhlen, Cushing was in charge of clinics conducted by members of the Oklahoma State Dental Society. Participants were G. E. Zinn, Wagoner; Fred H. Nowlin, C. L. White, J. B. Jenkins, Roy C. Daniel, A. C. Seids, and Alvin L. Fountaine, Oklahoma City; T. H. Williams, Chickasha; A. F. Kennedy, Walters; A. M. Bradley, W. T. Jacobs, and G. D. Carl, Muskogee; E. A. Hodges, Newkirk; I. E. Cordrey, Blackwell; L. H. Johnston, Vinita; J. M. Temples, Tulsa; W. Hopkinson, Miami; W. D. Rush, Cleveland; C. A. Ruhlen, Cushing; E. H. Hart, A. F. Sebert, and John Goeringer, Clinton; C. B. Ball, Frederick; and D. E. La Mont, Gotebo. Dr. A. B. Walker, president of the Society, was scheduled to present a clinic on "A Method of Tin-foiling a Waxed-up Denture." Because of a sudden attack of illness, however, Dr. Walker spent the week in a Kansas City hospital and was unable to attend any of the meetings. His presidential address was read by Dr. L. M. Doss, president-elect.

— 6 —

FOR THE FALL term of 1923, a dental department was established in the University of Oklahoma Hospital, Oklahoma City. Dr. Francis J. Reichmann, later an outstanding editor of the *Bulletin*, secretary and president of the State Society, has recently narrated this experience:

"My career in dentistry in Oklahoma was really started before I arrived in the state. In my senior year at Ann Arbor, Michigan, 1922–23, Dr. Chalmers Lyons, who was chief of the oral surgery department, told me he had received a letter from the University of Oklahoma asking that a dentist be sent to the University Hospital in Oklahoma City to start the department of dentistry in that institution. Dr. Lyons said he thought I could handle the job and suggested I go over to the University Hospital at Ann Arbor and work with the oral surgery department until time to graduate, that they would give me special training in gunshot wounds and fractures as I would probably need them very much down in Oklahoma.

"I followed his instructions and in due time arrived in Oklahoma for the first time in my life. I found the University Hospital had very limited equipment for the practice of dental surgery. In fact, I was given two instruments, and $175 to buy what I wanted. The dental supply houses in Oklahoma City practically gave me all the things I wanted that were not new, and I spent almost all the money for new instruments.

"There were no oral surgeons affiliated with the hospital at that time. There were two exodontists in Oklahoma City but neither was interested in more than the removal of teeth. As a result, my training in oral surgery at the University Hospital was done by two very eminent surgeons, Dr. Leroy Long, Sr., and Dr. Samuel Cunningham. At that time Dr. Long was doing all the oral surgery at the University Hospital as well as a great deal of general surgery, and Dr. Cunningham did the orthopedic surgery, including fractures of the jaws and face. With these eminent gentlemen I was privileged to do much work assisting them and, later in my two years there, they assisted me and offered helpful suggestions on the basic principles of facial surgery."[12]

[12] Interview with Dr. F. J. Reichmann, July, 1953.

During the course of the impromptu interview, Dr. Reichmann paid tribute to the dental profession of Oklahoma: "After spending two years at University Hospital, I opened a dental office for the general practice of dentistry in Oklahoma City. The reason I stayed in Oklahoma was because of the fine spirit and co-operation of the Oklahoma County Dental Society. I was tremendously impressed by the eagerness of the members to advance in the profession. I learned something of their history, how humble they were and how anxious they were to learn more about dentistry. I learned about the Society bringing the most eminent teachers and practitioners from any place in the world to give postgraduate courses for their benefit and the benefit of their patients. Since professional relationships are most important in a professional man's life, this caused me to remain in Oklahoma City.

"In those first years my private practice did not keep me too busy, so I spent most of the mornings at the University Hospital, continuing my studies in oral surgery and attendance at the outpatient clinic. This I did until we had a full-time resident dentist out there to take my place. Then I would spent three mornings a week with that young man. For about six years I was the only dentist in Oklahoma City who made visits to the hospital. Gradually this changed, as resident dentists who had spent one year at the University Hospital, such as Dr. Ward Shaffer, Dr. J. Millard Robertson, and others, located in Oklahoma City. They began to make the morning visits, and we would alternate. As soon as there were four of us, we would alternate on three months' shifts, working with the full-time resident."

No attempt has been made to establish complete dental care for patients admitted to the University Hospital. Rather, concentration has been upon those conditions which contribute to the hospitalization of patients. Preventive dentistry, therefore, has received little attention. Over eight thousand teeth were extracted during the first year by the resident dentist.

After the Crippled Children's Hospital was added to the University Hospitals system in 1928, a dental hygienist was employed who examined the mouths of children, taught them simple rules of oral hygiene, and reported to the resident dentist on those who needed additional dental care. In 1935 the Crippled Children's Act was amended through the efforts of Joe Hamilton, then director of the hospital, Dr. T. W. Sorrels, and the Rotary Clubs of Oklahoma. Dental cripples were declared eligible for treatment, including children with cleft palates. Cleft lips and palates, singly or in combination, occur in about one out of nine hundred live births. The incidence in Oklahoma is about sixty-five a year. These deformities, frequently neglected, require the services of specialists for correction and rehabilitation. Those cases brought to the Crippled Children's Hospital have received care and corrective attention from dentists and physicians trained in oral surgery, plastic surgery, and orthodontics.

Meantime, before the state had provided hospital facilities for crippled children, the Oklahoma State Dental Society had continued its vigorous campaign for the teaching of oral hygiene in the public schools.

CHAPTER SEVEN

Oral Hygiene

— I —

THE TEACHING of preventive dentistry first sponsored by the Society in 1912 continued uninterruptedly. Best results were obtained in communities where school authorities introduced the teaching and practice of oral hygiene to students of the lower grades. Members of the Society, particularly in smaller communities, gave assistance to the program. Dr. Charles A. Hess, Idabel, kept a record of pupils examined by him in that city from 1913 to 1921. In 1920 he found 227 pupils with aggravated cases of diseased gums: 394 pupils had 813 cavities in their six-year molars. His summary of his findings for the first and last year of his study was as follows:[1]

	1913	1921
Number of pupils	385	549
Number of cavities	1,604	1,371
Number of pupils with no cavities	50	210
Number of pupils, cavities permanent teeth	231	178
Number of pupils, cavities temporary teeth	958	884
Number of fillings	62	465
Number of pupils with fillings	26	104
Number of abscesses	134	96
Number of pupils with abscesses	83	64

In 1924 the Lee School Parent-Teacher Association, Oklahoma City, began the sponsorship of a dental clinic. The Okla-

[1] *Bulletin*, February, 1921, p. 8. Succeeding issues of the *Bulletin* throughout the 1920's include articles relating to the oral hygiene movement.

homa County Dental Society furnished equipment for a vacant room in the school where a dentist spent one-half of the school week attending to dental needs of the children. All pupils were examined each year and charts showing oral conditions were prepared for each child, who took them home to show his parents. Only on written consent of the parents was corrective work undertaken at the school. Conditions found among the pupils during the first two years were as follows:

	1924	1925
Pupils Examined	1,002	1,027
Temporary Decay	1,642	1,524
Permanent Decay	192	142
Abscesses	202	88
Bad Gums	115	0
Emergencies	219	102
Work Done Outside Clinic	46	76

At the annual meeting of the American Dental Association held in Dallas, Texas, in November, 1924, Oklahoma's hygiene exhibit arranged by Dr. Hess attracted special attention. Charts showed conditions found in a diseased oral cavity and placards explained the dangers from neglect of the care of teeth. Of particular interest were the four cases of teeth in the Hess Collection. Two of the cases contained about 19,000 extracted teeth; two cases contained about 450 samples and combinations of extracted teeth, upper third molar fused to second molar, perforated roots, broken broaches, impactions, faulty bridge work, pulp stones, and other unusual conditions found during the course of general practice by Dr. Hess over a ten-year period.

The Oklahoma County Dental Society, working through a committee headed by Dr. J. B. Jenkins, exhibited an educational dental exhibit at the state fairs in Oklahoma City and Muskogee in 1925. The committee planned and executed greatly enlarged models in carvings and bas-reliefs in plaster of Paris, cross sections and longitudinal sections of the human jaws and tissues. These illustrated the inception and progress of caries (tooth decay) and pyorrhea. These sections were done in natural colors and mounted in Cornell board, twenty-four inches by thirty-six inches, which bore suitable explanatory text. The posters were arranged in logical order and formed the background of the display.

The carvings and bas-reliefs used in the models were the handiwork of Dr. Jenkins, whose hobby, in which he excelled, was sculpturing. He designed the beautiful silver plaque awarded Dr. George W. Andree, Tishomingo, by the state society in 1929 for the most successful clinic demonstrated at the annual meeting and that same year prepared a bronze bust of Dr. C. N. Johnson, Chicago, veteran dental leader and former president of the national association, which was presented to him that year. Dr. Jenkins also prepared busts of the first eight governors of Oklahoma, which are on exhibit in the Oklahoma Historical Society.

In addition to the plaster-of-Paris models prepared for the state fair exhibits, four illustrated models were included on malocclusions and orthodontics which showed conditions before and after treatment. Beneath these were placed a design ten feet in length, the "Health Highway." It was a symbolical representation of the two courses of life open to every new-born child. One pathway was bordered with tooth brushes, proper foods, evidences of good health, efficiency, happiness, and plenty; the other pathway, represented a life of indulgence of perverted appetite, negligence, ignorance, sickness, misery, and despair.

The exhibit also included an enlarged revolving model, run by an electric motor, of a lower denture which contrasted one-half of the teeth and tissues in perfect health and arrangement with the other half which showed every condition of disease and neglect. Included also was a table display of foods for a proper diet. Two illuminated radioscopes with suitable interpretations attracted much interest.

During each fair two dental nurses remained in charge of the exhibit. They gave informal talks on the significance of the display, the importance of proper diet, of frequent dental inspection, of thorough prophylactic measures, and the necessity of the prompt filling of all small cavities.

The exhibit attracted widespread attention. Lantern slides were prepared and shown before luncheon clubs, women's organizations, and the schools of the state. Dr. Carl Puckett, state health commissioner reported greatly increased sales of tooth brushes and dentrifices. With the advent of national radio programs, the sponsors of a popular radio team made all America conscious of the slogan, "Brush your teeth twice a day; see your dentist twice a year." During the summer of 1926 dentists made talks before teachers attending school at Alva, Edmond, Stillwater, and Tahlequah: Dr. E. L. Miley at Northwestern, Dr. L. M. Doss at Central, Dr. L. G. Mitchell at A. & M., and Dr. A. E. Bonnell at Northeastern. Dr. Doss continued in practice a custom he had established under his presidency in 1922: an annual award of a handsome ladies' wrist watch to the student at Central State Teachers' College, Edmond, who wrote the best essay of four hundred words on "Preventive Dentistry."

The Oral Hygiene Committee of the State Society, during the administration of Dr. W. T. Jacobs, Muskogee, in 1925 was composed of Dr. Charles A. Hess, Idabel; Dr. T. W. Sorrels, Oklahoma City; Dr. John M. Temples, Tulsa; Dr. G. H. Williams, Oklahoma City; and Dr. A. M. Bradley, Muskogee.

This committee worked out a program of co-operation in dental health education with the State Department of Public Instruction and the State Health Department that reached all parts of the state through its public school system. Dr. Puckett informally set up a Bureau of Mouth Hygiene in the State Health Department which obtained for distribution from the Public Health Service pamphlets on "Mouth Hygiene for Mother and Child," "To the Mother," "Food and the Teeth," "Care of the Mouth," and "How To Brush the Teeth."

Dr. T. W. Sorrels, while president of the Society in 1926, spent much of his time away from his practice in organizational work for the oral hygiene movement. During the legislative session of 1927 he led an unsuccessful attempt to gain an appropriation of $7,500 to support a Bureau of Mouth Hygiene in the Oklahoma Department of Public Health. Governor Henry S. Johnston's appointee to the position of state health commissioner, Dr. O. O. Hammonds, nevertheless, was able to budget $5,000 from his general appropriations for this purpose. Dr. Hammonds created the Bureau of Dental Health Education under the supervision of Miss Pearl Wilson, R. N.

Dr. Sorrels, as president, instituted a policy that has become a part of administrative practice: On September 8 he met in Oklahoma City with the presidents and secretaries of the district societies, when the officials discussed forthcoming meetings and reported on membership drives and work underway under the guidance of the Oral Hygiene and Educational Committee. Each year thereafter the president and president-elect of the Society have held annual meetings with district officers, usually in August or September.

When Dr. Charles A. Furrow, Tulsa, succeeded Dr. Sorrels in the presidency of the Society in April, 1927, the latter was appointed chairman of the Oral Hygiene and Educational Committee, which served as an advisory board to the Bureau of Dental Health Education. Other committee members were Dr. A. B. Rivers, Okmulgee; Dr. J. A. Wells, Shawnee; and Dr. J. B. Jenkins, Oklahoma City.

In order to co-operate more closely with the State Department of Public Health, district officers appointed a superintendent of dental health education in each county. Those appointed were:

Eastern District:

Adair County, Dr. W. M. McAnally, Stilwell
Atoka County, Dr. I. C. McDonough, Atoka
Cherokee County, Dr. T. J. Treadwell, Tahlequah
Coal County, Dr. E. B. Garrison, Coalgate
Haskell County, Dr. T. W. McKinley, Stigler
Hughes County, Dr. Roy A. Smith, Holdenville
Latimer County, Dr. Paul D. Coleman, Wilburton
Le Flore County, Dr. C. M. Murray, Poteau
Mayes County, Dr. J. H. Quinn, Pryor
Muskogee County, Dr. G. L. Dodson, Muskogee
Okmulgee County, Dr. A. B. Rivers, Okmulgee
Pittsburg County, Dr. W. S. Phillips, McAlester
Pushmataha County, Dr. O. E. Alexander, Antlers
Sequoyah County, Dr. T. F. Harmon, Sallisaw
Wagoner County, Dr. H. H. Deatheridge, Wagoner
McCurtain County, Dr. Charles A. Hess, Idabel
Choctaw County, Dr. C. A. Thompson, Hugo
Bryan County, Dr. W. S. Williams, Durant

Northern District:

Osage County, Dr. H. G. Carson, Pawhuska
Rogers County, Dr. H. H. Kaho, Claremore

Clinics: An Important Feature
of Oklahoma State Dental Association Meetings
Dr. Richard T. Oliver (*above*), of Tulsa, and Dr. T. A. Jones (*below*),
of Oklahoma City, presenting clinics.

To the Ladies
Dr. Douglas L. Rippeto with two winners of the Thomas A. Jones Award for Dental Assistants: Phyllis Terry, 1953 winner, at left, and Wanda George, 1954 winner.

Nowata County, Dr. J. F. Buxton, Nowata
Washington County, Dr. F. B. Collins, Bartlesville
Pawnee County, Dr. W. D. Rush, Cleveland
Payne County, Dr. J. W. Childs, Stillwater
Craig County, Dr. W. C. Reed, Vinita
Ottawa County, Dr. R. H. Cully, Miami
Creek County, Dr. R. E. Smoot, Bristow
Tulsa County, Dr. R. W. Williamson, Tulsa

Northwestern District:

Grant County, Dr. F. C. Gale, Pond Creek
Garfield County, Dr. R. G. Carl, Enid
Kingfisher County, Dr. L. C. Harness, Kingfisher
Alfalfa County, Dr. J. A. Brown, Cherokee
Woods County, Dr. A. W. Clark, Alva
Ellis County, Dr. E. G. Fulton, Shattuck
Blaine County, Dr. L. A. Williams, Watonga
Noble County, Dr. O. W. Boyer, Perry
Major County, Dr. W. R. Brown, Fairview
Texas County, Dr. I. M. Lightner, Guymon
Beaver County, Dr. Roy Harville, Forgan
Harper County, Dr. W. H. Griffith, Buffalo

Central District:

Canadian County, Dr. J. P. Neal, El Reno
Logan County, Dr. R. O. Hirschi, Guthrie
Cleveland County, Dr. A. B. Walker, Norman
Pottawatomie County, Dr. Roy Melugin, Shawnee
Pontotoc County, Dr. G. C. Alsbach, Ada
McClain County, Dr. S. D. Wilson, Purcell
Oklahoma County, Dr. I. M. Helmy, Oklahoma City
Garvin County, Dr. W. Robbins, Pauls Valley
Carter County, Dr. D. A. McKeller, Ardmore
Johnston County, Dr. George Andree, Tishomingo
Murray County, Dr. W. L. Shamel, Sulphur
Marshall County, Dr. Norman Miller, Madill

South Central District:

Grady County, Dr. A. W. Wallace, Chickasha
Stephens County, Dr. W. E. Ferguson, Marlow

Comanche County, Dr. F. D. Dole, Lawton
Jefferson County, Dr. A. H. Bartling, Ryan
Cotton County, Dr. Norman Scism, Walters
Caddo County, Dr. I. J. Thomas, Carnegie

Southwestern District:
Jackson County, Dr. M. H. Wooldridge, Altus
Tillman County, Dr. C. B. Ball, Frederick
Kiowa County, Dr. G. S. Ault, Hobart
Washita County, Dr. L. H. Lanier, Cordell
Custer County, Dr. E. H. Hart, Clinton
Greer County, Dr. C. E. Hill, Mangum
Beckham County, Dr. J. E. Brown, Elk City
Harmon County, Dr. B. B. Bell, Hollis

Dr. W. S. Williams, Durant, was one of the more active workers in the oral hygiene movement. Dr. Williams had established his practice in Durant in 1904; his tenure as a member of the Board of Dental Examiners, 1918–35, is the longest in the history of the state. He was joined in practice at Durant by his sons, John in 1919 and Earl in 1926.

He and his boys visited the Training School for Boys at Pauls Valley and corrected dental conditions of the 125 inmates; they visited the State Industrial School for Girls at Tecumseh and treated 240 girls. The elder Williams suggested to Dr. Sorrels that similar work should be undertaken at other state institutions by dentists. His suggestion was acted upon by members of the Southwestern Dental Society. Dr. F. C. Holmes, Mangum, president of the district group, Dr. Glenn S. Ault, Hobart, vice-president, and Dr. C. B. Ball, Frederick, secretary, interested businessmen of Frederick in providing equipment for a dental office for the orphanage at Tipton. Members of the district society examined the 189 children in the home; treatment was administered to 120 who needed corrective dental work. The group also visited the reformatory at Granite and performed a similar service.

— 2 —

AFTER A superintendent of dental health education was appointed in each county, in 1927, all agencies concerned with public health, including the State Department of Health, the Oklahoma Medical Association, the Medical, Pharmaceutical, and Dental Association, extension divisions of the universities and their affiliates, parent-teacher associations, district organizations of the Federated Women's Clubs, businessmen's clubs, school authorities, and parents reported increased interest in dental care for children.

The showing of films, illustrated lectures with lantern slides, discussion series, and distribution of literature on the subject focused attention on the problem, but remedial action was prompted in too few instances. The trouble here lay with the dentists themselves. When interested groups learned that some 557,000 of the 700,000 grade children in Oklahoma were in need of reparative and preventive dental service, they demanded remedial action. Too often, however, parents reported that when small children were taken to the local dentist, he advised them to do nothing about dental needs, as temporary teeth soon would be lost anyway. The dental profession was faced with a novel situation: the public ready for children's dentistry and asking for it, public agencies advising that it be done, but a general apathy throughout the state on the part of the profession and, in some sections, the complete ignoring of the problem.

The average dentist feels that a child dental patient is much more difficult to work with than an adult, quite often disturbing office routine and preventing the dentist's rendering the best service; a mother standing by the operating chair is not always conducive to best results. Some dentists hesitated to attempt reparative operations on the teeth of children because of the uncertainty of results and consequent injury to their professional reputations from unsatisfactory work.

Accomplishments in the counties varied according to the enthusiasm and co-operation of dentists, health authorities, and school officials. In Noble and Cleveland counties, 2,449 grade children were examined by dentists, 863 permanent teeth were filled, 531 temporary teeth filled, 147 permanent and 774 temporary teeth extracted. Five hundred and forty-three of the children had their teeth cleaned, while 40 children had additional dental work done, such as fillings and crown and gum treatments.

The Lions Club of Okmulgee assumed sponsorship of the movement for oral hygiene in the rural schools of Okmulgee County. Dr. I. M. Hauser was engaged to do the operative work in the rural schools; his salary and expenses were borne jointly by the civic club and the County Health Association in those instances where parents were unable to pay for his services. Dr. Hauser took portable equipment with him from school to school and thus was able to offer his services at on-site visitations. During the spring term of 1929, 648 rural children received dental aid by this method, 867 fillings were made, and 325 teeth extracted.

Blanchard, Oklahoma, gained state-wide recognition for the dental health program undertaken in the public schools. When reports of investigations made by members of the Dental Society were published that indicated about 85 per cent of the children in the grade schools of Oklahoma needed treatment for dirty, diseased conditions of the teeth and gums, J. E. Cannon, superintendent of schools at Blanchard, decided to make oral hygiene a community project. Pupils came from rural homes, and it became necessary for Cannon and his teachers to conduct an intensive community-wide campaign of education for preventive dentistry. In this attempt he was aided by Dr. S. D. Wilson of Purcell. Cannon was not satisfied with having his pupils taught facts about dental health; he wanted them to have needed correction of dental defects.

The Blanchard community responded to its needs; by pie suppers, school plays, and other means, funds were raised to invite an itinerant dentist to perform the necessary operative work. Dr. Wallace Fisher, Oklahoma City, was engaged for this purpose, and in April, 1927, his program began which led to nearly 100 per cent correction of all dental defects.

Dr. Mervin C. Howard, Oklahoma City, who at this time limited his practice to children up to the age of fourteen years, did similar corrective work among the rural school children of Oklahoma County in 1928 and 1929. The State Department of Health sponsored the activity as a demonstration of community organization for health service to children.

Dr. F. O. Pitney succeeded Dr. I. M. Helmy as dentist for the Oklahoma City school system at the beginning of the school term in 1927. Regular, periodic examinations of students in the grade schools were instituted by Dr. Pitney, and corrective work done for students of indigent parents through contributions from the Parent-Teacher Association.

An article appeared in the November, 1930, issue of *Oral*

Hygiene by Dr. J. B. Jenkins, Oklahoma City, which called attention to the importance of the use of X ray in diagnosis; by January, 1,183 dentists had written the publisher for reprints. The Society ran the article in the January *Bulletin*. Jenkins included these statements:

"We have been in the habit of employing the Roentgen ray for examination of only those teeth suspected of being non-vital or diseased, and using the ray only to verify our suspicions, when, in fact, there are at least twenty-three other possible abnormal conditions to be revealed by the radiograph. No one in this day of modern diagnostic aids has a right to guess at the condition which might lie hidden within the bone and gum tissues. If patients knew what we dentists know about conditions too frequently existing in the mouth, hidden to the eye, and the relationship that exists between these conditions and constitutional health, they would refuse to accept a diagnosis based upon visual examination alone, and would insist upon radiographic examination.

"We shall not permit the Roentgen ray to take away our eyesight, but we should remember that the important two-thirds of the tooth is hidden in the jaws."[2]

Jenkins had prepared an illustrated chart to show patients hidden causes of illness or malformations revealed by the X ray. He listed the following:

1. *An Abscess.* May result in a bone infection, toxins in the blood, systemic diseases, heart and other organic diseases. The tooth may seem sound and comfortable.

2. *A Granuloma.* Is evidence of infection and bone destruction; often breaks down into painful abscess and blood infection; always unsafe and should be removed.

3. *Infection in the Bone.* May remain many years after tooth is extracted. Frequently explains why patient fails to recover health by mere extraction of teeth. Diseased area should be removed also.

4. *Root Left in Jaw.* As likely to cause disease as an infected tooth. Usually unsuspected; painless; cause of many systemic chronic diseases. Should *Always* be removed.

5. *Root in Antrum.* Should never be allowed to remain, causes

[2] *Bulletin*, January, 1931, pp. 14–16. According to the *Bulletin*, p. 8, the article by Dr. Jenkins was also published in the January number of Spanish *Oral Hygiene*.

serious disorder, pains and complications. Should be removed as promptly as possible.

6. *Pyorrhea Infection.* Often in last stages before discovered. Usually painless. Always filthy, causes many diseases, much better check it in early stages.

7. *Tarter Deep under gum.* Frequently accounts for sore teeth, bleeding gums. One of the forerunners of pyorrhea. Must be found and removed or gum and bone may become infected.

8. *Irritating, Ill-fitting Dental Work.* X ray shows effect on the bone, how it wastes away under inflammation, forming pus pockets, and food-trap.

9. *Infected Cyst in Bone.* Usually unsuspected, frequently painless. Often results in complete fracture of bone. X ray will reveal true condition.

10. *Hidden Decay.* Long before the top breaks in, it may be undermined by decay and the tooth lost before trouble is discovered. Check up.

11. *Supernumerary (Extra) Teeth.* Frequently explain vague pains, neuralgias, eye disturbance, cyst, bone destruction, unerupted teeth and discomfort under plates.

12. *Broken Hypodermic Needle in Jaw.* Sometimes lost in the tissues following hypodermic injection. Should be removed promptly.

13. *Curved Roots that Break Easily.* Showing why some teeth are more difficult to extract than others. No one can foretell the size, length, shape or curvature of a root without X-ray examination. When roots break off they should be removed.

14. *Decay under Good-looking Fillings or Crowns.* The filling or crown may appear perfect. An X-ray picture may reveal recurrence of decay. All old dental work should be carefully examined to determine if it is worth keeping.

15. *Condensing Osteitis.* Inflammation and condensing of bone, presses upon large nerve trunk. Produces neuralgic pains in head and neck.

16. *Impacted Wisdom Teeth.* Often lie deep in the jaw out of sight, causing 22 different disorders, pain, neuralgia, neuritis, muscular and sensory paralysis, nervousness and frequent insanity. Should always be removed.

17. *Impacted Cuspids.* Frequently produce many of the fore-

going symptoms including eye disturbances, mental and nervous disorders. Never safe in these positions.

18. *Pus in Antrum.* Resulting from colds, influenza, poor drainage, abscessed tooth roots sloughing into the sinus, causing head and face pains, foul odor, fever, and other complications.

19. *Enlarged Root-ends That Break Easily.* Prevents easy extractions. Another reason why it is worth more to extract some teeth than others. Only the X ray will show this.

20. *Pulp Stones in Nerve Cavity.* Frequently explains why a sound appearing tooth may cause aches, pains, neuralgia and neuritis. It often irritates the nerve like a grain of sand.

21. *Root-end Necrosis.* Usually indicates death of tooth and bone, sloughing of the dead part, infection and poisoning the blood stream. Always advisable to extract even if patient is well.

22. *Broken Jaw Bone.* Frequently the jaw is fractured without knowing it. Attempted extraction of teeth, following injury, without X ray might prove serious. Better check up first.

23. *Bone Tumor.* Often discovered before doing much damage. Sore place or enlargement under a plate, or in the jaws might prove to be worthy of one's most careful attention.

24. *Osteomyelitis.* Frequently the bone becomes infected, destroying entire jaw and causing loss of teeth. Of long duration, requiring careful management. Swollen jaws should be carefully examined, using the X ray in all cases.

Copies of the chart were displayed in many offices of members of the Dental Society. This educational work contributed to public interest in the oral hygiene campaign.

During the school term 1931–32 an all-inclusive health program was put into effect in the Clinton public schools through the energy and effort of local groups and professional men. They received sustaining co-operation from George D. Hann, superintendent of schools, and his faculty. Every dentist in the community assisted in the program: Drs. A. F. Sebert, L. L. Patterson, H. G. Hays, L. E. Church, A. G. Hartzog, and A. L. Hartzog.

In the dental phase of the program an accurate examination was made and record kept of the condition of the teeth and gums and corrections needed. Parents were advised of the defects found. Five hundred and fifteen of the 1,205 school children examined needed corrective work; several cases of trench mouth were found, treated, and cured. In many instances bad gums were found and corrected. It was found, too, that children who needed the most corrective work, those with the worst cases of bad teeth, came from homes whose economic status was above average, homes where children were allowed to indulge in refreshments of soft drinks and candies between meals.

When Dr. E. E. Overmyer of Muskogee was president of the Oklahoma State Dental Society for the term 1933–34, Oklahoma co-operated with other states in a dental survey of school children sponsored by the American Dental Association and the United States Public Health Service.[3] In the survey, 1,438,318 school children in twenty-six states were examined by local dentists; in Oklahoma twenty-three counties were selected to take part in the survey. Members of the Oklahoma State Dental Society in the counties voluntarily assisted in the program; 18,677 Negro and white school children were examined.

The findings at McAlester, where Drs. Max Knarr, W. S. Phillips (who was to be president of the state society four years later), Edgar Porth, Ben C. Thompson, and the veteran dentist, Dr. H. A. Weeks, conducted the survey, were typical of results recorded in other parts of the country. The following table expresses in percentage the dental needs of the 1,504 children examined:[4]

		780 Boys			724 Girls		
	Age in Years	6–8	9–11	12–14	6–8	9–11	12–14
(a)	Present dental needs and						
	oral pathology	%	%	%	%	%	%
	Treatment needed:	95.2	99.3	99.3	95.9	98.6	97.1
	Prophylaxis	88.6	93.4	93.3	85.3	90.5	91.4
	Gingivitis	6.8	20.4	20.6	4.6	9.3	20.5
	Children with caries,						
	deciduous teeth	51.4	16.3	1.5	52.3	15.5	1.2
	Children with caries,						
	permanent teeth	36.2	63.5	70.3	38.6	66.1	74.6

[3] "Dental Survey of School Children, ages 6–14 Years Made in 1933–34 in 26 States," in *Public Health Bulletin No. 226* (May, 1936) (U. S. Treasury Department, Public Health Service, Washington, D. C.).

[4] The statistics were extracted from *Table X*, p. 165, of *Public Health Bulletin No. 226.*

	780 Boys			724 Girls		
Malocclusion, slight	17.5	21.2	23.0	14.6	26.5	20.6
Malocclusion, severe	2.1	8.0	6.4	2.9	5.1	4.5
Orthodontic treatment recommended	8.3	13.9	11.9	8.2	9.7	9.5
(b) Past dental treatment						
Treatment received prior to examination	24.1	41.9	44.9	21.4	38.6	43.1
Odontexesis	3.4	4.1	4.9	5.2	5.7	4.6
Children with filled deciduous teeth	13.7	11.6	4.6	7.3	9.7	5.4
Children with filled permanent teeth	3.9	12.6	18.5	5.8	16.1	20.7
Children with extracted permanent teeth	0	2.4	10.1	0	2.7	10.0

These conditions foretold findings of dentists attached to the Civilian Conservation Corps who were charged with the care of youths over seventeen years of age. Six to ten years later these same conditions forecast findings of dentists in the armed services during World War II. Children with diseased teeth and mouths, neglected during the depression years and oftentimes handicapped by nutritional deficiencies from improper diet, were too often found unfit for service when they reached the age and time of the country's greatest need.

— 3 —

WHEN Dr. Wallace Seccombe, superintendent of the Royal College of Dental Surgery, Toronto, Canada, lectured at the postgraduate course of the Dental Society in 1921 on the subjects "Preventive Dentistry" and "Diet in Relation to Dental Diseases," attention of the members centered on these problems. The following year members in attendance at the tri-state meeting, Kansas City, heard his lecture on "The Demineralization of Modern Foods—A Causative Factor in Dental Caries." Many attended the section on "Preventive Dentistry and Dietetics" conducted by him with the assistance of Dr. A. L. Walters, Tulsa. They learned of requirements of the body for calories, mineral constituents, and vitamins, and the importance of wholesome foods in the diet.

During the following two years Dr. Walters appeared before the Society at its annual conventions to lead discussions pertaining to dietetics and preventive dentistry. He represented the best thinking of the period and brought to his colleagues stimulating facts culled from the laboratories of medical research on the proper diet for a pregnant mother, a bottle-fed baby, a child from two to twelve years of age, and adults.

Dentists co-operated with physicians in bringing the story of proper diet to the public. An excerpt from a speech made by Dr. A. C. Seids, Oklahoma City, to a public gathering shows a typical presentation: "Our remarks naturally must begin with pregnancy, the formation of the foetus and its development. At the fourth month the foetus begins to take form and small nodules are noticed deposited, which, as development progresses, form the first or deciduous teeth. Let me stress here the need of care, and a clean mouth, if the expectant mother hopes to bring into the world a child that will be blessed with a strong body and good dentition. The most pitiful person the dentist encounters is an expectant mother with a mouthful of broken-down and abscessed teeth. In the name of God, what chance has this helpless forthcoming child? It already has two strikes and a foul against it. All obstetricians with whom I have come in contact are very careful to see that the expectant mother's diet is correct, and in addition prescribe the necessary elements to assure proper development of the child's body and teeth.

"After birth of the child, between its sixth and eighth month, the two lower central incisors make their appearance. These are immediately followed by the upper central incisors; others follow suit, and at thirty-two months the complete compliment of deciduous teeth should be in place. At the third year the child should be taken to the family dentist for inspection, and these visits should continue regularly at four to six months, depending entirely on the formation of the teeth and the incidence to decay.

"If you want to make me hot under the collar, ask me why baby teeth should be filled since they lose them anyway. I'll tell you why. A child is building a body, burning up energy, growing, and without the proper dentition to handle his food is headed toward ill health. It is far more important that a child's mouth be healthy than an adult's.

"At about six years of age the six-year molars make their appearance just back of the deciduous teeth. These are four in number, two up and two below. They are known as the keystone of the dental arch and should be watched carefully as they often come through with leaky pits and fissures. These should be repaired at once. With loss of the deciduous teeth and the advent of the permanent ones, eternal vigilance is necessary to maintain a healthy mouth.

"It might be well to go into the matter of orthodontics at this time. To my way of thinking the child who is unfortunate enough to have malformed teeth is in a serious position. The prospects of the child going through life with an ill-shaped mouth should be given serious consideration by parents, as it is my belief that malposed teeth have more to do with stunting one's personality than almost any other defect. Finger-sucking and other bad habits formed by infants which tend to cause ill-shaped mouth and jaws should have early care. The habit of sleeping in one position should be guarded against. Sleeping on the arm or hand may cause the mandible or lower jaw to become malposed or crooked.

"Not only the child but the adult as well should be taught to satisfy the craving for sweets with seasonable fruits. It is as easy to teach a child the habit of eating fruit as it is sweets. Milk has been spoken of as the perfect food and every child's diet should include one quart of milk each day. Plenty of fresh garden vegetables should be included in the diet. In recent years we have heard much about vitamins, and I am glad to submit a table of the vitamins, their source as well as importance . . . ."[5]

Dr. Seids also touched upon other problems affecting oral hygiene: "We lose our teeth generally from one of three causes, namely, decay, pyorrhea, or accident.

"The formation of the teeth come about from two or more points of development, depending on the tooth, the incisors and cuspids from two points, the bicuspids from four, and the molars from five or more. As the points of development merge to form the crown of the tooth—the crown is always formed first and it takes from one to three years for the roots to complete development after the tooth has completely filled its place in the dental

[5] Dr. Seids' manuscript is in the files of the Central Office, Oklahoma State Dental Association.

arch—quite often the enamel folds fail to unite. When this happens, small pits and fissures provide ingress of secretions which break down and destroy the structure of the tooth. Often the pits are so minute that many years may pass before the action of the secretion gets in its work. For these reasons, children should have regular dental inspections.

"We are also confronted with rapid decay. One may fill a tooth with all the care in the world then have the patient return in thirty days with another cavity in the same tooth. It has been suggested this condition may be retarded by the elimination of sugar from the diet. Whatever the cause, it is the one thing which all but drives your dentist to the mad-house.

"Now as to the blight of an unhappy people, pyorrhea, what is it and why? Let me say here and now that far more teeth are lost from the cause of pyorrhea than all other causes combined. In dental literature, three times as much has been written on this subject as on any other subject covering dentistry. Authorities differ as to the cause of this malady. It is generally recognized as being due to systemic or local conditions or a combination of both.

"If systemic, the condition may arise from several sources, such as faulty metabolism, endocrine disturbance, or diabetes. A person with pyorrhea suddenly comes aware that a tooth or teeth has become loose and seems sore under pressure. Seldom is pus or infection noticeable to any extent, but the gum tissue takes on a pale, grayish color and eventually the tooth must be removed. A thorough check up should be made as soon as possible so that the source of trouble may be isolated and treatment begun. An X-ray examination may show a degenerative condition of the bony structure of the jaw.

"Pyorrhea may be brought about by local conditions directly attributable to neglect. Deep deposits of calculi are found imbedded under the gum tissue adhering to the teeth, the gums become sore, bleed and, in advanced cases, severe swelling is noticeable. Pyorrhea may also develop from faulty-fitting crowns and fillings, from extractions where replacements have been neglected or teeth drifting from their original position to cause trauma or extreme pressure. If the case has not progressed too far, treatment should be begun which should prolong the usefulness of the teeth for a long time.

If, however, response is not immediate, the offending teeth should be removed and replaced with substitutes.

"Vincent's Angina or Trench Mouth is an infectious disease which America apparently inherited from World War I. I had personally never seen a case until our boys began coming back from Europe. This is a malady which attacks young and old, rich or poor, alike, and no distinction is shown for social standing. It may be acquired by drinking from an infected glass, eating from improperly sterilized dishes, using a face towel infected by another person, and especially from kissing. Early symptoms are soreness of the gums and intense bleeding from one or more places around or between the teeth. I have treated patients from ten months old to seventy years of age with this disease, but I have never encountered a case with patients wearing full upper and lower dentures. This shows conclusively that the point of ingress is about the natural teeth. Like all other infections, the sooner attention is given to the cause the more quickly will a cure be effected."

A younger dentist, Dr. Claud A. Northcutt, Ponca City, also became a leader in the movement for preventive dentistry. Reports of the satisfactory work he was doing were discussed in mothers' clubs and parent-teacher associations. He impressed upon prospective mothers their need for proper diet; he had pre-school children visit his office at regular intervals of three months. Dr. Northcutt established the system of administering to the dental needs of children on an annual-fee basis, in order to assure regular treatment.

An important contribution to the oral hygiene movement was made by Dr. Fletcher C. Gale, Pond Creek. Dr. Gale, who graduated from the Western Dental College in 1905, established his practice at Pond Creek ten years later. During the earlier years of his practice it was evident to him that too little professional attention had been paid by manufacturers to tooth-brush design. Most types were similar to miniature hair brushes. Dr. Gale devoted much time to research on the problem, and after many experiments, incorporating suggestions from members of the Society, a small two-row straight trimmed brush was developed which he began marketing in 1921 as the San-I-Ti tooth brush. He established the San-I-Ti Tooth Brush Company at Pond Creek; his product was highly prescribed by Oklahoma dentists; by 1927 more than 44,000 of the brushes were sold in the state. In 1930, Dr. Gale reported sales of 170,000, with at least 80 per cent sold as a result of prescriptions written by Oklahoma dentists.

Dr. Mervin C. Howard, in an article in the November, 1929, issue of the *Bulletin*, included these facts obtained from his work in the rural schools of Oklahoma County: "Upon a recent dental survey of all the 'well' children of a first-class rural school, of the children in the first four grades, it was found that in this prosperous community sending fifty children to these four grades, an average of twenty-two cavities per person was present. Vincent's infection, early stages of diseased gums, and foul breath abounded. Badly arranged teeth, due to prolonged retention of abscessed teeth and filth were present in numbers. Of these 'well' children, only four bore the evidence of a tooth brush. Most of the number examined had no tooth brush and had never had one. It is strange that boys and girls of these grades were considered 'well' yet were two and three grades behind in their classes."

Dr. Norman Scism, Walters, in the same issue of the *Bulletin* included a suggested outline for the care of children's teeth:

1. *Care of sound teeth.* This includes thorough prophylaxis by the dentist and instructions to the parent and child on proper methods of home care. The parent should brush the child's teeth as soon as they erupt, and some recommend salving the mouth with a saturated solution of boric acid before they erupt.

2. *Treatment of carious teeth, or teeth predisposed to caries.* This falls into three divisions.

    a. Filling all pits and fissures.

    b. Filling all cavities where adequate retention may be obtained.

    c. In cases where decay has progressed so far that obtaining retention is doubtful or impossible but the pulp is still vital, the tooth is cut down with a stone until the cavity is self-cleansing and treated with silver nitrate.

3. *Extraction.* All teeth with dead or infected pulps should be extracted for several reasons. Foci of infection. Soreness causes child to fail to properly masticate food. Injury to enamel of permanent teeth from fragments of unabsorbed roots of deciduous teeth.

Anesthesia is a problem in children's work. The Ethyl Chloride spray developed by the Forsythe Infirmary is excellent.

4. *Space retainers.* In order to obtain proper development of the face and arches, space retainers should be placed where teeth are lost prematurely. Failure to do this usually results in malocclusion, and the need of extensive orthodontic treatment.

5. *Orthodontics.* When you consider the very rapid growth of the face compared to the cranium and that the proper development of the arches and the position of the teeth shape or mis-shape the face, you can see how important this treatment is.

A poor appearance is not only an economic loss, but the attendant malocclusion makes proper mastication of the food impossible, and then nutritional disorders set in.

— 4 —

MEN WHOSE NAMES were known throughout the dental world were selected to conduct classes at the annual meeting of the state society held at the Mayo Hotel, Tulsa, April 30–May 3, 1928. Instructors included the scholarly teacher and writer, Dr. C. N. Johnson, Chicago, president of the American Dental Association; Dr. Dayton Dunbar Campbell of Kansas City; the brother dentists, Drs. James C. Mortonson and Morton H. Mortonson of Milwaukee; and Dr. Phil Thomas of Minneapolis, one of the first of his profession to devote his practice exclusively to children.

Dr. Thomas presented an illustrated lecture on the dental needs of children in which he brought out the ill effects on the general health of the child from neglect of proper care of the deciduous teeth. The Program Committee, composed of Dr. C. A. Furrow, president of the Society, Dr. W. J. Scruton, Oklahoma City, president-elect who succeeded Furrow at the close of the session, and Dr. Roy H. Ellis, Okmulgee, secretary, who moved up to the position of president-elect, also arranged to have L. W. Kibler of the Extension Division, University of Oklahoma, appear before the Society. Kibler's topic was "Dental Education by Extension Plan." He explained a successful plan recently inaugurated by the University in co-operation with the Oklahoma Medical Association whereby lecturers in specialized fields of medicine visited group meetings of physicians in various parts of the state.

After discussion a motion was offered by Dr. C. R. Lawrence which was adopted. It provided that Dr. W. J. Scruton should appoint a committee of three to work with the Extension Division of the University on offering a postgraduate course in children's dentistry. Dr. Scruton appointed Drs. T. W. Sorrels, Roy Ellis, and E. E. Sanger, who met with Dr. O. O. Hammonds of the State Department of Public Health, Miss Pearl Wilson, his director of Dental Health Education, Dr. Paul L. Vogt, dean of the University of Oklahoma Extension Division, and L. W. Kibler. This group worked out a plan which was presented to the dentists over the state at the next district meeting and was enthusiastically accepted. Dr. Phillip Thomas was selected to give the series of lectures, demonstrations, and clinics. The enrollment fee was set at twenty-five dollars, and it was proposed to offer the course extending over a six-weeks period in November and December.

Unfortunately, the postgraduate course was unexpectedly postponed. Dr. Thomas came to Oklahoma in mid-November to begin the course before the Central District Dental Society, Oklahoma City. Dr. J. A. Wells, president, Shawnee; Dr. A. B. Walker, vice-president, Norman; and Dr. Harry Sorrels, secretary-treasurer, of the host city, had created enthusiasm for the meeting, which inspired the largest turnout of members and attracted seventeen additional dentists who became members of the organization. On Wednesday, November 14, the date for the opening of the meeting, Dr. Thomas became suddenly and seriously ill; he was rushed to the University Hospital and died the next morning. Dr. C. L. White was delegated by the Society as an escort to accompany the body to Minneapolis; a committee composed of Dr. Harry Sorrels, Dr. W. E. Flesher, and Dr. J. B. Jenkins drew up resolutions in honor of Dr. Thomas which were forwarded to Mrs. Thomas, the *American Dental Journal*, the *Oklahoma State Bulletin*, and the *State Dental Bulletin of Minnesota*.

The untimely death of Dr. Thomas delayed presentation of the postgraduate courses at district level until after the annual meeting of the state society held at the Huckins Hotel, Oklahoma City, April 22–25, 1929. Dr. Thomas B. McCrum of the Kansas City Public School Clinic, Kansas City, Missouri, and Dr. Paul A. Barker of Denver, Colorado, both well-known pedodontists and widely acclaimed lecturers, were chosen to present instruction in children's dentistry and economics.

The schedule of meetings extended over a period of five weeks, Dr. McCrum conducting the course through the first three weeks and Dr. Barker the remainder. The first meeting was held at Hobart on Monday, April 29. Sessions followed at Duncan, Oklahoma City, Enid, Tulsa, and McAlester on successive days, and the Monday through Saturday schedule was kept up by the instructors until the courses were completed. Dr. Roy Ellis, president of the state society, accompanied the instructors on their man-killing schedule; years later he estimated that during his term he spent some 146 days away from his office on official business for the Society, a high mark of devotion to the Society's welfare.

Eighty-six members of the Society took the courses. Dr. Paul L. Vogt, dean of the University of Oklahoma Extension Division, had hoped that non-members would take advantage of the course of instruction, but none did.

Dean Vogt mailed a questionnaire to participants immediately after the course was completed and received enthusiastic replies from all but three of the dentists. Typical replies to one of the questions he asked, "In what way has the course helped improve your practice," were as follows:

"By strengthening the public confidence in me. I traveled ninety miles each week to get this course, and will take the next one offered if at all possible."

"I handle children and their mothers with more confidence."

"Can discuss children's dentistry so much more intelligently with their parents, and know it is helping me a great deal."

"Parents know I took the course and are bringing their children to me."

"I have made space retainers that would have otherwise been neglected."

Dr. E. E. Sanger, secretary of the Society, received inquiries from officers of nine other state societies in reference to the sponsorship of the postgraduate courses by the Extension Division of the University of Oklahoma. Again, national recognition in dental circles came to the state society for its success in achieving a new approach to dental education.

After the annual meeting of the Society in April, when Dr. Roy Ellis became president, the Educational–Oral Hygiene Committee was enlarged to include Drs. T. W. Sorrels, Oklahoma City; J. A. Wells, Shawnee; C. A. Northcutt, Ponca City; A. F. Sebert, Clinton; Norman Scism, Walters; W. R. Fisher, Edmond; and W. S. Phillips, McAlester. These gentlemen worked with Dean Vogt on the itinerant plan of postgraduate instruction. They secured the consent of Dr. Arthur D. Black, dean, Northwestern Dental College, Chicago to have him and faculty members give a six weeks' course of instruction beginning in November on a schedule similar to the one used in the early spring and summer months. The following schedule was followed with meetings held during each week, in rotation, at Oklahoma City, Lawton, Clinton, Enid, Tulsa, and Muskogee:

Week of November 11—"Children's Dentistry"—Dr. F. B. Rhobotham.

Week of November 18—"Vincent's Angina and Other Diseases of the Soft Tissues of the Mouth"—Dr. E. H. Hatton.

Week of November 25—"Pathology and The Surgical Treatment of Pyorrhea"—Dr. G. R. Lundquist.

Week of December 2—"Gold Inlay Technique"—Dr. R. E. Blackwell.

Week of December 9—"Focal Infections and Preventions in Dental Practice"—Dr. Arthur D. Black.

Week of December 16—"The Technique of Novocain Injections" —Dr. S. W. Clark.

The University of Oklahoma postgraduate plan of bringing the best dental instruction into all parts of the state continued until 1934. During the administration of Dr. C. A. D. Beer, Enid, in 1930, a course in dental economics was begun by the Extension Division, at the suggestion of Dr. C. R. Lawrence and Dr. A. E. Bonnell. The course extended over a period of three years. Drs. R. H. Miller, St. Louis, and John C. Warnock, Kansas City, taught courses in dental economics; Robert Sesline, Oklahoma City, on credits; Dan W. Hogan, prominent Oklahoma City banker, on money and banking. The University furnished the services of Professor J. M.

Ashton, who taught a course in public finance, and Mary C. Welch, who conducted office surveys and instructed in dental office orientation. The University furnished instruction for about twenty dentists and their dental assistants per month with follow-up consulting service and office-routine surveys. Dentists found the service practicable and timely as the full impact of the depression years greatly affected their practice.

Dr. W. P. Morrison, El Reno, member of the state Senate, was instrumental in getting legislation passed during the 1931 session of the legislature which provided the University $6,000 for each of the following two years to be used for dental education. This prompted Dr. W. B. Bizzell, president of the University, to announce: "Had it not been for the present economic depression, the University of Oklahoma before now would have had in operation a school of dentistry in Oklahoma City in connection with the University Hospital and the School of Medicine. It is our plan, just as soon as conditions permit, to ask the legislature to authorize dental instruction. It is proposed to start primarily with postgraduate work, bringing to the practicing dentists of Oklahoma the latest developments in their profession, and then gradually to extend the work to undergraduate study."[6]

Actually, the goal set by Dr. Bizzell has never been achieved, but the appropriation was timely in sustaining the postgraduate plan of instruction. Governor W. H. Murray cut the yearly appropriation to $5,475, and the Board of Regents of the University applied an additional cut of 10 per cent, which left $4,927.50 for use in dental education. Funds were used through 1933 by the University in helping the state society sustain its postgraduate programs of instruction at annual meetings and before the district societies. But because of depressed world conditions which affected the state's economy, the dental organization was unable to get an appropriation for this purpose from the legislature in 1933.

6 *Bulletin,* August, 1931, p. 4.

CHAPTER EIGHT

Revisions of the Dental Act

— I —

WHEN THE fifteenth legislature convened in January, 1935, the State Dental Society had prepared a proposed bill to revise dental legislation. Dr. F. J. Reichmann, editor of the *Bulletin*, set forth reasons for the proposal in the January issue: "The enforcement of our present dental law has been found impracticable on account of its ancient construction. While it was passed in 1919, the contents were copied from other state laws of more ancient vintage. A history of the activities of the Board of Dental Examiners demonstrates the improper construction of our present law, which has failed to provide the proper structure upon which to build protection of the public against dental charlatanism. These weaknesses have been repeatedly admitted by members of the Board of Examiners through their attempts to pass amendments to our present law, their blaming of the executive branch of the government for their actions in some instances, and for their failure to act in others. . . .

"The proposed new dental law removes the responsibility for the proper conduct of the dental profession from the shoulders of the Governor and places it on the profession, which the public has rightfully done, and where it belongs."

Groundwork for the proposed revision of the dental act began in 1933 when Dr. A. C. Seids was state president of the Society. That year the annual convention was held in Oklahoma City in November in conjunction with the meeting of the American Society of Orthodontists. Dr. W. E. Flesher was president of this national organization, and reported to members of the state society on qualifying limitations suggested by orthodontists that should be included in state legislation.

At the close of the session Dr. E. E. Overmyer, Muskogee, became president of the Society, and, through recommendations of the executive council, the following members of the Society were appointed to a legislative committee: W. E. Flesher, Oklahoma City; A. C. Seids, Oklahoma City; A. E. Bonnell, Muskogee; Charles L. White, Oklahoma City; Roy H. Ellis, Okmulgee; and G. A. Roelke, Tulsa. The first four were former presidents of the Society, active since statehood or before in the betterment of dentistry, who had learned to work with Oklahoma legislators when the dental laws of 1913 and 1919 were enacted. Dr. Ellis, a former president, and Dr. Roelke, who was to be president in 1943, contributed time and enthusiasm to the study. Later, Dr. Fred Sparks was appointed to the committee. Sparks added experience and a necessary personal contact with Governor E. W. Marland. Sparks had served on the territorial Board of Dental Examiners before statehood when he was a leader in the movement that led to enactment of the dental act of 1905. At the end of a second term on the Board, 1922–26, he joined the Marland Oil Company as industrial dentist of that organization; for years he had been Marland's personal dentist. Enthusiasm by the committee was heightened when he brought a personal letter from Marland in which the Governor stated he would sign any bill that the State Dental Society could put through both houses of the legislature.

The committee employed the Oklahoma City law firm of Hayes, Richardson, Shartel, Gilliland, and Jordan to prepare their suggestions as a proposed bill for legislation. Judge Samuel W. Hayes, senior member, was a former chief justice of the Supreme Court of Oklahoma. Dr. J. A. Wells, president of the Society during 1935 when the bill was before the legislature, has recently recalled that he asked a Shawnee attorney of wide experience if he knew Judge Hayes. "Sam Hayes," was the reply, "why, if I had a case in court against Judge Hayes I would just as soon have him act as judge on the merits of the dispute as any man I know!"

Recent legislation passed in other states was carefully screened by the committee in order to make the proposed bill the strongest and most equitable to the profession and public in the nation. The following illustration shows how seriously the committee undertook its study: Oregon in 1933 had revised its dental law to include a strongly prohibitory section which forbade advertising. A dentist in Portland who had advertised for years sued the Board of Dental Examiners of Oregon in the Federal District Court on the grounds that the act was an invasion of his rights set forth in the fourteenth amendment to the federal constitution, that provision which states: "No state shall make or enforce any law which shall abridge the privileges or immunities of citizens of the United States; nor shall any state deprive any person of life, liberty, or property, without due process of law." He presented evidence in court that he had faithfully and competently performed every technique and operation claimed by his advertisements. The District Court and, later, the Circuit Court of Appeals upheld the Oregon statute. The case was appealed to the United States Supreme Court.

When this case reached the Supreme Court in 1934 for decision during its October term, the American Dental Association interested component societies in contributing toward defense of the statute. The Oklahoma State Dental Society joined the crusade.

Charles Evans Hughes, chief justice, handed down the decision. The court found the statute valid, that the state could prevent a dentist from advertising professional superiority and prices, that "it is within the authority of the state to estimate the baleful effects of such advertising, and to protect the community not only against deception but against practices which, though they may be free from deception in particular instances, tend nevertheless to lower the standards of the profession and demoralize it."[1]

Chief Justice Hughes spoke out vigorously for professional standards: "The community is concerned with the maintenance of professional standards which will insure not only competency in individual practitioners, but protection against those who would prey upon a public peculiarly susceptible to imposition through alluring promises of physical relief. And the community is concerned in providing safeguards not only against deception but against practices which would tend to demoralize the profession by forcing its members into an unseemly rivalry which would enlarge the opportunities of the least scrupulous. What is generally called the 'ethics' of the profession is but the consensus of expert opinion as to the necessity of such standards."

The committee prepared for the bill a provision against ad-

[1] *Semler* v. *Oregon State Board of Dental Examiners,* 294 U. S. 608–13.

vertising stronger than appeared in the statutes of any other state. It provided: "It shall be unlawful for any person, firm or corporation to publish, directly or indirectly, or circulate, through the usual commercial channels, through the press, magazines and directories, by radio or sign display, any statements as to the skill or method of practice of any person or operator; or in any way to advertise to practice dentistry; or to claim or infer superiority over other dental practitioners; or in any way to advertise as having ability to diagnose and prescribe treatment for malposed teeth by use of impressions, or casts, made from natural teeth; or to publish reports of cases or certificates of same in any public advertising media; or to advertise as using any anesthetic, drug, formula, material, medicine, method or system; or to claim the use of any secret or patented methods, treatments, or appliances; or to offer free dental services or examinations, as an inducement to secure dental patronage; or to publish any amount as a price or fee for the service or services of any person engaged as principal or agent in the practice of dentistry, or for any material or materials whatsoever used or to be used, or offering to guarantee or warrant any dental service; or to employ 'cappers' or 'steerers' to obtain patronage; or to exhibit or use specimens of dental work, posters, or any other media calling attention of the public to any person engaged in the practice of dentistry; or to give a public demonstration of skill or methods of practicing dentistry upon or along the streets or highways or any place other than his office where he is known to be regularly engaged in the practice of his profession; and any person committing an offense against any of the provisions of this section shall, upon conviction, be subjected to such penalties as are provided in this Act; provided, that any person licensed under this Act may announce by way of a professional card containing only the name, title, degrees, office location, phone number, and residence address and phone number, if desired, and if he is registered in a specialty he may announce it, but such card shall not be greater in size than three and one-half (3½) inches by two (2) inches, and such information may be inserted in public print when not more than one column in width and two (2) inches in depth; or announce his change of place of business, absence from, or return to business, in the same manner; or issue appointment cards to his patients, when the information thereon is limited to matter pertaining to the time and place of appointment and instructions to patients, and that permitted on the professional card; or display the name of the licensee, on the premises where engaged in the profession, upon the windows thereof and by a door plate or name or office directory when the information is limited to that of the professional card."

Dr. Reichmann, in explaining these provisions to members of the Society, wrote:

"Experience has demonstrated that advertising dental services promotes the following evils:

"1. It puts the patient on his own buying power, inducing him to decide to make a purchase he is unable to determine he needs.

"2. It creates the impression that the tangible article is the object purchased, when a healthy normally functioning mouth is the real objective.

"3. It creates the evil of quantity production, in a health service, which is by its very nature an individual service.

"4. It sets a fixed fee for a certain type of service, when the time and energy expended varies greatly if the work is properly rendered in each case.

"5. It causes the dentist to publish thrilling and impossible statements about his skill, of which he at least is a prejudiced judge.

"6. It causes the dentist to rely on advertising to secure patronage, instead of the satisfaction of his patients.

"There are some arguments for advertising, but they are only superficial in their soundness, and amount to nothing in the face of the fact that over 95 per cent of all dentists do not advertise. It is proper to prohibit advertising because, all things considered, it is against the public good to permit such practices."[2]

Included in the bill was a comprehensive definition of dentistry and dental practices, methods to qualify for special licenses, the creation of the organization to be known as the registered dentists of Oklahoma, with a state board of governors.

In addition to a comprehensive definition of the practice of dentistry the bill provided that boards of education or any organized health service might employ registered hygienists to examine teeth and teach dental hygiene.

Dr. Reichmann offered the following recommendation for the inclusion of a section to issue a special license to those who limited

[2] *Bulletin*, January, 1935.

their practice in the profession: "This section is a modern development, found in all the newer medical and dental legislation, designed to render beneficial service in two ways: first it protects the public against the professional 'fence jumper,' who represents himself as being especially qualified to perform certain specific operations, and who, in case he is sued by a patient, hides under the plea that he is only required to exercise the average skill and diligence required of all general practitioners of dentistry; second, it protects the properly qualified specialists from the unfair claims of some unscrupulous general practitioners who seem to have the ability to pose as a 'specialist' in any kind of service the patient seems to require at that time. This is a rigid regulatory measure designed to protect the public."

The proposed legislation, actually written by Lynn Adams of the Oklahoma City law firm, included a provision for a legal entity, "The Registered Dentists of Oklahoma." This, a new idea in incorporation, has been adopted in several states. The organization was to be composed of all persons entitled to practice dentistry, or oral hygiene, in the state, could sue and be sued, could enter into contracts and be recognized in the courts. This was a great improvement over provisions of the dental act of 1919, under which individual members of the Board of Dental Examiners brought about prosecutions under the act and, as in the instance of Dr. J. D. Moon, were subject to countersuit. All licensed dentists and hygienists were to become members of the corporation; all, therefore, were to abide by provisions of the proposed bill or lose their membership, *viz*, their license to practice the profession.

The "Board of Governors of the Registered Dentists of Oklahoma" was to consist of eleven members: four chosen from the state-at-large, seven from districts. The choice of members was to rest with members of the organization.

At district meetings of the Society held in November, 1934, the proposed legislation was thoroughly discussed; petitions were circulated by the district secretaries and members went on record in favor of the proposed revisions. Under the chairmanship of Dr. D. L. Rippeto, Oklahoma City, a statistical compilation was made on every legislator elected in November, as well as on hold-over members of the state senate, in regard to their attitude toward a more effective dental act. Moreover, dentists in each county had contacted prospective legislators in regard to the remedial legislation before the election. When the legislature convened in Oklahoma City in January, 1935, Dr. Rippeto had a fairly complete file which he made available to those dentists in direct contact with legislators on the progress of the measure.

William O. Coe, representative from Oklahoma County and a close personal friend of Dr. Robert D. Lochridge, introduced the measure, House Bill 173, January 28.[3] Coe and fifteen colleagues were co-authors of the bill prepared by Adams and the Legislative Committee of the Dental Society. Two days later the bill was referred to the House Committee on the Practice of Medicine, composed of seventeen members. Records compiled by Dr. Rippeto disclosed that four of the committee members were definitely in opposition to any remedial legislation affecting the practice of dentistry. Dr. Flesher has recalled that, on account of the heavy work load imposed on this first legislative session under Governor Marland, it was somewhat difficult to secure a quorum of committee members to consider the bill. On February 28, however, nine members took the bill under consideration. Four were those known to be opposed to any changes in the present statute; as a result the bill was favorably reported back to the House by the slim margin of one vote.

Led by Coe, friends of the dental profession in the lower house of the legislature were able to get the bill advanced without any crippling amendments. It passed on final vote eighty-seven to ten on March 6 and was forwarded to the Senate for its consideration. Here, on March 11, it was referred to the Legal Advisory Committee, which gave a favorable report four days later.

Unexpected opposition, however, developed, according to Dr. Flesher: "As our bill approached third reading and final passage, each senator received a letter on stationery of the State Board of Dental Examiners denouncing the proposed law as an underhanded

[3] *Journal of the House of Representatives of the Regular Session of the Fifteenth Legislature of the State of Oklahoma*, January 8 to April 30, 1935 (Oklahoma City, Central Printing Company, 1935), 448. Complete references to the progress of House Bill 173 appear in the *Journal*, pp. 486, 1039–40, 1160, 1246–49, 1330, 1339, 3022–3023, 3037, 3158–61, 3165–66, 3167, 3313, 3331–33, 3513–14, 3542–43. For progress through the upper chamber, see *Senate Journal* (Oklahoma City, The Leader Press, 1935), pp. 777, 783, 884, 992, 1260, 1446–47, 1563–70, 1608, 1635, 1651, 1663–65, 1672, 1694–95, 1801, 1819, 1909.

scheme of a small group of selfish dentists to control the profession and raise the price of dentistry. This eleventh-hour falsehood was a serious menace to our bill, and had we not enough strength to refute the charge before a vote was taken, our bill would have been defeated."[4]

Senator Louis A. Fischl, Ardmore, led the mounting opposition to the bill, and on March 20 was successful in having it re-referred to the Committee on Public Health and Welfare. This was done, where it rested for two weeks without action. Finally, a hearing was held at which appeared the members of the Board opposed to the measure. They were also represented by an attorney. On April 3, Senator W. A. Carlile, chairman of the committee, returned the bill to the upper house without recommendation.

According to Dr. Flesher, "Every day our friends watched and waited, pushing every opportunity to give consideration to our bill. The opposition was weakening, but they were fighting every move for an early vote. Finally the Democratic floor leader, Senator James C. Nance, Walters, insisted that our profession was entitled to consideration of the bill, and an early vote was inevitable."

Nance assured the dentists the bill would not lose its regular place on the calendar. On April 11 it was up for advancement to third reading, but opponents postponed its consideration until April 16. Senator Claud Briggs, Wilburton, president *pro tempore* was instrumental in taking this action.

When discussion on the bill began early in the afternoon of April 16, there was a well-filled gallery to hear the arguments concerning the measure. Senator Tom Waldrep, Shawnee, after a denunciation of the "closed shop" aspects of the measure, immediately moved that it be indefinitely postponed. By a close vote his proposal was defeated. Then the veteran senator Paul A. Stewart, representing McCurtain and Pushmataha counties in his fifth legislative session, arose in opposition. He made a strong and determined plea to kill the measure, then offered a motion to postpone it indefinitely.

Stewart's motion was narrowly defeated. Senators W. A. Carlile, Sallisaw, and S. W. Carmack, Gould, also talked against the bill. The dentists had expected that Senator Carlile, chairman of the Public Health Committee, would oppose the measure, but were

[4] *Bulletin*, July, 1935.

surprised to find Senator Carmack in opposition. Carmack had been well informed by dentists of Greer and Harmon counties, his constituents, on the merits of the bill. A few days earlier he had indicated he might support it.

Senator Fischl caused the chief damage to the bill by winning the adoption of weakening amendments. A major change was made in section 6 relating to the choice of the Board of Governors. The original bill provided for selection of the members by the profession; the Fischl amendment provided that the Board should be appointed by the governor with advice and consent of the Senate. Senator Stewart attempted to delete the section pertaining to advertising restrictions and substitute a provision that "any dentist may fix and advertise the price of dental plates and/or false teeth." This was defeated by a vote of twenty-one to seventeen.

On roll call vote the amended measure passed, twenty-four to thirteen. Stewart served notice he would move to reconsider the vote; the following day his motion was tabled by a vote of nineteen to sixteen. On April 18 the amended bill was returned to the House of Representatives, but was immediately recalled for further consideration. Fifteen changes were made in the bill, including an amendment by Senator Homer Paul of Pauls Valley to keep the Board from raising prices for dental services.

Other minor changes were written into the measure by the Senate, and a major change was made by the deletion of section 29 pertaining to restrictions proposed on advertising. This was done by the adoption of an amendment proposed by Senator Fischl.

The amended bill was returned to the House on April 20 for consideration. Representative Coe and the other sponsors of the original bill refused to concur and a conference committee from both houses was appointed to consider points of differences. Leon C. Phillips, speaker of the House, appointed members preponderantly in favor of House Bill 173 without the emasculating amendments. President Briggs of the Senate appointed to the committee a majority opposed to the bill, Senators Fischl, Stewart, and W. O. Ray, Tishomingo. Senators E. P. Hill, McAlester, and H. M. Curnutt, Barnsdall, were minority members.

It appeared a deadlock was inevitable, that the legislative session might adjourn before differences could be resolved and hence the bill would be killed. The Legislative Committee of the Dental

Society consulted with the floor leader of the Senate, James C. Nance, in regard to the proper course to pursue. Nance and Hill had been chief proponents of the original bill. Senator Nance advised the dentists to accept the amended bill and lay plans to reinstate its original provisions at the next session of the legislature. Thus the dental committee advised House leaders to accept the measure with the crippling amendments imposed by senate action. House Bill 173, as amended, passed the lower house eighty-three to nineteen, April 25, and on the last day of the legislative session, April 30, it was forwarded to the Governor. Governor Marland approved the measure May 2 after it was examined by his attorneys.[5] The Governor stated he was sorry the dental profession did not get exactly the legislation desired, but expressed the view that it was a great improvement over the earlier statute.

Dr. Flesher credited members of the Dental Society with creating a favorable atmosphere in the legislature for a better dental law: "In giving credit to the various members of the House and Senate it is impossible to prevent neglecting to mention many fine men who helped us in our fight. Nothing was more gratifying than to approach a senator or representative and have him at once say, 'yes, Dr. —— spoke to me about it at home.' Many senators were opposed to the bill until they were called upon by men from their own district. The dentists are to be lauded for their unceasing efforts."

The prophecy by Senator Nance that the dentists probably could correct defects in the dental law at the next session of the legislature, in 1937, was fulfilled. Nance between sessions changed his residence from Walters to Purcell; he became a member of the House of Representatives from McClain County and was chosen floor leader for the sixteenth session of the legislature. He exerted influence in behalf of the dentists.

William O. Coe introduced House Bill 235 on January 27, which corrected dental legislation by deleting the crippling amendments imposed by the Senate two years before.[6] On April 5 the

---

[5] *Session Laws of 1935* (Oklahoma City, Harlow Publishing Company, 1935), Chapter 24, Article 4, pp. 39–49.

[6] *Session Laws of 1937, Sixteenth Legislature, Regular Session,* January 5 to May 11, 1937 (Oklahoma City, Harlow Publishing Company, 1935). House Bill 235 appears as Chapter 24, Article 9, pp. 66–68.

measure passed the lower house by a vote of ninety-one to fifteen. When the bill reached the upper house for consideration, chief opposition was broken when Senator Stewart's motion to table the bill was decisively beaten, nineteen to eight. By the same margin, Senator Joe Whittaker's attempt to insert section 6, *viz*, the appointment of members of the Board of Governors by the governor, was defeated. Senator E. P. Hill, who as a member of the House of Representatives had assisted in passing the dental act of 1913, warded off all proposed amendments with the help of Senator W. A. Fidler of Oklahoma City.

The most novel amendment proposed was one by Senator Felix Church of Miami: "Provided, no dentist shall ever charge more than $50.00 for a set of plates of any kind."[7] Senator Hill raised a point against this proposal, which was sustained. The Senate agreed with him that it could not, by law, limit prices charged for such services. Without any amendments the bill passed the Senate by a vote of twenty-eight to eight. Since an emergency provision was included in the bill, it became a law April 29 when Governor Marland signed it.

The dental profession has found it necessary to request only one revision in the dental act. This was made in April, 1943, and the vote on the measure by the legislature reflects the confidence imposed in the profession to regulate itself.[8] The bill passed the House by a vote of eighty-two to twenty-six; the Senate, twenty-five to none. The measure broadened the dental act to include under surveillance of the Board of Governors all persons purporting to be making dental plates.

— 2 —

NATION-WIDE recognition in the profession has been accorded the dental act of Oklahoma. It is comprised of forty-six sections.[9] It constituted an "organization to be known as the Registered Dentists of Oklahoma," with corporate powers including the right to employ an attorney for the purpose of advising on the administration and assisting in the enforcement of the act. All persons practicing dentistry or dental hygiene within the state are members.

[7] See *Journal of the Senate of the Regular Session of the Sixteenth Legislature of the State of Oklahoma*, April 21, p. 1782.

An administrative agency, the Board of Governors of the Registered Dentists of Oklahoma, was created. It consists of seven members elected by members of the organization. The act spells out district boundaries from which the seven members are chosen; each member holds office for a term of three years. The Board is charged with the executive functions of the organization and the enforcement of provisions of the act.

A specific and detailed definition of the practice of dentistry is included in the act, as well as the limiting duties of dental hygienists. Licensing provisions are included with a stipulation, however, that the Board may recognize a certificate granted by the National Board of Dental Examiners in lieu of examination. Provision is likewise included for the granting of reciprocal licenses to applicants, with resident qualifications, from states having equally stringent laws. A special license may be issued to applicants who can meet qualifications spelled out in the act to limit their practice to one of the recognized branches of the dental profession. Dentists cannot practice dentistry under the name of a corporation, company, association, or trade name; they cannot advertise, other than by use of the ordinary professional card or inclusion of name, address, title, telephone number in city or telephone directories, or by having name stenciled on office window or door.

The Board of Governors not only grants licenses; it may revoke licenses for violations of the act, for court conviction of a crime involving moral turpitude, for persistent drunkenness or addiction to drugs. Any appeal, however, from a decision of the Board of Governors which involves revocation of license may be reviewed by the Supreme Court. A lengthy section sets forth procedures to be followed in hearing a case that might involve revocation or suspension of license. Provision is included to issue a writ of injunction against anyone who attempts to practice dentistry after his license has been revoked; conviction under this provision is punishable by a fine not exceeding five hundred dollars, by a one-year jail sentence, or both.

[8] See *House Journal, Nineteenth Legislature,* February 26, pp. 2079–81, and *Senate Journal, same session,* March 30, p. 1397. House Bill 303 appears in the *Session Laws* of 1943 (Guthrie, Co-operative Publishing Company, 1943), under Title 59, Chapter 7, pp. 131–33.

[9] *Compiled Statutes of Oklahoma* of 1951, Title 59.

Members of the organization pay an annual licensing fee of five dollars to the state treasurer, who maintains as a separate account the state dental fund. This fund is used to maintain regular and investigative duties of the Board of Governors.

Members of the organization are exempt from jury service.

This all-inclusive dental act is an advanced departure from earlier statutes. For the first time in Oklahoma clearly defined ethical practices were written into the act, and the changing Board of Governors has been zealous in maintaining discipline among members of the profession. Their interest in maintaining the highest standard of professional ethics has been of greatest assurance to the public; in one instance the Supreme Court overruled a disciplinary action which called for a license suspension for two years. The Court admitted that the action taken by the Board had doubtlessly been done in good faith, "yet the same was erroneous, and in law constitutes an abuse of discretion."[10]

In another instance where the Board ordered the suspension of the license of a member of the organization for sixty days, on information furnished by an investigating committee, the Supreme Court reversed the ruling.[11] The Court pointed out that the Board of Governors has no authority to appoint an investigating committee to hear charges, and that "before a member of the Registered Dentists of Oklahoma may be disciplined by the Board of Governors of said Organization, the member must be charged, notified, and given a hearing, as provided by the State Dental Act." "The Board of Governors," so the Supreme Court ruled, "acts in a dual capacity. It is the executive head of the Organization charged with the enforcement of the provisions of the act, and it also acts as a Board of Dental Examiners. Its duties and powers in each of these two capacities are specifically defined and the nature of the powers conferred and of the duties imposed show clearly a well-defined separation of those powers and duties. When the Board sits as a Board of Dental Examiners its powers and duties are expressly defined and limited. When sitting as the Board of Governors of the Registered Dentists of Oklahoma it acts in an executive capacity under broad powers and may exercise quasi-judicial discretion."

[10] *Board of Governors of the Registered Dentists of Oklahoma* v. *Brown,* 182 *Oklahoma,* 244.

[11] *State* ex rel *Board of Governors of Registered Dentists of Oklahoma* v. *Rifleman,* 203 *Oklahoma,* 294.

Dr. B. L. Shobe   Dr. Charles W. Day   Dr. Albert E. Bonnell

Dr. C. R. Lawrence   Dr. C. L. White   Dr. Arthur C. Seids

Shobe Memorial Award Recipients

U. S. Public Health Topical Fluoride Team
in Action in Oklahoma, 1949

On the two other occasions when actions of the Board of Governors have been brought under review by the Supreme Court, the Board has been sustained. One involved a dentist who was convicted in California for issuing a check with intent to defraud. Charges of moral turpitude against him were filed with the Board of Governors. The charges were sustained and his license to practice dentistry revoked. This action was upheld by the Supreme Court.[12]

The other instance involved an interpretation of the following provision of the act: "No person, firm or corporation shall advertise in any manner to the general public, that is, to persons other than members of 'The Organization,' that he, they, or it can or will sell, supply, furnish, construct, reproduce or repair prosthetic dentures (sometimes called plates), bridges, or other appliances to be used or worn as substitutes for natural teeth, or for the regulation thereof; and no person not licensed to practice dentistry in this State shall sell or furnish, or offer to sell or furnish, any such products or services."

Horace D. Ballaine, district judge, Tulsa, issued an injunction against the United Dental Laboratory of that city because advertisements of the firm appeared on baseball score-cards, in the Tulsa papers, and in the telephone directory. The guilt of the firm was sustained on appeal to the Supreme Court. The Court had ruled in an earlier case against the United Dental Laboratory for violation of the dental act of 1935, "that the state may enact legislation of this type for the protection of citizens is well settled."[13]

The provision of the dental act relating to the granting, after examination, of special licenses to those dentists who limit their practice was an innovation in legislation. Since the adoption of this law in 1935 by Oklahoma, other states have passed similar statutes which provide for an examination of those who wish to specialize in any of the fields of dentistry.

[12] *Bancroft* v. *Board of Governors of the Registered Dentists of Oklahoma*, 202 *Oklahoma*, 108.

[13] *Curtis* v. *Registered Dentists of Oklahoma*, 193 *Oklahoma*, 233–36, and 201 *Oklahoma*, 430–32. In *Curtis* v. *State*, 78 *Oklahoma C. R.*, 282–93, Judge Bert B. Barefoot wrote the opinion of the Criminal Court of Appeals. The decision, given March 29, 1944, includes this paragraph: "It is well known that the masses of the public do not comprehend or understand the skill that is necessary in the making of proper dentures and the proper charges to be made for such services. Such persons are often attracted by the advertisements of the quack and charlatan and seek his services."

Dr. Reichmann has explained how oral surgery has been limited to dentistry: "The specialty of oral surgery has grown as a specialty of dentistry in Oklahoma since World War I. In 1918 the American Medical Association section on oral surgery was abandoned and the Society of Oral Surgeons and Exodontists was created in conjunction with the American Dental Association. The organization at that time was very small but it was composed of a determined group of surgeons whose essential degree was that of dentistry. Since that time the term 'exodontia' has become obsolete and the term 'oral surgery' has become all-inclusive. The name of the organization has been changed to the American Society of Oral Surgeons.[14] It is compulsory to have a Doctor of Dental Surgery degree to become a member. Many of the members are also Doctors of Medicine.

"With the passage of our new law which included the specialist's licensing provision, examinations for the practice of oral surgery have been in conformity with professional training available throughout the country. Whereas in 1925 there were only two places in the United States to obtain recognized training in oral surgery, now there are dozens of hospitals and educational institutions that offer qualified, intensive two- and three-year courses. The development of the specialty has been a distinct benefit to the dental profession and to the public."

Dentists have limited their practice in other recognized branches of their profession: orthodontists, to the straightening of teeth and correction of malocclusions; prosthodontists, to complete or partial dentures; periodontists, to the treatment of pyorrhea; pedodontists, to the care of children's teeth.

[14] Dr. Menifee R. Howard, Denver, Colorado, and twenty-eight other oral surgeons organized and founded the American Society of Oral Surgeons in 1918. Dr. Howard received an Oklahoma license in 1906 and practiced for a limited time at Shattuck, Oklahoma. He recently related that while a dental student in 1905 he watched the performance of a traveling medicine show at Woodward, Oklahoma. The traveling "dentist" offered to remove teeth at a bargain rate. The "dentist" used his clenched fist to produce anesthesia, broke off teeth, and left roots to cause harmful after-effects in the mouths of his victims. See "Menifee Howard to Harry Sorrels," December 8, 1954, in files of the Central Office, Oklahoma State Dental Association; also, *Dental Survey*, Volume XXX (May, 1954), 642.

— 3 —

In 1936 the Oklahoma State Dental Society held its annual meeting in conjunction with the Texas State Dental Society at Dallas, August 31–September 4. This was the year of the Texas Centennial Exposition; it was not difficult to get competent, notable lecturers to attend the joint meeting and enjoy famed Texas hospitality. Among the special guests invited to lecture before the societies were Dr. C. R. Lawrence and Dr. A. L. Walters. Dr. Lawrence talked to the general assembly Thursday, September 3, on the subject, "Economic Factors in the Management of a Dental Office." The following morning Dr. Walters lectured on "Our Nutritional Requirements." Much favorable comment was heard by the 108 Oklahoma dentists in attendance on the presentations made by their colleagues.

Enthusiasm engendered here gave emphasis to a proposal for a Southwest Dental Congress to be held in Oklahoma City in 1939. With the completion of Civic Center, show place of civic pride, including the Auditorium with a seating capacity of 6,500 and the Zebra Room with thousands of square feet for exhibit purposes, and the building of the Biltmore Hotel, one of the largest hotels of the Southwest, Oklahoma City was to become one of the most active convention centers in the United States.

Formal invitations to dental societies of adjoining states to take part in the Southwest Dental Congress were extended after the annual meeting of the state society in 1938. A special journal edited by Dr. N. Dea Griffith, the *Southwest Dental News*, was issued in June and October, 1938, and February and April, 1939. The congress was scheduled for April 24–27, 1939.

Responses to the invitations foretold a successful meeting. On June 26 of the preceding year representatives of six states met in Oklahoma City to perfect the organization of the congress.[15] Officials of the Oklahoma Dental Society were made officers of the permanent organization: Dr. F. J. Reichmann, president; Dr. N. Dea Griffith, secretary; Dr. A. C. Seids, treasurer; and Dr. Harry Sorrels, general chairman. This group of Oklahoma City dentists spent much of their time in the ensuing months making arrangements for

[15] *Southwestern Dental News* (Oklahoma City), October, 1938.

the congress. The general chairman, Dr. Harry Sorrels, enlisted the aid of 116 members of the Oklahoma County Dental Society. They served on thirty committees under definite, detailed assignments. Honorary co-chairmen for each committee were selected from component societies.

The Southwest Dental Congress was designated the official meeting in 1939 for the Kansas, Missouri, Arkansas, Oklahoma, and New Mexico state dental societies; co-operating states included Colorado, Louisiana, and Texas; societies in these states had already set the time of their annual meetings for later in the year. At this, the most important meeting ever sponsored by the Oklahoma State Dental Society, fifty prominent leaders of the profession appeared on various programs. These men came from states other than those which were members of the congress. Intensified postgraduate study was offered in public health, oral surgery, prosthodontia, amalgam restorations, orthodontia, children's dentistry, periodontia, root surgery, and cast restorations.

During the first two days of the meeting, Monday and Tuesday, April 24 and 25, general lectures were offered and specialized work was dealt with in the sectional meetings.[16] Wednesday was reserved for business meetings of the societies, for the 200 table clinics offered and the thirty-nine scientific exhibits. Accredited members of the American Medical Association had been invited to attend the congress; fifteen of the physicians in Oklahoma City presented scientific exhibits. The University of Oklahoma School of Medicine, the Kansas City Western Dental College, Baylor Dental College, Washington University School of Dentistry, the College of Dentistry, University of Nebraska, the St. Louis University School of Dentistry, and the Southwestern Society of Orthodontists, as well as individual members of the dental profession, also entered scientific exhibits.

Physicians from Oklahoma City who prepared scientific exhibits were: Patrick Nagle, "Correlation of Dental Surgery and Plastic Surgery"; Lee K. Emenhiser, "Temporo Mandibular Joint Syndrome"; Ralph Bowen, "Nasal Allergy Problems as Seen in Children"; John Heatly, "Pathology of Lower Jaw"; E. Goldfain, "Dental Pathology in Arthritic Cases"; Earl McBride, Elias

[16] Program for the Southwest Dental Congress, April 24–28, 1939. A copy of the seventy-two-page program is in the files of the Oklahoma State Dental Association.

Margo, and Howard Shorbe, "Surgical Problems of the Mandible"; George H. Kimball, "Plastic Surgery"; William K. Ishmael, "Relationship of Dental Infection to Rheumatic Disease"; Henry H. Turner, "Clinical Endocrinology"; Curt Von Wedel, "Plastic Surgery of the Face"; John F. Burton, "Plastic Surgery of Face and Mouth." All the exhibits attracted special attention, from the character and reputation in the medical world of participating physicians as well as from the presentations.

Booth number thirty-one among the scientific exhibits on "Electro-Galvanic Phenomena Oral Cavity" was of special interest. It was prepared by Dr. Everett Lain, nationally known dermatologist of Oklahoma City, and Dr. Sherrill Caughron, whose father had interested Dr. Lain in making the first X-ray pictures of teeth in Oklahoma shortly after statehood. The Lain-Caughron exhibit was the result of observations upon the effect on the health of patients of the use of dissimilar metals in dentures.

The doctors had found from clinical tests that "human saliva contains the necessary elements for a good electrolyte, whether its chemical reaction is neutral, acid, or alkaline; therefore, a galvanic battery has been constructed in every oral cavity where restorations have been made from two or more electropotentially dissimilar metals."[17] Although medical and dental literature since 1878 had included brief mention of the action, Drs. Lain and Caughron startled visiting dentists and physicians with the results of their clinical studies. They suggested that an electric cell could easily be formed by dental fillings, for example one of gold and the other amalgam, with the saliva normal to the mouth. Their findings indicated that certain pathologic conditions were relieved by removal of the dental fillings or by changing all fillings to the same kind of metal.[18]

[17] Everett S. Lain, M. D., and G. Sherrill Caughron, D. D. S., "Electrogalvanic Phenomena of the Oral Cavity Caused by Dissimilar Metallic Restorations," in *Journal of the American Dental Association*, Vol. XXIII (1936), 1641–53.

[18] Dr. Everett Lain was awarded a "Diploma for Original Research" at the annual meeting of the American Medical Association, June, 1933, for his work in this field. An article by Lain, "Chemical and Electrolytic Lesions of the Mouth Caused by Artificial Dentures" appeared in *Archives of Dermatology and Syphilology*, Vol. XXV (January, 1932), 21–31. "Electrogalvanic Lesions of the Oral Cavity produced by Metallic Dentures," in the *Journal of the American Medical Association*, Vol. C (March, 1933), 717–20. "Electric Phenomena in the Oral Cavity," in the *Dental Digest*, June, 1934. He was co-author with Dr. Caughron and Dr. William Schriever of the article, "Problem of Electrogalvanism in the Oral Cavity Caused by Dissimilar

On Tuesday afternoon, Dr. Charles A. Furrow, Tulsa, presented an hour-long clinic on "Osteosynthesis in Metal Root Implantation," and on Tuesday and Thursday afternoons, after 4:15 P.M., Drs. John A. Wadlin, G. A. Roelke, W. D. Rush, and O. F. Sinks, all of Tulsa, presented a clinic on "A Complete Denture Technique for Full and Partial Dentures."

The final two days of the meeting were devoted to the specialized postgraduate lectures. Classes were dismissed early enough each afternoon to allow the dentists ample time to visit the ninety-five educational commercial exhibits in the Zebra Room. Each afternoon during the week motion picture films on related subjects were shown as supplementary aids to the postgraduate courses.

Newspapers and radio stations of Oklahoma City gave the congress wide publicity; the *Daily Oklahoman* and *Oklahoma City Times* assigned reporters and photographers to the convention and used most of their products; each of the four radio stations released time for two thirty-minute programs which featured guest speakers on dentistry. From the corps of distinguished visitors were selected speakers who appeared before fourteen business, professional, and luncheon groups at their weekly meetings; sixteen of the junior-senior high schools arranged programs for speakers to appear before the student assemblies; every means of communication was used to stimulate interest in oral hygiene.

Varied entertainment, too, was offered the visitors: trap and skeet shooting, horseshoe pitching, a golf tournament, stag party, college alumni banquets, fraternity luncheons, dinner dances, and luncheons and style shows for the ladies.

The Southwest Dental Congress had official registrations from thirty-six states and two foreign countries; more than 2,000 dentists, assistants, and members of the auxiliary were in attendance. Four hundred and twenty-nine dentists registered from Oklahoma, the largest number ever to attend an annual meeting. Dr. O. F.

Dental Metals," which appeared in the *Journal of the American Dental Association*, Vol. XXVII (November, 1940), 1765–72. Dr. William Schriever, of the Department of Physics, University of Oklahoma, and Dr. Louis E. Diamond, of the Department of Biochemistry, University of Oklahoma School of Medicine, recently collaborated on a project negotiated by the University of Oklahoma Research Institute. A publication of their findings appeared under the title, "Electromotive Forces and Electric Currents Caused by Metallic Dental Fillings," in the *Journal of Dental Research*, Vol. XXI (April, 1952), 205–29.

Sinks, president-elect, who had helped organize the meeting, succeeded Dr. Reichmann as president of the state society, and Dr.
Harry Sorrels was rewarded for his work as general chairman of
the congress by being chosen president-elect.

National recognition again came to the Oklahoma State Dental
Society on account of the successful staging of the Southwest Dental Congress. And when the American Dental Association met in
Milwaukee, July 17–21, state delegates from the Southwest, as
has been related previously, led a spontaneous movement that
lacked only four votes in achieving their aim: the choice of Dr. C. R.
Lawrence, Enid, as president-elect. Without organization, with no
pre-convention plans, the movement almost succeeded.

CHAPTER NINE

World War II and After

— I —

THE FOREBODING THREAT to the nation's welfare overshadowed the usual activities of the Society during the presidency of Dr. Harry Sorrels. In June, 1940, Hitler's forces overran France; Goering's promise to bomb England into destruction and his boast that then Germany would "stick the fat pig across the Atlantic" awakened Congress and the public to the world crisis. During the summer, dentists who were members of the Oklahoma National Guard took part in the Third Army maneuvers in Texas and Louisiana; in September, the famed Forty-Fifth Division, which included the Oklahoma Guard unit, was called to active service; in October, registration and selection of civilians for active duty began under provisions of the National Selective Service Act.

Dr. Sorrels, aware of the mounting tension in the country, had Brigadier General Leigh C. Fairbank appear as principal speaker at the annual meeting of the Society in Oklahoma City in April, 1941.[1] General Fairbank, chief of the Dental Division in the Surgeon General's Office, United States Army, spoke on the subject, "The Dental Profession in Our Preparedness Program."

When the Society had revised its constitution and by-laws in 1936, one of the standing committees created was the Military Affairs Committee. It was composed of three members, whose principal duties in the 1930's had been to assemble and disseminate information on federal activities relating to dentistry in the armed services and the Civilian Conservation Corps. Committee members

[1] The source of this and subsequent material relating to Oklahoma dentistry during the war are issues of the *Bulletin*, January, 1941–January, 1946.

during this period were Earl Williams, John Smiley, W. E. Overmyer, F. J. Reichmann, A. E. Bonnell, Jr., and F. J. Brandenburg.

As the nation called on its reserves of man power in the movement from defense to war economy, more Oklahoma dentists entered the armed services. By December, 1940, 132 members of the
Society held commissions in the United States Army Dental Corps.
The Military Affairs Committee, whose members were F. J. Brandenburg and Earl and John Williams, served as a clearing house for
the Society on mobilization information. Articles were prepared for
the *Bulletin* and correspondence carried on in regard to man-power
requirements of dental branches of the armed services. Before their
term on the committee ended, these men were in uniform. They
were succeeded by others during the period when the country was
at war, all of whom, except the older members, entered service:
R. C. Meyer, G. S. Ault, L. V. Swift, J. A. Brown, A. B. Rivers,
C. R. Swander, C. A. D. Beer, and L. W. Cheek.

In 1942, when Dr. George Roland was president of the Society,
he appointed Dr. A. C. Seids state chairman of procurement and
assignment. In this position, Dr. Seids worked in close co-operation
with Colonel Clive E. Murray, director of selective service for the
state. He acted as consultant and adviser to the local boards whenever the status of a dentist came under consideration. Through
local county chairmen, Dr. Seids was able to determine in individual
cases whether members of the profession should enter the armed
services or be deferred to take care of civilian practice. Each doctor
was rated according to age and physical defects. All dentists not
called to active duty were urged to take part in civilian defense.

By July, 1943, 144 members of the Society were in active service, 25 per cent above the state's allotted quota. Appendix Q includes
the names of those in service, previously listed in issues of the
Bulletin.

Occasionally letters appeared in the *Bulletin* from those in
active service. Here are excerpts from one written in February,
1943, by Dr. L. L. Willis: "Our work, since the first few weeks of
the war, has been pretty much routine. But have had plenty of that.
After 18 months afloat doing all that is possible to rehabilitate the
oral conditions of our young men—I have come to one definite con-
clusion. That is that something must and will be done after the war
to improve the present debilitated oral condition of the average

American. If the organized profession doesn't propose a practical plan, the government will, and we will be on the outside looking in whether we like it or not. Figures don't lie. Of the first 2,000,000 of the country's best, examined for service, almost 1,000,000 were rejected because of their oral condition. To get the men, standards were lowered; now, dental troubles are taking more man hours than any other physical defect. These figures go into Washington from every ship in the Navy every month.

"It's been interesting to observe the dentition of the people in various localities and the oral manifestations of diseases not seen in Oklahoma. For instance, among the Polynesians of the South Pacific where oranges, tangerines, and lemons grow wild in bountiful quantities, scurvy is very prevalent. Rarely do you see a native forty years of age who hasn't lost most of his or her teeth due to scurvy. They have never developed a taste for citrus fruits and nobody can educate them. The dentist and physician I met on one particular island have tried to educate them to the importance of Vitamin C, but with no avail. The natives are of such a happy-go-lucky carefree nature, they just don't give a damn about losing their teeth if saving them means eating citrus fruits. . . .

"The most interesting of my off ship observations has been with that of leprosy, its oral and general manifestations. I was fortunate in getting permission to take the ship's photographer with me last week to a colony and we got some excellent clinical photos. After you have seen some of the worst cases, you will no doubt be a believer in euthanasia."

Dr. Paul C. Bonnette, assigned to the heavy cruiser *U.S.S. Louisville*, Pacific Fleet, wrote in January, 1944: "Haven't been seasick as yet and have been through some heavy seas but I'm not bragging too much—it can still come.

"Am doing a lot of dentistry—mostly exodontia. We're well equipped—Ritter senior unit—X-ray, etc., and no foot motors, as some of my colleagues in other branches of the service have to put up with.

"The food is delicious and plentiful, have my own single room (I'm senior Lt. aboard). We have a soda fountain, canteen, and ship's service. Have our own laundry—shirts 4 cents, uniform pants 7 cents, etc., and get a weekly service on it too. Carry our barbers and haircuts are free as against $1.00 in California. We're a miniature city wrapped in steel and its a great life—nothing like salt air, good food and lots of sleep to combat old age."

Dr. Albert Bonnell, Jr., wrote in October, 1943: ". . . We started in combat back on the southwest coast of Sicily last July and have moved quite a distance since then. I see a few Oklahoma dentists occasionally. Among them are Lt. Col. Reichmann of Oklahoma City and Maj. Clarence T. Richardson of Cushing. Colonel Reichmann is a busy man and from the information I gather, he has been doing a commendable job in handling a very responsible position.

"Capt. Charles J. Blum of Hominy, Capt. Hugh G. Hays of Clinton, Capt. Bishop Shields of Enid, and Capt. Clifford LeHew of Pawnee should all be able to give interesting clinics upon their return on 'Dentistry Under The Trees' or 'Exodontia and Operative Dentistry, accompanied by artillery shells and air raids.' Captain Leonard W. Cheek of Ada has developed into an itinerant prosthodontist and he has a tremendous business. He will be full of clinical possibilities. He wrote home from Sicily that 'he was not half so scared under fire as he had expected to be.' In explaining the statement after it appeared in the *Ada Evening News* he said the statement was correct—that he had not expected the sphincter muscles to hold but that they held.

"The dentists here have really been doing a commendable job, going right on through combat with the troops, doing emergency dentistry there and assisting the surgeons in the care of battle casualties. When we go into a 'rest area' then we are busier than in combat, doing the necessary operative work while the troops are available for it. The basic principles of such work haven't changed any since Otto Hine was doing it twenty-six years ago, and some of the other things he might wonder about haven't changed either."

The *Bulletin* also quoted an item that appeared in the column of Ernie Pyle, famed war correspondent, August 19, from Sicily, which included reference to a front-line clearing station where Dr. Leonard Cheek was on active duty: "A front-line clearing station is made up of physicians and dentists and men who were ordinary, normal people back home. But here they live a rough and tumble life. They sleep on the ground, work ghastly hours, sometimes are under fire, and they handle a flow of wounded that would sicken and dishearten a person less immune to it. They'll get little glory back home when its all over, but they have some recompense right here in the gratitude of the men they treat. Time and again as I lay in my tent I heard wounded soldiers discussing among themselves the wonderful treatment they had received."

Dr. Eugene W. Wise, editor of the *Bulletin,* published a letter in the April, 1945, issue from Dr. Ward L. Shaffer relating to service in the Pacific area: "Sure, it seems good to be back! Have thought of all of you often but restrictions have been such the past two and a half years, both here and overseas, that there was little I could say. The organization with which I served, as the oral surgeon member of the Maxillo-facial team, was the 21st Evacuation Hospital, a very large outfit. J. M. Robertson, Marion Flesher, and I were together throughout. We spent 13 months on the California desert on maneuvers before being sent over to the Southwest Pacific. It was good training all right for after that desert, any place they might send you would be an improvement. We got used to shaking the centipedes out of our blankets every night and turning the lizards out of our shoes every morning. Stood us in good stead for in our journeying thru Noumea, New Caledonia, Guadalcanal, and Bougainville for 14 months; you live among an amazing assortment of other varmints and insects, beetles, flies, spiders, ants, termites, scorpions, butterflies, hermit crabs, land crabs, and more fungi and moulds than you ever knew existed. After a while you get quite used to them.

"Life on an advanced island base in the combat zone was the most interesting and exiciting of all. Living on 1 per cent of a place where the other 99 per cent was and still is occupied by Japanese made up for a lot of sad deficiencies. Incidentally, a year ago, during what was generally spoken of around there as 'the push' our hospital was located between our artillery and the enemy line. Shells were going over back and forth all the time and in addition to the usual protection, the hospital area was historically guarded by Fiji Scouts who were so loyal and courageous their memory will always be respected by all who came to know them.

"It was such a screwy war there that at times it seemed only half real. But what made it real enough was what you used to see and hear every day, the crunching noise that the wheels of the ambulance make when they stop on the gravel at the door of 'Receiving' —the noise of the back door of the ambulance when it opens, then the clang of the iron step as it came down. Then what followed . . . .

"We were in the earthquake belt and slight earthquakes were almost a daily occurrence, and you could count on a big one about once a week to nearly shake your tent down. Everything we had was under tents. The only thing between you and nature was a mosquito net. And by the way, the radio system there was called 'The Mosquito Network.' Movies were the main escape from reality. And talk about the rain, it rained every day—every day. The annual rainfall in those parts is measured in feet instead of inches. A magnificent volcano about six thousand feet high was only a few miles away, but was in enemy territory so all you could do was admire it. Steam and smoke a mile high was nearly always pouring out the top of its cone.

"Bill Cole dropped in and spent a few days with us on Guadalcanal. He arrived on Christmas 1943 and to see him was like getting another Christmas present from home. He soon departed for his new assignment on the Russels. F. D. Entriken of Enid soon afterwards joined Bill Cole on this same ship. Both were recently in Australia on leave.

"Robertson and Flesher are in the Philippines now, their letters have been dated from there the past month. . . ."

In the January, 1943, issue of the *Bulletin* appeared an item on Dr. Charles E. McCracken, Tulsa, then serving in New Guinea:

"Young Doctor McCracken, who now answers to the title of Captain in the United States Army, is such a whiz at fixing up ailing American molars amidst the humid jungle scenery that he rated a special story on his prowess by George Weller, *Chicago Daily News* foreign service correspondent.

"Weller refers to McCracken as a 'middle-sized, plumpish tooth and gum man who has settled down among the American fighter pilots and has his fingers in the mouth of practically everybody of importance who is septic in Papua. And that is a lot of people.'

"Dr. McCracken has been in New Guinea since May 18 and has been in the Army dental corps about two years. He started his front-line tooth pulling when he could practically swing around the revolving chair and inspect Jap sniping posts.

" 'Lacking a bone chisel in those days,' Weller reported in his dispatch from New Guinea, 'McCracken made one from a screw driver. The motor for his drill was purloined from a refrigerator. He worked nine hours daily. Now, with the Japs driven across the Owen Stanley range, McCracken has two chairs instead of one, and he often works from 10 to 12 hours daily.'

"A grass hut similar to those of fabled South Sea charm is Captain McCracken's office and laboratory now. His screened-in laboratory hut with a thatched roof and hip-high thatched walls was built by bush-headed Papuans without a single nail."

Weller had mentioned in the quoted article that "fliers, especially fighter pilots, are at their prime in cloud warfare at the age when wisdom teeth are just emerging. And teeth are very susceptible to high altitudes where our Airacobras and Kittyhawks lock with Jap Zeros. Wisdom teeth, especially, begin to give pain at 20,000 feet. Consequently, when a pilot's need for vigilance is greatest, he may suddenly be stabbed with a toothache."

Older members of the profession, too, were accepted for active service, including such veterans of World War I as Dr. O. W. Boyer, Perry, and Dr. E. E. Sanger, Yukon, who served at training centers within the United States. The very excellent dental care given service men stationed at training centers has recently been explained by Dr. Sanger: "We found, by keeping correct records, that 1,000 officers and men would require 4,600 fillings and 1,560 extractions. The same 1,000 officers and men would require crown replacements and partial dentures or full dentures to the number of 360 to 380. Complete examinations were given all men in service, X rays were made of teeth or a complete X ray of the mouth where necessary. The men were given the best dental service that we knew at the time to perform. In my mind this advanced dentistry twenty years ahead of where it would have been. Dentistry owes much to the service performed during that period; many men and officers who had neglected the care of their mouths and teeth for the first time found out what really could be done for them and how it should be done."

Dr. Francis J. Reichmann, veteran of World War I, was a line officer during World War II. Reichmann, just out of high school when the United States entered World War I, enlisted and served with an artillery unit throughout the war. Years later, while Reichmann was practicing in Oklahoma City, Charles F. Barrett, adjutant general of Oklahoma, persuaded him to take an examination to be a second lieutenant in a national guard unit. Successful, Reichmann served in the field artillery and in general staff work up until World War II. He served in Sicily, Italy, central Europe, and southern France as assistant chief of staff of the Forty-fifth Division. In April, 1949, he became assistant division commander of the Ninety-fifth Division, a reserve unit of the Fourth Army, with the rank of brigadier general. In April, 1954, Dr. Reichmann for the first time missed an annual convention of the Oklahoma State Dental Association, when stateside. He had been selected by Division officers to go to New York City and return to Oklahoma the battle flags of the Forty-fifth Division.

Dr. E. E. Ogle, Wewoka, and Dr. W. J. Adams, Oklahoma City, also saw active combat service in branches other than their regular profession: Dr. Ogle in field artillery, Dr. Adams with a cavalry unit.

At the suggestion of Dr. Harry Sorrels, that portion of the *Bulletin* devoted to news from district societies, beginning in 1945, listed dentists in active service. This prompted district secretaries to include references to men in service. In the July, 1945, issue, Dr. I. E. Alfholder, secretary for the Northwestern District included the following:

"Captain Jules A. Weinberger (Guthrie) is in Europe with the Dental Corps.

"Lieutenant Commander M. O. Austbo (Blackwell) is now on *U.S.S. Refuge*—a hospital ship—somewhere near Okinawa.

"Capt. Otto R. Whiteneck is back in Ft. Sill—and would be glad to have you call at the Dental Clinic No. 1.

"Dr. C. A. D. Beer is back in home in Enid from a tour of duty with the army.

"Capt. Wilbur Whiteneck is stationed in California.

"Capt. Bishop Shields, son of Dr. H. B. Shields and formerly with the 45th Division, is now serving in Paris in a base hospital.

"Capt. Thurman Warrick, son of Dr. H. O. Warrick, Enid, expects a leave soon to visit with home folks—after a year overseas.

"Fred Entriken, Lt. Sr. Gr. is in New Caledonia. His father, Dr. H. L. of Enid, told us that Fred and Dr. M. O. Austbo had a visit over there.

"Dr. Roy Carl, now in Manila, P. I., is looking toward the good old U. S. A. He has been through the scrap of New Guinea."

In the same issue Dr. L. E. Tennis, Central District, reported that "Lt. Donald Granger is now stationed at the Naval Base, Norman, after his return from 21 months service in the Pacific Theatre.

"Capt. Bill Smith was through Ada last month on his way to Denver, Colorado for a new assignment. Bill has been at Sheppard Field Hospital, Wichita Falls, Texas, for the past three years."

Dr. Fred Sims, from the Northern District, reported:

"Bob Baker has been promoted from Captain to Major and is with the army in England.

"Lt. Jack Wadlin, who has been with the 1st Marines in the South Pacific, is having a variety of experiences. He was stationed at Saipan, thence to Okinawa. He was acting liaison officer between the air and ground forces.

"The Purple Heart has been presented to Lieut. Hugh D. Thomason. Lieut. Thomason was wounded in action while serving aboard the aircraft carrier *Sangamon* in the Pacific."

Dr. Frank P. Bertram included the following items of news from the Oklahoma County District:

"Major J. M. Robertson is back in the states from the Philippines.

"Dr. J. E. Brown, Jr. is again Capt. J. E. Brown, Jr. Jim was called back to the army, ten days before expiration of his terminal leave. As someone said, 'They can't do that to you, Jim, but they sure have.'

"Capt. R. F. Rhodes is on his terminal leave from the army and expects to relocate in Oklahoma City."

Dr. Roy Ellis, secretary for the Eastern District, included a paragraph on Dr. A. W. Grove. "Capt. Arthur W. Grove recently visited Okmulgee friends. A. W. had just returned from nearly two years service in England and North Africa. He was squadron dental surgeon Hdq., 379th Bomb. Group, 8th Air Force. Co-operation among medical and dental staffs was all that could be desired. Morale of the squadron of the 8th A. F. was of the highest at all times and competition of the different groups was keen. Their monthly reports of missions, tons of bombs dropped, etc., also carried summaries of dental services. That indicates the dental surgeons were on the alert. A. W. reports to Dallas for reassignment."

As the war drew to a close in the summer of 1945 and demobilization began, more of the dentists were returned to civilian practice. The October issue of the *Bulletin* reported the following men had received honorable discharges: Capt. J. D. Moore, Ada; Capt. C. E. Davis, Wewoka; Capt. L. C. McGee, Newkirk; Capt. E. R. Barnes, Oklahoma City; Capt. John Glass, Jr., Tulsa; Capt. Kenneth Shepard, Chickasha; Lt. J. H. Halloman, Frederick; Maj. Frank Miller, Anadarko; Maj. Ward L. Shaffer, Oklahoma City; Maj. O. H. Randall, Oklahoma City; Maj. V. A. Boucher, Bartlesville; Maj. C. A. D. Beer, Enid; Maj. Ralph Cully, Miami; Lt. Col. J. J. Cornett, Oklahoma City.

One member of the Society failed to return. Captain Cowan M. Masters, Tahlequah, died of wounds in Germany, March 3, 1945. Dr. Masters was a graduate of the Kansas City Western Dental College, class of 1943, and shortly after graduation entered service. And one—Lieutenant Commander Harry B. McInnis, Enid, was captured on Guam in December, 1941. Dr. McInnis was taken to Japan the following month and released to American forces at Yokohama on September 11, 1945.

By the first of December, 1945, an increasing number of dentists had returned to private practice. In the January, 1946, *Bulletin*, Dr. A. A. Pounds of the South Central District reported the following members still in service: Capt. S. Max Barrett; Lt. Col. Leon L. Cole; Lt. Cdr. P. E. Greenan; Capt. Virgil C. Holdreith; Capt. J. P. Lansden; Lt. Cdr. John E. Lewis; Capt. L. R. Moore; Maj. W. H. Pretty; Capt. W. L. Rhodes; Maj. W. L. Shamel; Lt. Col. E. E. Sanger; Capt. Gordon L. Sanger; Capt. L. K. Turnbull; Capt. John C. York.

Drs. Kenneth T. Shepard and P. A. Cornish, Ardmore, and Dr. Ray F. Rhodes, Purcell, had returned to private practice.

Dr. L. E. Tennis included information on returnees in the Central District:

"Dr. L. W. Cheek has now opened offices with Dr. Tom R. Granger, Ada. Both boys are just back from service. Dr. Cheek served five years and six days in E. T. O., Africa—Sicily—Italy—Germany. Dr. Tom Granger served four years and one month with the Army Air Forces, San Antonio. He served with seven different branches.

"Dr. Donald Granger is opening his office with Dr. Ed Granger. He served in the navy 23 months, 18 months of this time in the South Pacific.

229

"Dr. Rex Talley is back at work now after serving in the navy for three years.

"Dr. Todd McLarty has returned to Holdenville."

Dr. Fred Sims of the Northern District included the most comprehensive review of the status of members in service or returning to private practice:

"The following members of the Northern District are still in service: Capt. R. O. Beauchamp, Lt. H. S. Born, Capt. Earl Cunningham, Lt. (jg) John G. Gerard, Lt. H. P. Jones, Lt. Cdr. Jack Atkins, Capt. H. E. Lamborn, Lt. Clifford H. Le Hew, Lt. Don B. McAllister, Lt. Ernest L. Miller, Lt. R. C. Mitchell, Lt. C. D. Neal, Lt. Fred D. Riddle, Capt. T. E. Schoeni, Capt. Harry L. Workman.

"Major Bob Baker, who enlisted in June, 1942, and served in the European Theatre, is now home on terminal leave which ends in February '46.

"Dr. Chas. Blum of Hominy served with the 179th Infantry of the 45th Division, European Theatre, from January 27, 1941. He was presented with two Purple Hearts, the Bronze Star and one cluster. Hominy will be glad to have him back in his office. He was discharged as a major.

"Dr. F. J. Brandenburg is now located at 917 Medical Arts Bld., after services as Lt. Colonel from July 18, 1942 to August 20, 1945.

"Dr. Casey Childs, who entered service in May, 1941 and since 1943 has been in New Guinea and the Philippines, is now on terminal leave which ends in February. He was Chief of Dental Surgery with the 551st General Hospital. Dr. Childs attained the rank of full Colonel. He earned combat stars for work in oral surgery and as a member of Maxillo Surgery team.

"Dr. Bob Ingram served thirty-five months from December, 1942, to November 4, 1945, as a full lieutenant in the navy. He is now located at 301 Medical Arts Building.

"Dr. Chas. McCracken enlisted December 15, 1940, and served in the Southwest Pacific with the 8th Service Command. His terminal leave will end January 13. He received the Unit Citation, three battle stars and pre-Pearl Harbor ribbons. The shingle hanging out at 1307 South Main was probably the most desired decoration; he entered service as a first lieutenant, he is now a major.

"Dr. Hugh A. Sims, who was a full lieutenant, U.S.N., was inducted in 1943 and returned to Great Lakes for separation December 1, 1945. He served one year at Great Lakes and was transferred to the First Marine Division with which he served for seventeen months in the South Pacific.

"Major C. T. Richardson of Cushing is remaining in the service. He has recently completed two and one-half years service in a general hospital with the 5th Army in Italy.

"Dr. Joe Trimble reported for service in September, 1942. He was discharged in October, 1945. He has been stationed at the Marine Boot Camp at Parris Island as head of Oral Surgery for the Navy.

"Dr. Charles H. Glass enlisted June 6, 1942, and will be discharged January 26, 1946. He attained the rank of Captain and served in the European Theatre, receiving five battle stars.

"Captain John Glass spent nine months with ground forces and three and one-half years with Air Corps stationed at Camp Bowie, then with the Air Technical Training Command, Fort Logan, Colorado. He was later transferred to Chillicothe, Missouri, and more recently to the Air Forces Redistribution station at Atlantic City. He is now in practice with his father, Dr. John N. Glass, at 216 National Mutual Building, Tulsa.

"Dr. Hugh Thomason, who was in the Naval Reserve, was in active service from September 5, 1943, to October 5, 1945, in the Asiatic Theatre. He received a Purple Heart, four major battle ribbons, and a Bronze Star.

"Dr. L. C. Trotter, as Lt. Commander U.S.N., ends his terminal leave December 11. He entered service October 1, 1941, and saw service in the American and Pacific Theatres.

"Lt. Jack Wadlin, U.S.N., was transferred to the Marines early in his term of service and spent eighteen months in the Pacific Theatre. He will be eligible for discharge as soon as he is released from the hospital at Norman."

Dr. Roy Ellis reported on the following members from the Eastern District:

"Lt. Ingram Ogden, U.S.N.R., spent late November and early December with friends and relatives in Henryetta. Lt. Ogden has been in the service some eighteen months, most of that time in the Southwest Pacific. Said he'd like to be home as a civilian but the bachelors just don't rate enough points.

"Dr. F. E. Dickson, recently relieved from duty with the U.S.N.R., resumed practice at Haskell, November 1.

"Major Albert E. Bonnell, Jr., Major R. R. Ebersole, and Major W. E. Overmyer are now Al—Randy—Bill again, glad to be greeted in the old familiar way."

Dr. I. E. Alfholder, Blackwell, wrote in the January *Bulletin:* "It was my privilege to be in the Borden General Hospital in Chickasha on the morning of October 1. There appeared a gentleman in his first 'civies' in several years. Everywhere we went about the wards and halls all eyes and smiles and handclasps were for the veteran. From the Commanding Officer to the kitchen force, all showed radiant signs of being glad to see him." Dr. Alfholder referred to Dr. Phillip Earl Williams, son of the pioneer dentist, Dr. W. S. Williams, Durant. He was retiring as chief of dental service, Borden General Hospital, where he had been stationed since January, 1943; at the October meeting of the State Society he lectured on "Oral Surgery and Oral Pathology."

These veterans and others of the Society in service were anxious to return to private practice. Like millions of other young Americans who gave up three to six years of normal life in behalf of national security, they wanted to return to their families and homes, jobs and professional duties. Dr. A. C. Seids, chairman of the procurement and assignment service for dentists, reported in April, 1944, that there were 575 dentists practicing in Oklahoma. This number included lady and Negro dentists; all but 63 were born before 1901. He wrote: "What with three years of war, with few replacements, and with the number of deaths and retirements, it is easy to see we have about given our all."

Another survey of the dental population of the state was made in August, 1945, during the presidency of Dr. Charles Hess, Durant. It revealed that Oklahoma had 553 practicing dentists, located in 136 cities. Two counties were without dental service. Dr. Hess stressed the importance of the survey in his address to the annual convention in October, postponed from the usual April date because of transportation limitations. Dr. Hess suggested the Society should offer a refresher course to returning veterans and included this statement in his remarks: "What of the dentist returning from the service: What will be your attitude toward him? Will you be helpful and glad he is back; will you want to share your patients with him? He has been fighting for us, for our liberty, for the things we hold dear. It is my earnest request and appeal that you give the returning dentist all the aid you can to get him reestablished; he is deserving and entitled to it. You have enjoyed an immense practice the last four years. Why? Because of the war conditions, inflated pay checks. Now let's share the practice."

Meantime, those dentists too old to serve or deferred from active service kept alive interest in the Society. They took part in war-bond drives, served on local draft boards, participated in scrap drives, and worked longer hours in taking care of civilian dental needs.

— 2 —

DURING the administrations of Dr. George Roland and Dr. G. A. Roelke, 1943–44, Drs. Fred Pitney, James Miller, R. M. Dunn, Ira McCarty, and Fred Sims served on committees that developed insurance programs for members of the Society. These included a Malpractice Liability Insurance plan and a Health and Accident Insurance plan, which were extended to include those members returning from service.

A legislative committee composed of Dr. A. C. Seids, Dr. D. L. Rippeto, and Dr. W. C. Travis, through concerted action of other Society members, experienced little difficulty in having the dental act amended, in April, 1943, to provide for the regulation of dental laboratories.[2] This provision made the dental act one of the strongest in the United States; it has remained unchanged. The next forward step taken by the Society was to study how to improve its organization.

In July, 1945, Dr. T. W. Sorrels addressed a letter to the Executive Council which was published in the *Bulletin*. He pointed out that business details pertaining to the Society were too time-consuming for practicing dentists; he suggested the employment of a full-time business manager or executive secretary and the establishment of a central office.

[2] *Session Laws of 1943* (Guthrie, 1943), Title 59, Chapter 7, pp. 131–33.

Dr. Eugene W. Wise, Tulsa, secretary-editor for the Society, in succeeding issues of the *Bulletin* likewise advocated centralized control of business affairs of the organization. In April, 1946, Dr. H. O. Warrick, president, appointed a fact-finding committee whose members were Drs. David W. Matteson, T. W. Sorrels, N. Dea Griffith, A. C. Seids, and Frank Bertram. The committee report unanimously favored the employment of an executive secretary to be placed in charge of a central office in Oklahoma City. It was suggested that the expense could be borne by charging Society members additional dues of one dollar a month; that the constitution should be revised to incorporate these suggestions.

Dr. Warrick appointed Drs. Fred Seids, R. E. Stewart, and G. W. Anderson, who, assisted by Drs. T. W. and Harry Sorrels, completely revised the constitution and by-laws. In order to win unanimity of opinion among the members for the proposed changes and for the employment of an executive secretary, Dr. Max Armstrong, president-elect, Tulsa; Dr. W. C. Travis, treasurer, Chickasha; Dr. E. W. Wise, Tulsa; and Dr. J. B. Ratliff, a former president, Hobart, visited all the district meetings in 1946, where details were discussed and explained. At the fortieth annual convention of the Society, on April 14, 1947, the revised constitution and by-laws were adopted.

Under the constitution the name of the organization was changed to the Oklahoma State Dental Association. Provision was made to include honorary and nonresident, as well as active, members. The honorary office of vice-president likewise was created. Executive control was more clearly defined as centering in the Executive Council, whose membership consists of the president, president-elect, secretary-treasurer, a member from each component society with less than 100 members and one additional member for each corresponding increase in number, or fractional increase. Twenty-four standing committees were created.

The by-laws provided that 10 per cent of the members constituted a quorum; six voting members of the Executive Council were a quorum for that governing body. Duties of the executive secretary were clearly defined. These included his services as managing editor of the official publication; and designating his office as headquarters for the Association, where up-to-date membership records, clerical files, and fiscal accountings are maintained. He and the elected treasurer are bonded for $15,000 each; treasurers and secretaries of the component societies are bonded for $2,000 each. Funds are placed on deposit only in the name of the Association and a certified public accountant makes regular monthly audits of all financial records. State dues of members were raised from five to seventeen dollars.

The by-laws also provided for the Women's Auxiliary and the Dental Assistants Society. A standing committee of the Association, the Auxiliary Societies Committee, provides guidance on all business policies and projects of these organizations.

Chapter twenty-two of the by-laws included provisions relating to special members of the Association. Active members for twenty-five consecutive years are entitled to Silver Certificates; holders of Silver Certificates who have practiced dentistry fifty years are awarded Gold Certificates and presented gold keys by the Dental Association.

— 3 —

IN 1946, under the administration of Dr. J. B. Ratliff, the Oklahoma Dental Laboratory Society was formed. Claude Kibler started the first dental laboratory in the state in May, 1908. It was located in Oklahoma City under the name of the New State Laboratory and is still in operation by the founder. A few months later Victor Miller, Tulsa, started the Vic Miller Laboratory in that city. During the intervening forty-seven years more than fifty laboratories have become established which conform to the statutory provisions of the dental act and maintain high standards of service for the dental profession.

At the first meeting, held in Tulsa in March, 1946, Paul Hass, Tulsa, was elected president; Emory G. Lux, Oklahoma City, vice-president; Dale Havely, Tulsa, secretary-treasurer, and a board of directors chosen, composed of G. K. Peerson and L. J. Daniels, Tulsa; Fred M. Fuller and E. P. Hall, Oklahoma City. The following laboratories joined the Society at that time:

Bartlesville: Walter Cooper Dental Laboratory; Chickasha: Elkins & Powell Dental Laboratory; Enid: Hall Dental Laboratory; Frederick: Davidson Dental Laboratory; McAlester: White Dental Laboratory; Miami: Frank Fiorello Laboratory, Fred W.

Scoggins; Muskogee: Beard Dental Laboratory, Blaylock Dental Laboratory; Oklahoma City: Cole Dental Laboratory, Fine Arts Dental Laboratory, Fred Fuller Dental Laboratory, Hettinger Bros. Mfg. Co., Lux Dental Laboratory, Vernon C. McConaghie Laboratory, New State Dental Laboratory, Peterson Dental Laboratory, Piatt Brothers Dental Laboratory, Floyd Spiva Dental Laboratory, Tebow & Wayt Dental Laboratory; Okmulgee: Price Dental Laboratory; Stillwater: Myrle F. Dixon Dental Laboratory; Tulsa: Crosbie Dental Laboratory, Frank Fiorello Dental Laboratory, Glen Balboa Dental Laboratory, P. J. Hass Dental Laboratory, Dale Havely Laboratory, Hettinger Bros. Mfg. Co., Paul M. Jensen, Vic Miller Dental Laboratory, Morse Dental Laboratory, G. K. Peerson Dental Art, John Richmond Dental Laboratory, and Tulsa Dental Laboratory.

Members of the Laboratory Society resolved to abide by the code of ethics of the American Dental Association, to adhere to state dental laws, and to co-operate with the state association. They also resolved that "no dental laboratory shall advertise services, technique, or quote prices in or on any newspaper, magazine, radio, periodical, or any other means available to the public generally, or advertise prices in any dental publications, or in any other way than by enclosures in an envelope addressed to a licensed, registered dentist; nor shall any window or other outside signs be displayed by any such laboratory to attract the attention of the general public."

The following year a special laboratory committee was established by the Dental Association to work with dental laboratories of the state in creating better understanding and unity of purpose. This committee, originally composed of Drs. Earl Sillers, Jack Moore, I. E. Alfholder, and J. E. Brown has had a changing membership; Dr. H. O. Warrick and Dr. Max Armstrong, past presidents of the Association, and Dr. Ira T. Parker, Tulsa, have taken a particular interest in the Dental Laboratory Society. Eternal vigilance by ethical operators and the dental profession has been necessary to protect the public: On April 14, 1954, for example, a news item in the *Daily Oklahoman* reported that charges of practicing dentistry without a license were filed against operators of four Oklahoma City dental laboratories on information furnished by the Board of Governors; none of the four was a member of the Dental Laboratory Society. A spokesman for the Society stated: "Dentures should not be made in dark, dirty cellars or unclean bathrooms. Dentures should be made in clean, modern, up-to-date laboratories. Our members are ethical laboratory operators—businessmen in this community—people who have a stake in the area—interested in the public welfare." A feeling of mutual responsibility toward the public has been engendered by working relationships existing between the Dental Association and the Laboratory Society.

On October 3, 1950, Articles of Incorporation for the Association were filed with the Secretary of State of Oklahoma, signed by Dr. Fred O. Pitney, Oklahoma City, president; Dr. Harry N. Wagner, Henryetta, president-elect; and Dr. Rolla C. Calkin, Guthrie, secretary-treasurer.

The following year, while Dr. Harry N. Wagner, Henryetta, was president, the constitution and by-laws of the Association were revised under the direction of Dr. R. J. Melugin, Shawnee; Dr. R. C. Shurr, Muskogee; and Dr. W. H. Wilson, Tulsa; assisted by the executive secretary, H. Leon Snow. Minor revisions were made in accordance with provisions of the constitution and by-laws of the American Dental Association; these included a requirement that component societies hold at least two scientific meetings each year, and the number of standing committees was reduced from twenty-four to seventeen. Provision was made for a Payment Plan Commission to have charge of any post-payment plan adopted or sponsored by the Association. The by-laws also set forth the order of doing business for meetings at annual sessions.

The quarterly publication, the *Bulletin*, with revised format, appeared as *The Journal of the Oklahoma State Dental Association* in July, 1951. This title was officially incorporated in the by-laws adopted at the April, 1951, meeting. President Wagner, in his address to the members on April 21, explained the change: "Webster defines a bulletin as a publication containing the proceedings of a society while a journal is defined as a periodical publication or magazine. Our publication has advanced to the point that it contains much more than just the proceedings of our society. It is now a truly scientific and newsworthy publication. . . ." An examination of contributions made in recent years reveals the basis of Dr. Wagner's statement; on two occasions the *Journal* has been judged the best type of trade and professional publication in Oklahoma; every year it ranks among the top dental publications in the country. There is issued in months when the *Journal* does not appear the Oklahoma State Dental Association *New Letter*, mailed to members, containing items of current interest.

— 4 —

IN 1948, Dr. Frank P. Bertram, director of the Division of Preventive Dentistry, Oklahoma Department of Health, interested the Association in demonstrations offered by the United States Public Health Service in the technique of topical fluoride application for the control of dental caries of children. Congress appropriated $1,000,000 to the Public Health Service for the demonstrations from July 1, 1948, to June 30, 1949. Mobile topical fluoride demonstration teams were formed, and Oklahoma obtained the use of a unit. Each unit or demonstration team consisted of a dentist, two dental hygienists, and a clerk.

Clinical experience proved that four applications made at one-week intervals of a 2 per cent solution of sodium fluoride to properly cleaned teeth of children resulted in a 40 per cent reduction in the incidence of dental caries. The Public Health Service suggested that a series of applications should be given to children at the ages of three, seven, ten, and thirteen years, varied in accordance with the tooth eruption pattern of the individual child. It was suggested that an application at three years of age would provide protection for the deciduous teeth during the period of changing dentition: the incisors and first molars at age seven, the bicuspids and cuspids at age ten, and the second molars at age thirteen.

The topical fluoride team worked in the elementary schools of Oklahoma during the school term, demonstrating the technique to the dentists of the state. Accompanying publicity encouraged parents to continue the preventive treatment, and in some communities where water supplies do not contain fluoride, organizations such as local Parent-Teacher Associations have sponsored a continuation of the program.

The fluoridation of community water supplies was recommended in 1950 by the American Dental Association as a safe and effective procedure for reducing the incidence of dental caries.[3] Dr. Frederick S. McKay, of Colorado Springs, where a surplus amount

[3] *Daily Oklahoman*, July 6, 1954.

of fluoride in the water causes mottled enamel, began experiments relating to the condition more than forty years before, and, in 1931, Dr. H. Trendley Dean, Chicago, began studies of the relationship between fluorine and dental decay. These and other studies proved that one part fluorine added to one million parts water would reduce the incidence of tooth decay with remarkable success among children who, from babyhood, used the treated water. In 1953, a survey was made in Grand Rapids, Michigan, where fluoridation began in 1945, which showed that six-year-old children who had been drinking fluoridated water since their birth had 70.8 per cent less tooth decay than children of the same age group in a near-by community where the water did not contain fluoride. The incidence lessened, however, among older age groups, particularly those in Grand Rapids whose earlier years of experience antedated the fluoride treatment era: seven-year-old children, 52.5 per cent; eight, 49.2 per cent; nine, 48.1 per cent; thirteen, 39.7 per cent. Similar surveys have demonstrated the rate of reduction in tooth decay are approximately the same in all parts of the country where public water supplies are fluoridated.[4]

At a meeting of the Executive Council of the Oklahoma State Dental Association, March, 4, 1951, the fluoridation of water supplies in Oklahoma was approved; it also has the blessing of the Oklahoma Medical Association. Any community that undertakes this health-protection measure must meet the following requirements: a certificate of necessity must be validated by the local or county dental society, the local or county medical society, local public health officials, and the city commissioners or town governing agency. Finally, an ordinance must be adopted by the city in order to meet legal requirements.

Dr. William P. Ringo, president of the Dental Association, reported at the annual meeting in April, 1953: "Here in Oklahoma we have made a creditable start with eight cities that have approved fluoridation and a number of other cities in the process of approving. I am very proud that the first city in the state to establish this practice was the place where I was born and reared, Nowata. And the second place to establish fluoridation was the place in which I now live, Bartlesville."[5] Other cities listed by Dr. Ringo were

[4] "Information Bulletin," American Dental Association, May, 1954.
[5] The *Journal of the Oklahoma State Dental Association*, July, 1953, p. 9.

Guthrie, Ardmore, Tulsa, Clinton, Altus, and Mangum. In June, 1954, Oklahoma City added the process.

Since World War II the dental and medical associations have combined efforts with interested groups on other projects for health betterment: a cancer symposium and the Oklahoma Medical Research Foundation.

During the week October 6–10, 1947, the Oklahoma State Dental Association, Oklahoma State Medical Association, and the Oklahoma Department of Health joined forces with the Oklahoma Division, American Cancer Society, to conduct postgraduate symposia on cancer. Afternoon and evening sessions were held on consecutive days at Tulsa, Muskogee, McAlester, Durant, and Ada. They were conducted by nationally known physicians and oral surgeons on malignancies of the mouth, breast, and chest, and on the subject of radiology in its application to the diagnosis and treatment of the malignancies. Similar subjects were presented by a like team of experts at the same time in Oklahoma City, Enid, Woodward, Clinton, and Duncan. Dr. James B. Smith, head of the Department of Oral Surgery, George F. Geisinger Hospital, Donville, Pennsylvania, lectured and presented slides on malignancies of the mouth with the team of physicians and surgeons visiting the East Side of the state, while the same subject was presented at joint meetings of physicians and dentists on the West Side by Dr. Fred A. Henny, Department of Oral Surgery, Henry Ford Hospital, Detroit, Michigan. Dr. J. Millard Robertson, whose interest in the symposia reflected the attitude of many physicians and dentists in attendance, said, "If each practitioner of our profession detected only one malignancy of the mouth annually, think of the number of lives which might be saved, to say nothing of the suffering spared."

The late Dr. Tom Lowry, while dean of the School of Medicine of the University of Oklahoma, conceived the idea of the Oklahoma Medical Research Foundation. In 1947, shortly after his death, the medical fraternity redoubled efforts toward realization of his dream; laymen, physicians and surgeons, dentists, pharmacists, and nurses were united in an effort to raise $3,000,000 for a building on the hospital grounds, Oklahoma City, for laboratory equipment, and for the necessary complement of personnel.

The Dental Association at its annual meeting in April endorsed the Research Foundation idea. Dr. Charles Hess, Durant; Dr.

Charles J. Halm, Sand Springs; Dr. Fred C. Seids, Perry; Drs. Harry Sorrels and David Matteson, Oklahoma City, on June 8 met with Mr. Ancel Earp, Dr. J. P. Gray, and Mr. Charles A. Herschleb of the Foundation Committee for a general discussion of contributions dentistry could make and expect from the project. Out of this meeting and others that followed, plans for co-operation by Oklahoma dentistry were formulated. The Association pledged $250,000 to be paid over a ten-year period; teams of dentists under the direction of Dr. Fred O. Pitney visited all districts to receive personal pledges from members of the profession.

At the dedicatory ceremony for the Foundation, July 3, 1949, Dr. Fred C. Seids, vice-president of the Dental Association, spoke as representative of his profession; remarks of Dr. Max G. Armstrong, president, were recorded, and later used at district meetings. Dr. Francis P. Reichmann had been appointed a member of the Foundation Building Committee; Dr. A. L. Frew, Jr., the dental representative on the Research Committee of the Foundation.

Sir Alexander Flemming, the British scientist who discovered penicillin, delivered the principal address at the opening ceremonies. Later, at the request of the Foundation directors, Dr. A. L. Frew, Jr., accompanied the famous Britisher to the Mayo Clinic in Rochester, to Detroit, and to New York seeking information on dental research. Finally, in 1953, Dr. Reichmann and Dr. Matteson, representatives of the Dental Association, and Dr. Charles D. Kochakian, co-ordinator of research at the Foundation, worked out plans for a research fellowship in dentistry. One-half of the funds to support the fellowship are contributed by members of the Association; these are matched by the Foundation. On September 1, 1953, Dr. P. W. Goaz joined the staff of the Foundation to devote full time to dental research.

Meantime, military action to halt aggravated Communist assault in Korea began June 25, 1950. President Harry S. Truman signed Public Law 779 on September 9, 1950, to assure that adequate professional man power, physicians and dentists, would be at full strength for the armed services, and the army and navy called dental reserve officers back into service.

The draft law provided that every dentist up to the age of fifty was required to register and established the following order of priority to call them into service:

241

1. Dentists who received all or part of their training by enrolling in the ASTP or Navy V-12 programs and who had had no active duty as commissioned officers.

2. Dentists who received ASTP or Navy V-12 training and had served on active duty as commissioned officers less than twenty-one months.

3. Dentists who received no training at government expense and had had less than ninety days' duty.

4. Dentists with less than twenty-one months of active service.

The Association completed a survey the following February that placed Oklahoma dentists in one of the military classifications. Eighteen dentists were in priority 1 of the draft act; 9 in priority 2; 107 in priority 3; 75 in priority 4. A total of 150 dentists were reserve officers; 33 were already in service.

The State Association's Military Liaison Committee, with Dr. Volney V. Jones as chairman, worked out a point system to determine availability for military service. One point was allowed for each year of age, one point for each month of prior military service, two points for each dependent, and three points for each combat-earned decoration.

Again, to meet a national emergency, two national guard units were called to active duty in September, 1950: the famed Forty-fifth Division, which includes the Oklahoma unit, and the Fortieth Division, the California unit. With the guard went a full complement of dental officers. These, together with reserve officers called to service and voluntary enlistments, filled the quota from Oklahoma. The Executive Council of the Association, at a meeting December 9, 1950, waived state dues for members during their tours of duty. A roster of members of the Association who served during the crisis appears in Appendix Q.

In 1951, Tulsa members of the Northern District Dental Society inaugurated a program in celebration of National Children's Dental Health Day, February 5, that brought favorable publicity. Dr. Charles E. McCracken, president, was instrumental in having George Stoner, mayor, issue a proclamation which declared February 5 Children's Dental Health Day in the city of Tulsa. McCracken enlisted the aid of Noel Kaho, who prepared a thirty-minute television show for a local station. Kaho wrote the script and arranged for posters, models, and pictures. Attention was directed to the result of neglecting the teeth and lack of dental care by the appearance on the program of a boy and a girl both of whom have full upper and lower dentures. Drs. McCracken, Kaho, Robert E. Wright, Norton Wheeler, and Hugh Sims also appeared on the program. Posters were displayed in downtown stores throughout the week, and dentists spoke to business and professional luncheon groups on the importance of preventive dentistry.[6]

The Oklahoma County Dental Society adopted a somewhat similar program in 1955 which will be continued in succeeding years. Volunteer members of the Society during January examined the mouths of all junior high school students enrolled in classes in physical education; on national Children's Dental Health Day, awards were made to the boy and girl judged best in oral hygiene.

Two insurance plans of benefit to members of the Association have been developed during the past decade. While Dr. G. A. Roelke was president, in 1944, he appointed Dr. Fred Pitney chairman of an insurance committee to examine the possibilities of a group malpractice insurance plan, a type of protection extended to doctors and surgeons. No matter how careful the doctor, how ethical the practitioner, how infallible his judgment, an accident may occur for which he is held accountable. For example, on May 3, 1935 an able, veteran Muskogee dentist, Dr. C. C. Youmans, extracted some upper teeth for George W. Fabian of that city. On August 26, Fabian commenced action in district court against Dr. Youmans on the grounds his health was impaired because the roots of some of the teeth remained in his mouth and caused serious infection. Dr. Youmans died the following month; the suit was continued against his estate, and in November, 1938, the Supreme Court of Oklahoma awarded Fabian $1,300 in damages.[7] Through Dr. Pitney's efforts, the company that handled malpractice insurance for the Oklahoma State Medical Society provided a similar plan for the dentists.

At the same time another committee—Drs. R. M. Dunn, Ira E. McCarty, and Fred Sims—worked out a group health and accident insurance plan. During the administration of Dr. Rolla C. Calkin a detailed report in regard to the program was made at the annual convention in Oklahoma City, April 20, 1954. The Insur-

[6] *Bulletin*, April, 1951, pp. 37 and 45.
[7] *Griesel, Ex'r. v. Fabian,* 184 *Oklahoma* 42.

ance Committee, composed of Drs. R. D. Lochridge, T. H. Miley, and R. W. Conger, reported that from the time the Association adopted a group plan, June 1, 1944, to January 1, 1954, 308 members had been paid claims amounting to $174,350. Forty-eight of the claims were for amounts in excess of $1,000 for serious illnesses, accidents, and accidental deaths. The largest amount paid, $7,050, was to the estate of Dr. L. L. Barnes following his death November 24, 1947, from injuries received in an automobile accident near Norman.

Dr. Alvin L. Ball of Alva had a serious automobile accident during the summer of 1953. While confined to the hospital for two months, he was paid $2,000; as long as the disability keeps him from practice, he will be paid $400 a month. The majority of the members of the Association are now covered by liability or malpractice insurance and belong to one of the group health and accident plans in effect.

Another project sponsored by the Association that has gained favor with the profession and public is the post-payment plan for dental care. This was approved by the Executive Council in December, 1951, during the administration of Dr. H. N. Wagner and put into operation the following February. The Liberty National Bank and Trust Company of Oklahoma City handles the paper work; member dentists are freed from burdensome bookkeeping and collection responsibilities.

A single application form and note—signed by the patient in the dentist's office—are the only paper work necessary. These permit the patient to get the dental work needed while the dentist receives his fee immediately from the bank, which assumes full responsibility for collecting on the note. The post-payment plan has been considered an effective stop-gap against socialized dentistry.

Members of the Payment Plan Commission in 1954 included Dr. R. J. Melugin, Shawnee; Dr. H. N. Wagner, Henryetta; Dr. R. C. Mitchell, Tulsa; Dr. J. M. Ozmun, El Reno; Dr. V. C. Tisdal, Elk City; Dr. G. I. McBride, Enid; and Dr. L. A. Lucas, chairman, Oklahoma City. Dr. Lucas reported to the annual meeting in April, 1954, that 359 dentists were participating in the plan. The Liberty National Bank had handled 5,807 notes amounting to $1,087,177. Of this amount, payments received amounted to $796,-915, leaving an outstanding balance of $290,262. Notes that are delinquent over ninety days are turned to a collection agency whose fees are 50 per cent. Only a small number have been referred to the agency. Bank charges are 7 per cent: 6 per cent for interest and 1 per cent for insurance.

These, and other advances made by the Association, already discussed, have strengthened it in public relationship. Other actions of personal significance to members of the organization have been taken within its recent history.

CHAPTER TEN

Awards and Accomplishments

— I —

THE TWENTY-FIFTH anniversary of the state society was observed at the annual meeting in April, 1932, in Muskogee, site of the first meeting after statehood.[1] Here was begun a custom that has become traditional at annual conventions: the presentation of a Silver Certificate to those who have been members of the Society for twenty-five consecutive years.

On the first occasion, in a colorful ceremony at the annual banquet, Dr. Martin Dewey, president of the American Dental Association, presented Silver Certificates to twenty-three members. Dr. Dewey paid high tribute to the recipients. Four had been presidents of territorial associations. Seven were former presidents of the state association and two others were destined to fill that honored position within the next three years. Three were vice-presidents during the early years of the state organization. The other members had all held positions of trust and leadership in district societies or served on state and national committees. Dr. Dewey recounted that these gentlemen were of that small corps who became charter members of the state organization. He then traced the forward steps taken by the young society which marked it one of the most progressive of state dental organizations: the inception and remarkable success of the postgraduate plan that revolutionized professional meetings in the nation, the evolution to student participation in postgraduate courses, the co-operative success of tri-state meetings, the advanced

---

[1] All material used for this chapter, unless otherwise cited, was taken from the quarterly publication of the Oklahoma State Dental Association. The publication was called the *Bulletin* through the April, 1951, issue; succeeding issues, beginning in July, 1951, are the *Journal*.

idea of bringing the best of dentistry to the grass roots by sending lecturers of national reputation from district to district. He also paid tribute to those members who, though never rewarded with high office by the Society, nevertheless had supported goals of attainment set by its leaders and by their support added strength to the organization and raised standards of dentistry within the state.

Additional recognition has been accorded senior members of the Association. In December, 1946, the Executive Council approved a plan to honor those dentists with fifty years' service in the profession who had received Silver Certificates. It was planned to make them Gold Certificate members and present them with gold keys. The first ceremony was held at the annual meeting the following April when the revised constitution and by-laws were adopted. Dr. A. B. Walker, member of the Executive Council, a former president, made the presentation. Remarks he made then have been used at presentations of later years:

"Some fifty, sixty, seventy years ago, from the north and from the south, from the east and from the west, men and women with pioneer blood in their veins began to come into what is now Oklahoma. They came because it was a new land, a land of opportunity, a land in which there was plenty of room to live and grow.

"Among those who came were some who had taken up the profession of dentistry as their life work. They, too, came because it was a new land, a land of opportunity, a land in which there was plenty of room to live and grow. Many of them were poorly equipped for their work; some suffered actual hardships; but they soon grew to love this new land and neither heat nor cold nor drought nor flood could drive them away. They were the pioneers in dentistry in Oklahoma and they laid broad and deep the foundations on which the profession of dentistry in Oklahoma now stands. Many of them have gone to their reward but some are still with us, and their eyes still shine with that enthusiasm that shone in them fifty years ago."

Presentations were made to Drs. T. H. Williams, Chickasha; W. S. Williams, Durant; Fred Seids, Perry; Fred Sparks, Ponca City; R. H. Pendleton, Norman; C. S. Ferner and C. I. Trimble, Tulsa. A complete listing of those who have been thus honored appears in Appendix P.

In 1931 the Shobe Memorial was placed in the lobby of the

Medical and Dental Arts Building, Tulsa. Dr. B. L. Shobe, father of the Oklahoma Way, died in October, 1917. At the eleventh annual meeting of the Oklahoma State Dental Society the following April a committee composed of Dr. J. Q. Waddell, Kingfisher; Dr. C. W. Day, Tulsa; and Dr. A. E. Bonnell, Muskogee, was appointed to make plans for a suitable memorial.

The committee decided the best remembrance for their leader would be the furtherance of educational and research purposes through the use of funds raised by voluntary contributions. Dr. A. L. Walters, who was class captain in the course offered by Dr. Elmer S. Best, Minneapolis, in root canal fillings and focal infections, told the class members of the memorial plan. Donations were made; Walters visited other classes and received voluntary contributions that amounted to more than one hundred dollars, which were turned over to the Society's treasurer.

During the intervening years, to 1930, the idea for an endowment plan for educational and research purposes was allowed to lapse. With the opening of the Medical and Dental Arts Building in Tulsa in 1929, plans were revived for a memorial. Drs. Fred Lenhart, Earl Ammons, and A. L. Walters, Tulsa, the appointed committee, selected the beautiful bronze tablet that draws the attention of all who enter the building.

The Memorial now bears the names of five other former leaders of Oklahoma dentistry: Dr. C. W. Day, Tulsa; Dr. A. E. Bonnell, Muskogee; Dr. C. R. Lawrence, Enid; Drs. C. L. White and A. C. Seids, Oklahoma City. The pattern followed in the selection of Dr. C. W. Day for the honor has subsequently been followed in the selection of others. The Tulsa County Dental Society on February 4, 1934, petitioned the Executive Council to give consideration to the placing of the name of Dr. C. W. Day on the Shobe Memorial. The Executive Council recommended its consideration to the general assembly at its next meeting.

On May 7, 1934, the general assembly of the Society, in session at the tri-state meeting in Kansas City, adopted the following resolution offered by Dr. Walters: "Resolved, that the Oklahoma State Dental Society, through its Executive Council, shall determine the worthiness and recommend the name of any deceased member of the Society whose name may be proposed to grace the Shobe Memorial Tablet in the lobby of the Medical and Dental Arts Building in the city of Tulsa, Oklahoma, that the recommendation of the Executive Council be approved by the Society at its annual business meeting, and that the action of the Society be final." The resolution was adopted and remains in effect as a standing rule of the Association.

The Society made one of its finest gestures by honoring Dr. A. E. Bonnell with a testimonial dinner at the annual meeting in Enid in April, 1935. Bonnell is the oldest name in Oklahoma dentistry: since 1888, when he opened an office in Muskogee, principal city of Indian Territory, his profession has been represented by him or his son Dr. A. E. Bonnell, Jr., at that location. He was joined in practice by Dr. A. A. Pfeiffer in 1908 and by his son, president of the Society, 1954–55, in 1929.

Dr. Bonnell's record in dentistry was more than statewide. He had held the principal offices of the territorial and state associations and guided the State Board of Dental Examiners as a member during its first ten years of existence when precedents were established and ethics of practice formulated. He had given numerous clinics before the American Dental Association, had appeared before the Eighth International Dental Congress in Philadelphia, and on two different occasions before the Chicago Mid-Winter Clinic.

He represented the state society as a member of the House of Delegates of the American Dental Association for fifteen years, and, at the time of the banquet in his honor, he was a member of the important Judicial Council of that organization. For the term 1929–30, he was vice-president of the American Dental Association, the first Oklahoman to receive this high honor.

Dr. Bonnell was a regular attendant at district and state meetings of the Society; during the previous year he had missed the annual convention because he had gone abroad to appear on the program of the American Dental Society of Europe at The Hague, on May 20, 1934.

He was an active participant in the life of his community. For forty-six years he served as superintendent of the Methodist church Sunday school and was president for three years of the Oklahoma State Sunday School Association. He was a charter member and past-president of the Lions Club of his city, had served on the local school board for ten years, and for six years was a member of the Muskogee City Council.

When the Executive Council of the Society met November 26, 1934, Dr. J. A. Wells, Shawnee, proposed the testimonial dinner, and Dr. C. R. Lawrence, Dr. A. L. Walters, and Dr. C. L. White were appointed to make the necessary arrangements. These gentlemen had been closely associated with Dr. Bonnell in all the progressive advances made by dentistry in Oklahoma, and Walters had looked upon him as his preceptor from territorial days at Checotah. Bonnell was his dentist and extracted a third molar for Walters shortly after statehood. Some twenty years later Walters performed a similar operation for Bonnell.

At the time of the testimonial dinner, short addresses were made by Drs. A. A. Pfeiffer, A. L. Walters, F. J. Reichmann, and C. R. Lawrence. An unusual gift cherished by Dr. Bonnell was a bound volume which contained almost one hundred letters of personal tribute from members of the profession throughout the country. The Society had calculated well the timeliness of the deserved tribute; within a year Bonnell's name was engraved on the Shobe Memorial as one of the past leaders in Oklahoma dentistry.

In the mid-twenties, when Dr. C. N. Johnson, Chicago, great teacher of dentistry, was asked to comment on the postgraduate plan of instruction in Oklahoma, he replied: "This has been one of the most forward-looking steps taken by any profession, but why continue to go out of the state for instructors when you have developed such talent as Bonnell and Jacobs and Bradley of Muskogee, Walters, Temples, and Furrow at Tulsa, Weir and Barnes of Oklahoma City, Sebert of Clinton, and dozens of others, the best talent of any state?"

His criticism was just. In the smaller communities and larger cities of the state, dentists with inquiring minds, supple hands, and interest in professional advancement developed skills and techniques which were recognized nationally. All attributed their interest in better work to inspiration gained from postgraduate courses of instruction and interest shown by other members of the Society.

Dr. A. F. Sebert, who established his practice at Kaw City fresh from dental college in 1910, has recently related how these influences affected him: "When I graduated from dental college, I was the real thing; like many young professionals I thought I knew as much about dentistry as the professors. As for the men who had been practicing ten or twenty years, I had nothing but pity for them. Poor fellows, how little they knew!

"I located at Kaw City and intended to stay there just long enough to get a little money ahead so I could go to a large city where my wonderful work would be appreciated. During my spare time I stood at the bottom of the steps and watched the pretty girls go by. I knew all there was in dentistry worth knowing, so what was the need for me to study or experiment.

"Then the State Society put on their first postgraduate course. I went more to show the other fellows what I knew than to learn myself. It took two of these courses to show that I knew nothing of real dentistry, but when the light broke, I was left beaten and hopeless and thought that I should give up my profession.

"Just at this time Dr. Fred Sparks offered me needed encouragement. He convinced me all that I needed was to go into my laboratory, experiment, and study. This I did. . . ."[2] Dr. Sebert stayed at Kaw City eight years, then moved to Clinton. His technique in crown and bridge work and ceramics will be known and acknowledged long after he gives up active practice.

One other example illustrates how Oklahomans have benefited from advanced skills and techniques of members in the dental profession. Carl B. Anderson, at the port of embarkation in 1943 awaiting an overseas tour of duty with the armed services, was sent to a prominent practitioner in New York City for a dental check-up. Upon examination, the dentist thought there might be leakage around an inlay and decided to drill through the filling.

After a few moments the dentist inquired: "How long have you had this inlay?"

"About twenty years," was the reply.

"Who did the work?"

"J. R. Gossett."

"He must be in one of our larger cities?"

"Oh, no!" was the answer. "He has practiced at the small inland town of Temple, Oklahoma, since before statehood."

After the dentist had completed the work, he commented: "I should never have destroyed that inlay. There was nothing wrong with it. We have a clientele here in New York City that gladly would pay $1,000 for such excellent workmanship."

[2] Recorded interview with Dr. A. F. Sebert, Clinton, in July, 1953.

In order to stimulate competition among clinicians at the annual meeting in 1929, Dr. Otto Hine, Muskogee, clinical director, offered a prize to best clinician, the winner to be selected by popular vote of the membership who saw the clinics. Dr. J. B. Jenkins designed a trophy, done in silver, with a hand-hammered background of oxidized silver, and a scroll and a banner bearing the word "Excelsior" onlaid in silver with a satin finish. Dr. W. J. Scruton, president of the Society, presented the trophy to Dr. G. W. Andree, Tishomingo.

It was proposed to add names of subsequent winners during the ensuing years but, unfortunately, when Dr. Andree's office was destroyed by fire, the total loss included the prized trophy.

During the term of Dr. A. C. Seids as president of the Dental Society in 1933, he revived the custom of awarding a trophy to the best clinician at state meetings. This award, a handsome silver trophy, designated as the Arthur C. Seids Memorial Cup, in later years has been sponsored by the Oklahoma County Dental Society. Three judges from among the membership, whose identities remain unknown, are selected by the president, president-elect, and secretary of the Society. The cup is awarded to the clinician who receives the highest grade based upon the following scores:

1. 40%: value of clinic to advancement of dentistry.
2. 10%: originality.
3. 10%: presentation.
4. 15%: practicability.
5. 10%: simplicity.
6. 10%: neatness.
7. 5%: punctuality.

The cup is retired when won three years in succession by the same clinician, who cannot repeat a winning clinic. On two occasions the cup has become the permanent possession of dentists: Dr. L. A. Lucas, for staging winning clinics in 1941–43, and Dr. Norton Wheeler, 1944–46. Each year the four highest participants are invited to represent the state society at the national meeting of the American Dental Association.

At the first meeting Dr. Scott P. Bowyer of Tulsa won the award. In 1934 the state meeting was part of the tri-state convention at Kansas City. Seventeen Oklahoma dentists offered clinics:

A. M. Bradley and W. T. Jacobs, Muskogee; J. B. Herring, I. M. Helmy, J. R. Caughron, V. V. Jones, J. E. Brown, Harry H. Sorrels, Ward L. Shaffer, and L. V. Swift, Oklahoma City; G. W. Andree, Tishomingo; A. F. Sebert, Clinton; H. O. Warrick, Enid; M. R. Williams, Chickasha; and J. N. Glass, Norton Wheeler, and S. P. Bowyer, Tulsa. Dr. H. O. Warrick, Enid, who in 1947 was to become president of the Society and in 1953 the third Oklahoma dentist to be honored with the vice-presidency of the American Dental Association, was declared the winner. In succeeding years competition for the award has been equally keen.

— 2 —

WHEN THE state association was new and travel to convention cities from outlying points of the state limited to the railroads, few wives accompanied their husbands on trips to annual conventions. For the few who did attend, wives of local dentists arranged teas, theater parties, or automobile rides over the city. For example, those who accompanied their husbands in attendance at the first postgraduate course, at Oklahoma City in March, 1912, were entertained with a theater party and an afternoon with the Arts and Crafts Embroidery Club at the home of Mrs. G. A. Nichols.[3]

The following year more wives showed up to enjoy the comforts of the new Skirvin Hotel, to see the local sights, and to go on shopping tours. And when the convention opened at the Lee Huckins Hotel in March, 1914, the urbane Dr. R. S. Parsons took cognizance of their presence and in his presidential address suggested a ladies' auxiliary to be sponsored by the Society. His gallant and diplomatic gesture was received with considerable lack of enthusiasm by the members, however. A committee composed of A. L. Walters, J. M. Temples, and L. G. Mitchell was appointed to consider recommendations made by the president. Dr. Parsons had made other worthwhile recommendations, all enthusiastically adopted after the committee report was presented. But the members, in closed session, agreed with the committee: "We advise that a Ladies Auxiliary be not considered in any official manner at this time for many reasons which are unnecessary to mention."[4]

[3] *Daily Oklahoman*, March 27, 1912.
[4] Minutes of the Oklahoma State Dental Society, March 30, 1914.

253

Whatever the reasons that were unnecessary to mention, wives continued to accompany their husbands to convention cities. Their sex was leaving a period of disfranchisement, of high-button shoes, cotton stockings, ankle-length skirts, hat and hairpins, and transformations. They were entering an era that brought the right to vote, beauty parlors, the shortening of skirts and of hair, the staccato of high heels in business offices, highway improvements, and common use of the automobile. American business and professional men belatedly learned that their careers could be furthered if their wives occasionally left home limits to assist at the office or accompany them to conventions.

Visiting wives especially liked the gracious hospitality afforded by Tulsa. Its population by 1930 was over 140,000; twenty downtown buildings were ten to twenty-seven stories high. Although there were fifty-seven larger cities in the United States, Tulsa ranked twelfth among American cities in the number of buildings more than ten stories high.[5] Beautifully landscaped residential areas were showplaces; hospitals and churches were outstanding in architectural design; hotels and downtown shops were of quality and national rank.

The Society recognized inroads on its privacy from the influence of the ladies by proposing an amendment to its by-laws at the April meeting, 1940. The constitution provided that any proposed amendment lay over until the next annual meeting. In April, 1941, the amendment was adopted: "This Society shall foster and promote a Women's Auxiliary Society, their function to be the promotion of a well-designed organization drawn upon the functional and geographical lines of the Society. Their constitution and any amendments to be sanctioned by the Executive Council of the Society."

This was after-the-fact recognition of the organization already brought into being. At the meeting of the Society in Tulsa in 1937, plans were made which led to the organization of the Women's Auxiliary. Dr. A. B. Rivers, Okmulgee, president of the Society, Dr. W. S. Phillips, McAlester, president-elect, Dr. O. F. Sinks and Dr. S. P. Bowyer, Tulsa, who were to serve the Society as presidents in 1939 and 1941 respectively, met at the Mayo Hotel, on

[5] *Population, Number and Distribution of Inhabitants,* Fifteenth Census of the United States for 1930, Vol. I, Table II, pp. 18–20.

April 7 with a group of the wives of dentists in attendance at the meeting and advised them on procedures.

The following officers were elected: Mrs. L. G. Smith, Tulsa, president; Mrs. W. S. Phillips, McAlester, first vice-president; Mrs. A. J. T. Beatty, Oklahoma City, second vice-president; Mrs. E. E. Overmyer, Muskogee, third vice-president; Mrs. E. W. Wise, Tulsa, recording secretary; Mrs. E. L. Moore, Stillwater, corresponding secretary; and Mrs. H. G. Carson, Pawhuska, treasurer.

Charter members included Mesdames A. J. T. Beatty, Oklahoma City; Arthur L. Lynn, Medford; A. N. Dow, Ponca City; Rolla C. Calkin, Guthrie; Robert W. Conger, Pawhuska; H. B. Sherrod, Stillwater; C. A. Furrow, Tulsa; Norton Wheeler, Tulsa; John Glass, Tulsa; Robert Shira, Pawhuska; E. L. Moore, Stillwater; J. L. Mayfield, Norman; W. D. Rush, Tulsa; L. R. Moore, Chelsea; L. G. Smith, Tulsa; W. B. Haynes, Tulsa; John A. Wadlin, Tulsa; C. A. D. Beer, Enid; W. S. Phillips, McAlester; E. D. Sillers, Tulsa; Jack Childs, Tulsa; Fred E. Sims, Tulsa; J. M. Asbury, Oklahoma City; F. C. Seids, Perry; H. G. Carson, Pawhuska; E. E. Overmyer, Muskogee; A. C. Seids, Oklahoma City; S. G. Weiss, Muskogee; O. F. Sinks, Tulsa; E. W. Wise, Tulsa.[6]

A constitution was adopted which included among its objectives the following:

1. to bring its members into more active affiliation with the dental profession;

2. to initiate or assist in any activity that may be approved by the Dental Society;

3. to extend the aims of the dental profession to all organizations which seek the advancement of dental health and education;

4. to promote fellowship between the families of dentists;

5. to promote the welfare of dentistry.

Since the organization of the Women's Auxiliary its membership has grown to more than three hundred; special programs are prepared for state meetings in conjunction with the parent organization, and the lady members now look forward to the comming-

[6] "History of Women's Auxiliary to the Oklahoma State Dental Society," prepared by Mrs. L. G. Smith, Tulsa, in 1949. The manuscript is in the files of the Central Office, Oklahoma State Dental Association.

ling of interests with those of their husbands, and special sessions for lectures, and teas and dinner-dances that afford social relaxation.

The Auxiliary sponsors other projects, too, devoted to the purpose of the organization. Mrs. L. A. Lucas, secretary in 1951 of the Women's Auxiliary, Oklahoma County Dental Society, has listed worthwhile projects sponsored by the state group and has cited how the local auxiliary has met its obligations.[7] In the late 1930's the Oklahoma County Dental Society, through members, donated time to the care of teeth of indigent children at the Salvation Army clinic. The Auxiliary provided transportation for the children, donated money to buy amalgam for the clinic, sponsored puppet shows put on in the grade schools as a dental education program, and made contributions to help support needy families.

Typical entries from the minutes of the local Auxiliary reveal:

1941-42—Puppet shows held for four weeks in grade schools.
Amalgam for Salvation Army Clinics.
Donated $15.00 to State Auxiliary project of placing book of *Teeth, Health, and Appearance* in city schools; in addition, each member donated $1.00 for additional books.

1944-45—438 tooth brushes for schools.
433,695 surgical dressings for Red Cross.
Magazines for veterans' hospitals.

1947-48—Buying and pledging $100.00 bond each year for ten years to be given to the Research Foundation to be used for dental research.
Contribute $10.00 each to Red Cross, Community Fund, and cancer drive.
Bought 597 tooth brushes for grade-school children.
Donated $12.95 to polio drive.

1950-51—$70.00 worth of tooth brushes bought for grade schools.
$100.00 to Research Foundation.
Films for dental hygiene for schools.
$10.00 to Red Cross; $10.00 to Community Fund.

These and similar activities sponsored throughout the state by

[7] Margaret F. Lucas to Harry Sorrels, March 4, 1951. The letter and enclosures are in the files of the Central Office, Oklahoma State Dental Association.

the Auxiliary have proved its worth to the Association. Even small things, such as the use of the color scheme of dentistry, lilac, at annual banquets indicate the influence of the wives on the profession.

Officials of the Association have arranged for nationally known speakers to appear on programs of the Auxiliary. In 1942, for example, Dr. George W. Crane, popular author and writer of a syndicated newspaper column on psychology, spoke to the Association on "Psychology of Professional Practice" and before the luncheon meeting of the Women's Auxiliary on "How a Wife Can Make or Break a Dentist."

The Oklahoma State Dental Assistants Association, too, has merited the approval of the parent organization. Leaders in dentistry appear on its programs, and many of the dentists have had Miss G. Archanna Morrison, a former executive dental assistant in Boston, author of the well-known book, *In the Dentist's Office*,[8] visit their offices and offer professional advice to hygienists, assistants, and secretaries. Table clinics prepared by assistants for presentation at annual conventions attract large attendance from members of the Association. Dr. T. A. Jones, Oklahoma City, inaugurated the custom in 1953 of awarding a silver cup to the assistant who presents the best clinic. Phyllis Pearson Terry, assistant in the office of Dr. Fred Pitney, won the trophy, which must be won by an assistant three times for permanent possession.

Shortly before Dr. Charles Lincoln White died, February 24, 1941, he presented to Dr. Harry Sorrels, a constant visitor at his bedside, an ivory billiard ball. Because ivory comes from the tusk of an elephant, Dr. White thought of it as a symbol of his profession. Sorrels, then state president of the Society, had the head of a gavel carved from the ball; the gavel, though chipped and retired from active use, is presented to incoming presidents of the Association as a symbol of the office. It reminds them of the intrinsic worthiness of service performed by their predecessors.

The Oklahoma County Dental Society has sponsored two projects in Oklahoma City which reflect a good public relations policy. The Oklahoma County Dental Study Club has placed books on dentistry and indices to dental periodical literature in the Oklahoma

---

[8] *In the Dentist's Office, A Guide for Auxiliary Dental Personnel* (Philadelphia, J. P. Lippincott and Company, 1948) is considered outstanding in its field.

Medical School Library.[9] Accessions are made yearly, sponsored by the Study Club, and the dental library is keeping abreast of expanding needs of the Medical Center.

The other project, the Salvation Army Children's Dental Clinic, was begun in 1933.[10] The clinic was held in the Salvation Army Citadel until 1941, when quarters were provided in the newly established Variety Club Health Center. In the early days of the clinic, Drs. L. V. Swift, N. Dea Griffith, and W. E. Flesher served on the board of directors; now, the current president of the Oklahoma County Dental Society serves as counsellor to the Oklahoma County Health Association, which is in charge of all the health services at the center. Dentists who have devoted much time to the children's clinic are Drs. L. L. Willis, James R. Miller, M. S. Taubman, Max Ward, D. A. Yeager, Leonard A. Newcomb, Charles S. Garland, A. C. Sales, Ronald C. Doll, L. F. Bates, William C. Hopkins, W. H. Doyle, Randel F. Whitton, Tully L. Lale, Robert H. Binkley, Jack Stewart, Floyd W. Trindle, Thomas C. Dunn, Harold Pollock, and Don S. Harp.

Growing old in service to dentistry, too, is the quarterly publication of the Association. Although established in 1911, it was not until 1914 that advertisements first appeared in the *Bulletin*. It is significant that three of these advertisers, the New State Dental Laboratory, Hettinger Brothers Manfacturing Co., and the Pearce Dental Supply Company, have taken space in all subsequent issues, a relationship that parallels that of C. H. Kibler, Clay Jewett, and Roscoe F. Turk of these firms with members of the Association. Through the quarterly, dentists keep abreast of current happenings in the profession, state and district meetings and programs, and Oklahoma personalities who make contributions to dental literature.

For several years Dr. Earl F. Ammons, who practiced at Tulsa from 1918 to 1950, had a national following among the profession for his column "The Dentalog," which appeared in the *Dental Survey*. During this period he made occasional contributions to the

[9] "History Dental Library, Oklahoma School of Medicine," submitted by Ward L. Shaffer, March 27, 1950. This manuscript is in the files of the Central Office, Oklahoma State Dental Association.

[10] "The Salvation Army Children's Clinic, Oklahoma City, Oklahoma," manuscript in the files of the Central Office, Oklahoma State Dental Association.

Bulletin on homely philosophy slanted towards dentistry. In the Society's publication of July, 1946, he included this:

"At a Texas State Dental Meeting several years ago, I saw my first dental talking and moving picture. The title of the picture was 'Third Molar Technic' starring the late Dr. George Winter with an all dental cast. Doctor Winter flipping out third molars with an elevator was as thrilling as a G-man bowling over gangsters with a sub-machine gun in a regular movie. The picture held the attention of the audience to the very end. These dental movies, now an every day occurrence, are a boon to timid dentists who never get closer than the outskirts of the clinic table. Like small strawberries that get jostled to the bottom of the box, these dentists have been watching clinicians for years from window sills, or standing on tip toes. I recall a clinic that Dr. Winter, in person, gave some years ago. He was extracting an impacted third molar. From my position back of the patient I couldn't even see Dr. Winter but I did get an occasional glimpse at his shiny elevators and forceps by watching their reflections in the bi-focal lenses of a doctor who had a ringside seat. I couldn't make out whether Dr. Winter was using his thumbnail or the patient's tonsil as a fulcrum for the elevators.

"Some predict that the dental meetings of the future will consist entirely of talking pictures. Unless a movie projector can be perfected that makes extemporaneous after dinner speeches, tells tall stories in hotel lobbies and plays a hand of poker, I believe the clinician, in person, will never go out of vogue."

His account in the July, 1944, *Bulletin* related how a dentist is happiest when his hands and mind are busily engaged in creative work: "My barber brought his five year old son to the office today. I registered surprise when he couldn't tell me how many teeth his boy should have and he said to me: 'Doc can you tell me how many hairs are on your kid's head?' Such is logic.

"Some of these hot afternoons, I can't tell whether I am tired or just lazy. The symptoms blend so beautifully that it's like differentiating between gingivitis and incipient pyorrhea.

"To me a broken appointment is not always a disappointment. Often I consider them as not so much money lost as time gained for puttering around the laboratory. At such times I do some of my best research work.

"Recently I have been studying the reactions of Mexican jumping beans to novocain, chloroform, and alcohol. I dissected away one side and cemented cellophane faces over the openings, giving them much the appearance of open-faced crowns.

"Through this window I studied and observed the family life of the worm that dwells in his one-room apartment, and gives the kick to the jumping bean. When someone calls me a worm I shall think of this little fellow who can sit in his own living room and with one flip of his tail knock his dwelling three or four times its own length. If we were as agile as this worm, we could lift ourselves over a fence by our own bootstraps. I injected a little alcohol into one bean and the worm inside got on a jag. His capers would make a flea look as inactive as a poppy seed on a French roll."

This nostalgic item appeared in October, 1945: "Mushbites— what pleasant memories they bring up, what fascination in kneading the yellow wax through the fingers like a miser fondling his gold. What can equal it for grooming the hands and nails after a week-end fishing trip!

"I have always been a collector of bees-wax. From that first mushbite taken in dental school I have accumulated through the years a hunk half as large as a bowling ball. How many successes and failures are tied up in that ball—how many sorrows and joys it contains—all blended now so that the griefs are almost obliterated, leaving only pleasant memories.

"At times I feel a little sad at the passing of the mushbite, just as many of the older generation bemoan the passing of the horse and buggy. The mushbite, like the horse and buggy, is a symbol of the past, and what we old sentimental boys want back is our youth. That's why, when things get a little too complicated, I take out the old bees-wax ball and gaze into it longingly, as a fortune teller into his crystal, and take a journey back to the good old mushbite days."

His "philosophy of education" was a tonic to the profession: "If I were running a dental school I would start the freshmen making stainless steel clasps the first day. Within an hour I could determine more about their future than from a dozen intelligence tests. I would give each a yard of heavy gauge stainless steel wire, a pair of cuckoo-beaked pliers, and a plaster model, and tell them to 'go to it.' But first I would demonstrate how simple it all was by making a sample. In this demonstration I would use annealed wire—not for deception, but to nourish that over-confidence of youth so necessary to bring out all the moral possibilities of the experience.

"I would then take a suitable position where I could study the expressions on their faces, and await developments. Some will be satisfied early and quit before getting much adaptation of the clasps to the plaster teeth; some will get that lucky twist that makes a good fit but, not satisfied, will give the wire one more zip—and all will be lost. Some will fuss around until the soft plaster teeth shape to the misfitted clasp, and they will smile and think they have succeeded. There will be those who know they have done a good job and will have the rare judgment to leave well enough alone. In after years when the boys are confronted with complexities perhaps they will recall this experience and strive a little harder for that elusive zip that makes for perfection.

"I wish my father, when I was at a tender impressionable age, would have given me a piece of stainless steel wire, and said, 'Son, take these pliers and blend the wire to the waistline of a summer squash. Whenever you get a fit so snug that a chigger can't crawl between the wire and the squash without removing its brassiere, you may come to supper.' I might have gone to bed hungry that night but, too, I might have absorbed a little of that quest for the elusive zip that keeps hope eternal in the breast of the twister. Now, it would take quite a bit of persuading to make me pliable enough for a bit of wire to teach me much. I just say 'nuts' to the stuff and hope that all my patients will stay on the gold standard."

A recent column which has added reader interest to the dental quarterly is "Aside from the Chair." This was begun under the editorship of Dr. J. Millard Robertson, continued by Dr. Bill Hopkins and the present editor, Dr. Albert R. Drescher, with occasional guest columns from one of the districts. It is usually concerned with dental personalities and their hobbies: Dr. T. W. Sorrels, his fishing exploits; Dr. Ford E. Bridges, his interest in astronomy; Dr. L. A. Lucas, who has over four hundred toy elephants in his office; Dr. Roy G. Carl, his interest in guns and feats of marksmanship; Dr. J. A. Wells, his registered Herefords; Drs. Tom Granger and Leonard W. Cheek, their ranches; Drs. L. E. Tennis and C. B. McDonald, their golfing exploits; Drs. Mervin C. Howard, W. H.

Doyle, and J. P. Neal, their stables of trained horses; Dr. F. E. L. Thomas, his woodworking tools, the hundreds of toys he builds and turns over to the Salvation Army; Dr. Roy A. Sikkink and hand-made ship models; Drs. J. H. McHenry and James W. Mayfield, "Ham" radio operators; Dr. A. F. Sebert, maker of trout flies and bass lures; Dr. L. E. Church, ranching and interest in soil con-servation; Drs. Ed Granger and Robert Epperson, farming; Dr. A. M. Crowder, indefatigable lodge worker; Drs. Roger Meyer, Alva Hill, I. M. Lightner, Rolla C. Calkin, civic leaders; Dr. Charles Hess, his dental museum, years of school-board member-ship, and interest in the Boy Scout movement; Dr. Claude R. Swander, his Boy Scout work since 1929 that has won local, state, and national recognition; and H. L. Anderson for his club work.

Apparently every dentist has a hobby; Dr. Drescher has in-exhaustible sources of material to exploit on this subject for the *Journal*. These may be as diverse as the farming operations of J. O. Wynn, the beautiful, variegated beds of iris of Fred Seids, the trap-shooting ability of Bill Bryant, the realistic landscapes and other oil paintings of L. E. Glass, the globe-trotting ambassadors of good will for the governor and state, Noel Kaho and Ross E. Waltzer, the inventive genius of F. D. Stalford, or the energy and public spirit of L. D. Wright in his work in the Oklahoma City Chamber of Commerce. The list seemingly is endless; for example, C. E. Pyatt, Kingfisher, became a scoutmaster at Cheyenne in 1928 and has served in Boy Scout work continuously since that time. At one time he had the only mounted troop in scouting; in 1948 he received the Silver Beaver for services rendered in the Great Plains Council of Oklahoma. And Dr. Bruce D. Storm, Elk City, became an assistant scoutmaster in 1927. Still active in the movement, he was a member of the executive board of the Last Frontier Council in 1954; he received the Silver Beaver award in 1943.

Older members of the Association, however, recall how J. M. Temples, former president, moved from Tulsa to Joplin, Missouri, in 1916 because of his interest in minerals of the tri-state area. Dr. Temples found there the necessary elements to form the base of an effective powder for cleansing teeth. He formed the highly successful Py-co-pay Company and diverted his interests from dentistry to mining operations and civic work. He served Joplin as mayor during two terms.

Older members, too, recall an incident in the life of the late Dr. E. K. Mabry, who began general practice at Holdenville in 1907 and later limited his practice to become one of the state's first exodontists. The incident occurred at the time America was undergoing great social changes, a transition in dress and personal appearance. Women were discarding ankle-length dresses and high buttoned or laced shoes and cotton stockings for stockings of silk or lisle, shorter skirts, and pumps, and beginning that onslaught on barbershops that heralded a booming new business in the making, the art of using the tools and materials that flooded the market for facial make-up. Men, too, were replacing ankle-high buttoned or laced shoes for low-cut footwear, discarding heavy cumbersome pocket-watches with log-chain effects adorned with lodge emblems banded across their vests for wrist-watches, and derbies for fedoras, while struggling out of the detachable-shirt-collar era into the ease and convenience of the soft shirt, complete with collar.

Mabry began working on the detachable soft collar in 1913. Recently, Dr. J. V. Cruzan, who has practiced in Oklahoma City since 1908, related his knowledge of Mabry's experience: "I was in Holdenville August 16, 1915, and after visiting with Dr. Mabry for quite a while, learned he was very elated over the fact he had a check in his pocket for ten thousand dollars. Some time previously he had worked up an idea of a buttonhole that you did not have to put the collar button through. He sold the idea to the Earl and Wilson Shirt Corporation for fifteen thousand dollars. Ten thousand dollars were paid in cash and the remainder was to be paid in royalties as shirts incorporating the idea came off the production-line.

"Dr. Mabry took a trip to California and spent most of the ten thousand. On the way back to Oklahoma he stopped at Reno and did nothing to replenish the ten thousand. He then came to Oklahoma City and opened an office, fully expecting to receive five thousand in royalty payments. Meanwhile the soft shirt with attached collar came into use, so the doctor did not collect, but, needless to say, in dentistry he did."[11]

The other column, "Do You Remember —," citing a year in the annals of Oklahoma dentistry which was begun by Dr. Drescher and is now prepared by Dr. Don M. Ishmael, associate editor, is a brief summary of happenings that draw marked attention to past

[11] Letter from J. V. Cruzan to J. S. Clark, May 25, 1954.

achievements. This column and one that occasionally appears by Dr. Harry Sorrels called "Historical Bridges" are invaluable sources for material on the history of the Association.

An article under the caption "Not Just Dentistry," by Dr. J. B. Ratliff, Hobart, has appeared in each issue of the *Bulletin* since July, 1951. His first experience in practicing in the "short-grass" country deserves notice. Fresh from college in 1919, and awaiting the date to appear before the Board of Examiners, he came to Hobart and took over the practice of Dr. D. M. Brenneman, pioneer dentist who came there shortly after the town was established in 1901. Dr. Ratliff was to fill in while Dr. Brenneman took a deserved two-weeks vacation.

On the first day the young dentist was in charge, an early patient was an Indian, the town loafer. Dr. Ratliff, elated to begin practice so soon, patiently and carefully turned out a workmanlike job of filling and capping badly neglected teeth. Upon leaving the chair, the Indian grunted: "Huh! Pay 'em next week!" Soon another appeared, another and another until most of the two weeks were spent at the chair, and nights in the laboratory performing services on the promise: "Pay 'em next week!"

Dr. Brenneman returned. His young assistant told him how busy he had been. "For whom did you do all this work?" he inquired.

"For Indians," and Ratliff started calling off their names.

"But," interrupted the veteran dentist, "where are the orders from the Indian agent at Anadarko?"

Ratliff then learned facts about practice for restricted Indians: that there would be no "pay 'em next week," because the practice was unauthorized.

As his column indicates, topics he discusses in the *Bulletin* often wander far afield from dentistry but he best portrays the profession he loves and personalities in the profession. Here are excerpts, the first, from the October, 1951 *Bulletin:*

"Did you ever have a patient ask you why you chose dentistry as your life's work? Most people will admit that dentists are a necessary evil, but most of them can't understand why anyone would want to be one. I have often thought the same thing, especially after one of those days when every tooth you try to extract, breaks, and three or four old ladies you have made dentures for, come in with complaints about this or that.

"I expect most of you were influenced like I was by some dentist. In my case he was John Glass, Sr., now of Tulsa, who was practicing in Hobart when I was in high school. John devitalized and made a large inlay for my left upper first bicuspid (which I still have); put in a small gold foil in a cuspid, seven or eight alloy fillings, and cleaned my teeth.

"The whole bill was eighteen dollars.

"Right there was when I decided to become a dentist. Having chopped cotton for ten cents an hour, I figured that if a dentist could make that much money so easy, I was going to be one.

"Get John to tell you sometime how he landed in Hobart in 1908. All he had was a foot engine, a case of hand instruments, and ten dollars. He increased his capital the first night in a poker game, and decided to stay. John Glass believes in dentistry and has encouraged a number of young men, including his two sons, to study dentistry. Years ago, John used to introduce me to people as one of his boys. He stopped when I began to look older than he."

This, from the January, 1953 issue:

"Lake Murray Lodge is about the best place in Oklahoma to hold a district meeting, and South Central really put on a fine meeting there in October.

"As usual my old friend, C. B. Ball, was the chief worker. There are a lot of remarkable dentists in Oklahoma, but I believe Ball is near the top as a worker for the association.

"We have a good many men who do a lot for ethical dentistry (as Willard Ogle would say), over a period of a few years, then they get tired or something and drop out of the picture. Not Ball. He has been at it for about forty years and is still going strong.

"I became interested in dentistry while in high school, and used to clean John Glass's office. I think it was about 1915 that I acted as a kind of errand boy for the South Western district meeting in Hobart. Just as at Ardmore this year, Ball was one of the chief workers at that meeting in 1915. While there has been plenty of water under the bridge since then, Ball doesn't seem any older to me now than he did then.

"He started in Frederick in 1913, and was secretary of our district for ten years, and is the only man to ever hold the office of president twice. He was treasurer of the state association for five years, and was our state president in 1936. Then in 1945, when most men his age would be thinking of a rocking chair in the sun, Ball moved to Ardmore. He was elected president of the South Central district the first year and has been one of their best workers since.

"It is hard to believe, but the guy has never missed his district or state meeting in forty years. If anyone in the state can top that record I would like to hear about it. I know it is customary to wait until a fellow is dead to write something like this, but the way he is going I probably won't be around then, so I am paying my respects now. Since Ball was present at my first dental meeting, he will probably still be going strong at the last one I attend."

A favorite topic under "Not Just Dentistry" has been Smokey, the Ratliff's pet cat; a favorite colleague is Dr. Harry Sorrels. Both were topics for discussion in the October, 1951, issue of the *Bulletin:*

"I have always heard about the power of the press and the value of advertising. Personally I didn't pay much attention to either. I never advertised and while I read the editorials in the papers, I usually disagree with them, but for the past two years I have begun to realize the value of advertising. When our daughter, Louise, was in the second or third grade, a friend gave her a kitten. Because of its color she named it 'Smokey.' As usual in cases of that kind it turned out to be a female, and it wasn't long until we began to have more kittens than we could take care of. While Louise was home, through grade school, junior high, and high school, we had no trouble, as each time a new family of kittens arrived, she had them promised to friends. The trouble began when Louise went away to college and Smokey continued to produce. I finally became desperate and inserted the following ad in the local paper: 'For Adoption: To those who can furnish proper references five part Persian kittens. Their mother 'Smokey' is one of the most highly respected cats in our neighborhood. Can't say so much for their father.' The result was startling. I believe we could have given away twenty kittens if Smokey had had that many. A few months later when Smokey's next family came along, I inserted the following ad: 'No birth control for Smokey. She has four more part Persian kittens that she would like to place in good homes.' Then a few months later another ad, as follows: 'Smokey is getting old and is losing her teeth, but hasn't lost her enthusiasm. She still has two of her last family of kittens to be placed in good homes.' The last two ads brought the same result as the first, only more so. We now have a waiting list for Smokey's families. I am happy to report that Smokey is still doing her part. She gave birth to three beautiful part Persian kittens sometime during the state meeting. I have no idea how much longer she will continue to increase the cat population of Hobart, but as long as she can stand it, I guess we can.

"Another thing I can't get enthused about is the seven thousand dollar history book that everyone but me voted for at the annual business meeting. Anyway I have a suggestion for Harry and his Special Historical Committee. If we ever have a dental museum, I know something that should be placed in it. Charlie Hess wouldn't part with it any time soon but he might leave it to a dental museum in his will. I am referring to his old Oliver typewriter. Anyone who has ever received a letter from Charlie in the past thirty or forty years will know what I am talking about. That typewriter has a personality all its own. If you have ever seen its old bold faced type, you will never forget it. Charlie is famous for his five beautiful daughters, and the fact he has saved all the teeth he has ever extracted. He should also be known as the fellow who owns the oldest usable typewriter in Oklahoma.

"I wonder what Harry Sorrels will take up when he is finished with this history of Oklahoma dentistry he has been working on so long. Usually as a person gets older it becomes harder to get enthused about things. He usually even loses interest in things that seemed very important when he was younger. Harry is an exception. I have known him a long time, and he is always enthused about something. He is a natural born organizer and promoter and isn't happy unless at work organizing or promoting something. Harry has done some fine things for our Association and deserves a lot of credit. I know some of the obstacles he has had to overcome in promoting this history and I don't believe any other member could have put it over. If you attended the last annual business meeting, you witnessed a good example of his salesmanship. He started out by saying he wasn't trying to sell the Association on the history, but it turned out to be one of the best sales talks I ever heard. It must have been because I didn't hear any 'no' votes except mine, and he almost made me feel like a heel for voting against him. I predict that it won't be long until Harry will find something else to promote, and when he does, I think I will be one of the first to fall in line. Might as well.

"It seems that Harry Sorrels is kinda monopolizing this column, but since I wrote the above, I have received a copy of his latest work. It is in the form of letters, supposed to be written to a senior in dental college giving advice on conducting a successful practice. It is the finest thing of its kind I have ever read and should be required reading for every dental college senior in the country. I have underestimated Harry. I thought the history was taking all his effort, but it seems he was working on these letters at the same time, and believe me it took a lot of work. Where does the guy get all the energy?"

Principal element, however, that has brought the dental quarterly journal status is the inclusion of scientific articles contributed by members of the Association. When Dr. C. R. Lawrence first began publication of the quarterly in 1911, and for many years thereafter, its major use was to create interest in annual meetings and growth of membership of the Society. Scientific articles by out-of-state clinicians were rare, as though added as an afterthought for space fillers. Still later, a series of articles by Dr. Al Walters on nutrition centered state attention on the subject. These were followed by articles by Dr. J. B. Jenkins on the use of X ray, Dr. T. W. Sorrels on orthodontia, and Dr. F. B. Reichmann on oral surgery—an indication Oklahoma dentistry had a story worthy of telling.

In January, 1942, Dr. L. A. Lucas made the first of a series of contributions on "Root Canal Therapy" and "Endodontics" that mark him one of the nation's outstanding specialists in dentistry; Dr. Scott P. Bowyer contributed to articles on "Exodontia" in the mid-forties, and the versatile veteran Al Walters prepared for publication in the July, 1946, *Bulletin* an article on "Prophylaxis" that brought national recognition.

When the Association formally approved the position of executive secretary, one of the many duties assigned the officer was to act as managing editor of the dental quarterly. Fortunately, the position has been filled by young men trained in journalism: Richard H. Tunnicliff, June, 1947, to August 1, 1948; H. Leon Snow to May, 1952; and Bill Howard, present incumbent. These employees of the Association have been directed and assisted by editors chosen from members of the organization.

Dr. Eugene W. Wise, Tulsa, edited the *Bulletin* during the period he was state secretary, 1941–48, with assistance from Dr. T. W. Sorrels. His was the last term in which the Society secretary was responsible for editing the publication. At the April, 1948, meeting in Tulsa, Dr. Wise was honored by his associates through elevation to the office of president-elect although he was ill and unable to attend the convention. This was his last illness; he died June 1.

Dr. T. W. Sorrels continued as associate editor another year while a group of earnest, hard-working younger members of the Oklahoma County Dental Society began to assume more responsibility for the publication. Drs. J. Millard Robertson, Bill Hopkins, and Albert Drescher deserve chief credit for the merit of the publication. Outstanding advances were made in format and content after H. Leon Snow was appointed executive secretary; the high calibre of the publication has been maintained by Bill Howard. Dr. J. Millard Robertson was editor for issues July, 1948, through April, 1949; Dr. Bill Hopkins, July, 1949, through April, 1951; and Dr. Albert R. Drescher for more recent issues. During the six-year period, however, all have alternated as associate editor and served on the editorial board, working in close harmony to produce a superior professional journal. Other members of the editorial board have been Dr. Don M. Ishmael, Dr. Robert G. Hirschi, and Dr. Frank W. Stewart.

Occasionally the editors include articles that are reprints from other journals, and also presentations made by out-of-state guests, but the great strength of the magazine rests upon scientific articles of research by Oklahoma dentists. Recent contributions have included an article by Dr. T. A. Jones, who began practice in territorial days; articles of general interest by Dr. Noel Kaho and Dr. T. H. Miley; learned articles by Drs. John G. Leftwich, L. A. Lucas, Dan E. Brannin, Frank Stewart, Carl Schow, Robert G. Hirschi, Eugene W. Lewis, Don M. Ishmael, Norton L. Wheeler, Douglas A. Yeager, William B. Swartz, Sumner Russman, Earl R. Cunningham, O. Gordon Sullivan, William H. Rose, Martin F. Anderson, W. H. Cooper, and David E. Heller. All specialties are under study, and articles appearing in the *Journal* attest to the interest of able young dentists in making improvements in their profession and their willingness to share their findings with others. And since the late 1930's, articles by Frank Bertram on preventive dentistry have appeared in the publication as a medium to keep the profession aware of public responsibility in this field of dentistry. Invaluable additions to the literature of dentistry are being made by Oklahoma dentists through the pages of the *Journal*.

CHAPTER ELEVEN

Looking Ahead

— I —

D R. REICHMANN stated in an interview in 1953: "Professional relationship is the most important thing in a professional man's life." The Oklahoma State Dental Association has grown strong on this premise; through district and state meetings experiences have been shared among colleagues and the best talent of the state and nation has brought new ideas and techniques to the membership.

Dr. Theo P. Bringhurst, president of the Oklahoma Territorial Dental Association in 1906, contrasted meetings of that era with the 1954 session: "In 1904 I was secretary of the Territorial Association, charged with arranging the annual program to be held in Shawnee. In those days good clinic material had to be obtained principally from members of the faculties of dental schools. Dr. C.N. Johnson, Chicago, and Dr. Thomas P. Hinman, Atlanta, accepted our invitation. Both were later honored by the national association presidency, and years later appeared as instructors in our postgraduate plan of instruction. From Atlanta, too, came Dr. William Crenshaw of the Atlanta Dental College, and from Nashville came Dr. Joseph P. Gray, dean of the Dental Department, University of Tennessee. The Kansas City schools sent the McMillens, Drury J., Harry, and Frank; Dr. J. P. Root, and Dr. F. G. Worthley, all of whom honored many similar meetings after statehood. The only guest on the program engaged in private practice was young Willis A. Coston of Ft. Scott, Kansas, who, even then, was recognized as a leader in the profession. Now, consider the contrast. We can still go to the colleges for guest instructors, but our profession has developed leaders in private practice upon whom we can depend and look for guidance. How happy I am that last year I had the good fortune to hear young Dr. Douglas A. Yeager of the Oklahoma County Society on the subject 'Periodontoclasia,' and this morning Dr. L. A. Lucas on 'Dental Roentgenology.' We have learned to use our best home talent and this is typical of our district meetings. The dentist is no longer merely a plugger of cavities and the puller of teeth, but he is a medical man with great knowledge of oral pathology."[1]

Although district and state meetings have been of incalculable value in raising the general level of professional service, additional means are being used to advance professional growth. In 1949 the University of Illinois began a telephone course in dentistry. Members of local societies at Tulsa, Enid, Shawnee, and Oklahoma City have gathered at convenient centers, arranged with the local telephone company for an amplifier, and listened to lectures originating in Chicago delivered by national authorities.

Local study groups, too, hold regular meetings throughout the year and observe clinics, listen to guest speakers, and give reviews or abstracts from current dental literature in order to keep abreast of latest developments. Enid, Oklahoma City, and Tulsa dentists have carried on this practice for years. Outstanding among the smaller groups has been the Payne County Study Club. Dr. C. A. Ruhlen, Cushing, president of the state association, 1923–24, originated the study club idea at that time. Currently active members of the Payne County Study Club include Drs. Lloyd P. Buikstra, C. R. Swander, Thomas F. Harrison, and George F. Bolinger, Cushing; Dr. P. F. Henson, Yale; Drs. E. L. Moore, J. W. Childs, A. E. Buikstra, Harry Glover, Raymond Beauchamp, William D. Harold, Howard B. Sherrod, Taylor Scott, David E. Heller, and Lionel B. Bair, Stillwater. Similar small groups engaged in specialized study will add to professional growth and fraternal understanding.

This intense concern with professional development is reflected by interest in the Oklahoma Medical Research Foundation. The institution is too new, its possibilities too great, to prophesy its accomplishments, but Dr. Paul W. Goaz, Dental Research Fellow for the Foundation, recently offered these comments. ". . . Dentistry

[1] Theo P. Bringhurst to J. S. Clark, May 6, 1954, in files of Central Office, Oklahoma State Dental Association.

will become more and more appreciative of the need and value of preventive procedures and there will be a slow swing away from purely restorative dentistry to preventive dentistry. This is becoming especially evident now that we are getting down to basic dental research and preventive measures appear to be conceivable and within the realm of possibility.

"Any changes or progress in dentistry will come as the result of changes in dental education. The dental schools have the responsibility of training men so they may be capable of participating in the growth of dentistry along scientific and biologic lines. They will be trained to understand and interpret local and systemic factors of health and disease, and will be able to utilize all available biological knowledge in the solution of dental problems.

". . . My impression of dentistry in the next fifty years is not one of a medical specialty, but as a necessary collaborator with physicians who have come to recognize the fact that dental consultation is something as indispensable to the physician as is the medical consultation to the dentist. We can then expect that this co-operative association will enhance the vigor and usefulness of both professions and hasten the solution of important problems that are common to both."[2]

Evidences of this spirit of co-operation have been cited; in recent years the Oklahoma dental and medical associations have exchanged clinicians and speakers at stated meetings. In 1946, Dr. Michael J. Welsh of San Diego lectured at Oklahoma City to members, wives, and assistants of both organizations on nutrition as a factor in the health of people. He appeared again the following year before the associations, with Dr. Francis M. Pottinger, Jr., of Monrovia, California, and Dr. Douglas Gordon Campbell of San Francisco. In 1948, Dr. William A. Albrecht of Columbia, Missouri, addressed a joint meeting on soil deficiencies that result in health impairment. And the cancer symposia of 1947 pointed up mutual responsibilities toward this dreaded affliction.

Dr. Frank Stewart, Oklahoma City, in a discussion of "Cancer and the General Practitioner," which appeared in the *Journal*, July, 1953, elaborated on the responsibility dentists have toward their patients in the first phase of discovery and diagnosis of mouth can-

[2] Paul W. Goaz to Harry H. Sorrels, October 27, 1953, in files of Central Office, Oklahoma State Dental Association.

cer. He warned: "The progress of cancer in the mouth and the oropharynx is often quite rapid. Often, within two to four weeks, a small cancer of the mouth may be transformed from a localized lesion into one that is infiltrating. Delay in determining the nature of either small nodular lesions or fissures, because of failure to evaluate the clinical data and to do a biopsy, has permitted many an early and easily treatable cancer to reach an advanced stage of metastasis." Dr. Stewart pointed out that when a malignant tumor first appears in the gums, the hard palate, the edge of the tongue or the cheek, the location of the lesion and the mild character of the symptoms usually suggest to the patient the apparent trouble originates with the teeth. Probably, he stated, 80 per cent of deaths caused by cancer of the mouth could be averted by early diagnosis and adequate treatment. With increasing awareness by the public of the dangers from cancer, the general practitioner performs a real service by calling to the attention of the patient all abnormalities of the mouth. He not only centers attention upon the abnormality but insists that remediable action be taken.

Dr. Goaz in his comments on the future of dentistry stressed the increasing demands of formal college training, a subject of much interest to the Oklahoma State Dental Association. Looking backward, it is difficult to define how near the Association has come to a realization of the dream of a dental college. Only conjecture can indicate why the Billupp Bill in the first session of the legislature was killed which would have established a College of Dentistry in the University of Oklahoma School of Medicine. More certainly the Epworth College of Dentistry was doomed by the schism of Methodism and the financial straits of Epworth University. Twenty years later Dr. W. B. Bizzell, president of the University of Oklahoma, visualized a state-supported dental school, but the vision vanished with the depression years.

The need for a dental college is constantly being appraised; the solution, not readily apparent. A temporary expedient was worked out during the administration of Governor Roy J. Turner in 1951 through the Southern Regional Education Board. Oklahoma belongs to a compact formed by Southern states wherein various states accept students from other members who have no educational facilities in veterinary medicine, medicine, dentistry, and social work.[3] The home states of students provide funds for out-of-state tuition;

in dentistry, this amounts to $1,500 a year. Five Oklahoma dental students, two of whom are Negro, have been attending southern schools under this plan. However, Turner's successor, Governor Johnston Murray, failed to provide state funds for a continuation of the program. At best, it has been only a gesture toward present dental educational needs. There were 168 Oklahomans studying dentistry in twenty-one out-of-state colleges in 1954, but experience indicates that not all of them will return to the state after completing their courses. More attractive opportunities, because of the national shortage of dentists, usually beckon in the state or locale where they spend their four years of formal education.

The average dentist in Oklahoma in 1950 was over fifty years of age—one of the highest age averages in the nation.[4] There was one dentist in the state for every 2,788 persons, and the ratio is expected to improve only slightly in future years; nation-wide the ratio is 1 to 2,200. More serious, perhaps, is the unequal distribution of dental man power in the state. The population of Oklahoma in 1950 was 2,233,351. Of this number 1,100,285 resided in thirteen counties which have a land area of 10,833 square miles. The remaining sixty-four counties with a land area of 58,148 square miles had 1,133,066 inhabitants. Density of population in the thirteen counties was 101.1 per square mile; in the sixty-four counties, 19.5. Twenty-six counties have from 0 to 2 dentists in practice per county.

Members of the Association are still hopeful that, at some future date, the state will add a dental school to present medical facilities. One of the last official acts of Dr. Rolla C. Calkin, presiding at the April, 1954, annual convention, was to present to the membership a proposition for a survey on dental needs in Oklahoma. Dr. Albert E. Bonnell, Jr., announced in midsummer that the United States Public Health Service of the Department of Health, Education, and Welfare would undertake the survey to determine whether or not dental-training facilities should be established. It has been estimated that physical equipment for a school capable of handling 150 students will cost about $1,500,000, and the annual expense will be $400,000.

[3] Statement of Dr. Mel Nash, chancellor, Board of Regents of Higher Education, State Capitol, Oklahoma City, to J. S. Clark, April 10, 1954.

[4] "State's Dentist Shortage Cited in School Plea," *Sunday Oklahoman* (Oklahoma City), January 17, 1954, Section A, p. 11.

Dr. James R. Miller reported in August, 1954, that basic standards for hospital service at the University and Crippled Childrens' Hospitals had been approved by the Council on Hospital Service of the American Dental Association. Dr. F. J. Reichmann reported to the Executive Council on July 17 that he felt the National Advisory Dental Research Council would make a favorable report on the dental research project presented by the Oklahoma Medical Research Foundation. If the project is accepted for financial support, it will almost double the dental research at the Foundation.[5]

The young man or woman in Oklahoma who wants to prepare for a career in dentistry finds it is an expensive undertaking. Present costs for out-of-state tuition vary from $620 to $1,200 per year. Most schools require a minimum of ninety college semester hours for admission and accept only students of Junior class standing who successfully pass aptitude tests and are above average rank. Four years of additional study are required for graduation.

In addition to the financial drain necessary to obtain a degree, the young dentist enters a profession that requires a minimum investment in equipment and facilities in excess of $7,500. Dr. E. E. Sanger, who has had a son and daughter receive dental degrees and has another son in dental college, commented last summer that a dentist at the turn of the century with a foot engine, a spool-case for his instruments, and a cutaway coat, standard equipment of the time, could open an office and treat any ills of the oral cavity. New and advanced equipment, X-ray machines, drugs and materials, office space and furnishings place a heavier financial burden upon the dentist than that imposed upon other professional men.

In recent years, dentists, like members of other professions, have established their practice in bungalow offices in suburban areas; many have office and home under the same roof. In the larger cities where parking accommodations are more convenient away from the downtown area, the professional man can become a working member of the residential community where he establishes his office, belong to the local P.-T.A., luncheon clubs in the immediate area, attend a church in the neighborhood, and broaden his acquaintance among the businessmen and home owners where he lives.

Dr. A. B. Walker likes to remind colleagues that his was the

[5] *News Letter*, Oklahoma State Dental Association, August 1, 1954 (Oklahoma City).

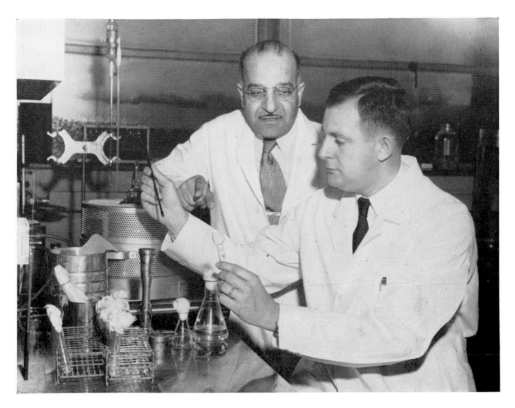

Rallying Point of Oklahoma Dentistry—
"That more may live longer."
Paul W. Goaz, D.D.S., and Charles D. Kochakian, Ph.D., work together at the Oklahoma Research Foundation, Oklahoma City.

Mike Smith, Taft Junior High School   Judy Flow, Northeast Junior High School

Oklahoma City "Smile of the Year" Winners, 1955

This contest, launched by the Oklahoma County District Dental Society to focus the attention of the community on the full meaning of National Children's Dental Health Day, has been established as an annual event in the junior high schools.

first bungalow office in Oklahoma Territory: a 12x12 unpainted building erected on the dusty, wind-blown main street of Fairview in 1902. Certainly the dispersal to residential areas is not new: In 1921, Dr. J. R. Caughron moved his office out on West Tenth Street in Oklahoma City, the first to leave the downtown, upstairs type of office. When Dr. Charles Hess moved from Idabel to Durant in 1934, it was into a modern bungalow-type office. Regardless of who established the pattern, it has been followed with increasing favor in recent years; in many instances the office stands alone on a residential street or well-traveled avenue; at other points it may be part of a medical group adjoining the office of a pediatrician, gynecologist, obstetrician, or general practitioner. At all points it is attractively and efficiently arranged, modern in design, and conveniently located at street level.

This trend becomes more apparent from the following statistics. The most recent telephone directory for Oklahoma City lists the office addresses of 155 dentists: 72 of the listings are out of the downtown areas of the city and Capitol Hill. The Tulsa directory lists 142, with only 85 in the heart of the city. The trend is equally pronounced in the smaller cities. District news in any of the recent *Journals* of the Association carry new listings. The October, 1953, issue, for example, lists five: Dr. Rhame Wood's, Nowata; Dr. J. G. Gerard's, Dewey; Dr. Vic Holdreith's, Chickasha; Dr. Kenneth Shepard's, Chickasha; and Dr. W. D. Atkins', Holdenville. Approximately one dental office in four in the state is now at street level, and the trend toward attractive bungalow offices may be expected to continue.

It has been stressed that in looking ahead toward better dentistry in Oklahoma, public education must play a vital part, and a chief factor will be the leadership and aids furnished by the State Department of Public Health.

A State Board of Health was created in 1945, composed of eight members appointed by the governor. Members served staggered terms in order to assure exemption from domination by any politically minded chief executive; this assures appointees in the state department freedom from political domination. Dentistry has always been represented on the Board of Health; first by Dr. Fred Seids, Perry, more recently by Dr. O. R. Whiteneck, Enid.

Dr. Frank P. Bertram, who has been in charge of the Division of Preventive Dentistry in the Health Department since 1936, recently explained some of the accomplishments and aims of the state agency: "After leaving the University Hospital following my year's residency in 1930, I practiced here in Oklahoma City until 1936. At that time I became interested in the public health program, which, prior to that time, had not had a dentist directing that phase of the program. Public health work was directed in the State Public Health Department by nurses and educators who conducted dental health educational programs. With the addition of federal funds, through grants-in-aid of public health funds to states, it was thought timely and proper to start the Division of Preventive Dentistry in the State Health Department. This was done by administrative act of the State Health Commissioner. I was employed to develop the program.

"Of course, I've seen quite a lot of changes. We've learned a great deal about preventive dentistry. There have been remarkably significant changes and discoveries which portend much better dental health for the public generally. It has been a pleasure to be part of that program.

"Incidentally, Oklahoma has made its contribution to these new discoveries. We have had excellent research men who have contributed to the knowledge and science of dentistry.

"We have been geographically fortunate in having a wide variety of geological formations; waters have different types of minerals that contribute to different carious and dental conditions over the state.

"Guymon is in an area where the chemical, fluorine, is prevalent in the water, which gives children a natural immunity to dental decay. In fact, they have a little too much fluorine in the water out there, and Dr. I. M. Lightner has a very apt description for the teeth, which he calls 'pinto teeth.' They are colored like a pinto pony, when fluorine is too high. We strive to control the fluorine content of water to one part per million. Out in the Panhandle of Oklahoma a lot of those waters will run two and three parts per million; this causes the mottling of enamel and results in the 'pinto' appearance, as Dr. Lightner calls it.

"The Panhandle isn't the only area in Oklahoma with waters of high fluoride content. Water supplies for Blue Jacket, and Maud, a number of oil camps near Fox and Healdton are high in content.

El Reno and Miami run exactly right—one part per million. This ratio reduces decay among children at least one-half and gives adults some immunity also."

It has previously been mentioned that nine Oklahoma cities now add fluorine to community water supplies. Other cities installing equipment or making plans for the fluoridation of water supplies in 1954 were Alva, Chickasha, Holdenville, Ponca City, and Tonkawa. When these cities are added to the group already using the fluorine process, more than one-fifth of the state's population will benefit, especially children who from infancy can enjoy this protective measure. Annual per capita costs vary from four to fourteen cents; the average, about nine cents. Education of the public by local dentists and physicians should assure more widespread adoption of fluoridation throughout the state in communities where the fluorine content of water is below the ratio of one to one million parts.

The legal right of a city to add the fluoridation process to municipal water has been thoroughly tested in Oklahoma courts.[6] The Tulsa city council passed Ordinance 6565 on March 3, 1953, authorizing fluoridation. The ordinance was to become effective upon its passage, approval, and publication. Certain taxpayers of Tulsa attacked it as an unwarranted exercise of police power in violation of the Fourteenth Amendment to the Constitution, as an exercise of power beyond that delegated to the city by the state legislature, on the grounds that it was an infringement on freedom of religion, and that it violated the provision of Section 196, Title 63 of the Compiled Statutes of Oklahoma in 1951, which forbids the manufacture and sale of "food" to which "fluorine compounds" have been added. Section 183 of the act defines "food" as "articles of food, meat, drink . . . beverage . . . ."

Judge Elmer Adams, District Court of Tulsa, ruled against the plaintiffs, who appealed to the Supreme Court. The right of the city to issue the ordinance was sustained in every particular; pertinent comments in the unanimous decision were: "We think the weight of well-reasoned modern precedent sustains the right of municipalities to adopt such reasonable and undiscriminating

---

[6] *Dowell et al* v. *City of Tulsa*, case # 36068, Supreme Court of Oklahoma, reported in the *Journal* of the Oklahoma Bar Association, Vol. XXV, No. 24 (June 19, 1954), 1168–74.

measures to improve their water supplies as are necessary to protect and improve the public health, even though no epidemic is imminent and no contagious disease or virus is directly involved.

"As knowledge in both the medical and dental fields has increased, the subject of health in both these spheres has become more important, and modern experience shows that private convenience and individual freedom of action are required to yield to the public good in instances where formerly there was observed no necessity for legislative interference."

The plaintiffs conceded that cities had the right to chlorinate water to kill germs and purify water, but contended that treatment of water with fluorides was an unlicensed practice of medicine. The court held: "We think that if the putting of chlorides in public water supplies will in fact promote the public health, the distinction sought to be drawn by plaintiffs is immaterial. To us it seems ridiculous and of no consequence in considering the public health phase of the case that the substance to be added to the water may be classed as a mineral rather than a drug, antiseptic, or germ killer. ... There can be no distinction on principle between [fluoridation] and compulsory vaccination or inoculation which, for many years, has been well established as a valid exercise of police power."

". . . The relation of dental hygiene to the health of the body generally is now so well recognized as to warrant judicial notice. Accordingly we hold that in establishing the fluoridation prescribed in Ordinance 6565, as effective to reduce dental caries, the evidence also sufficiently established it, as a health measure, to be a proper subject for exercise of the police power possessed by the City of Tulsa."

The plaintiffs had also alleged that fluoridation was a violation of the First Amendment to the Constitution of the United States, which includes, among its provisions, freedom of religion. The allegation was based on the premise that the use of medicine is abjured by certain religious sects or faiths. In disposing of this charge, the court held: "In contemplating fluoridation the City of Tulsa is no more practicing medicine or dentistry or manufacturing, preparing, compounding or selling a drug, than a mother would be who furnishes her children a well-balanced diet including vitamin D and calcium to harden bones and prevent rickets, or lean meat and milk to prevent pellagra." It appears, therefore, that if city ordinances in Oklahoma are properly drawn, no legal obstacles can be interposed to fluoridation.

The Division of Preventive Dentistry, in co-operation with the University of Oklahoma, recently made a twelve-minute health-education film, "Target Tooth Decay," which received the approval of the Council on Dental Health of the American Dental Association. Several state health departments have purchased prints of the film, and dental associations, including those of Puerto Rico and Hawaii, use the film in dental health programs.

Dr. Bertram gives public health lectures on preventive dentistry to members of the Junior and Senior classes of the medical school; he and his staff meet with workshop groups during the summer months at teachers' colleges and universities; unnumbered appearances are made before parent-teacher associations and civic groups each year. Only a limitation in state appropriations will narrow the range of achievement.

Another goal of the Association is the improvement of dental conditions among inmates of state eleemosynary and charitable institutions. Dr. B. C. Thompson, McAlester, conducted a survey in 1950 which revealed glaring deficiencies in dental care of patients.[7] The Eastern State Hospital, Vinita, has offered inmates dental service since 1925; a full-time dentist has been employed at the Central State Hospital, Norman, since 1929. In that year a dentist was employed and quarters furnished at the Western State Hospital, Fort Supply; after World War II, although population of the institution was above 1,300, dental service has been available only for one-half day per week. Since 1945, Dr. Louis R. Richardson has been employed at Enid; at the Pauls Valley State Hospital a local dentist spends one afternoon a week at the institution and two hours

[7] Correspondence Covering the Work of the Committee on Institutions, April 14, 1950. This collection is in the files of the Central Office, Oklahoma State Dental Association. At the time the survey was made the following dentists were serving state institutions on a full or part-time basis: B. C. Singleton, Central State Hospital, Norman; Willis C. Reed, Eastern Oklahoma State Hospital, Vinita; Thomas L. Richardson, Enid State School, Enid; James P. Neville, Oklahoma State Penitentiary, McAlester; Thomas M. Lansden, Oklahoma State Reformatory, Granite; F. W. Cates, Oklahoma State Tuberculosis Sanatorium, Talihina; Dougal McKellar, Veterans' Hospital, Sulphur; W. H. Goldsbury, Pauls Valley State Hospital, Pauls Valley; Lloyd E. Church, Western Oklahoma Tuberculosis Sanatorium, Clinton; T. N. Niles, Western State Hospital, Fort Supply; and Earl T. Davis, Whitaker State Home for White Children, Pryor.

each week at his office making extractions and fillings and impressions for dentures.

The Western Oklahoma Tuberculosis Sanatorium, Clinton, depends upon a private practitioner who devotes from one to one and one-half hours per week to practice for the inmates. At the State Tuberculosis Sanatorium, Talihina, similar inadequate care is maintained by the state.

Adequate dental care has been maintained at the Whitaker State Home, Pryor. Dr. H. H. Taylor, local dentist, checked the mouth of every child in 1948, and in the summer of 1949 the federal mobile dental clinic visited the home to treat the teeth of all the children with sodium fluoride. One morning each week is reserved by Dr. Taylor for children from the home.

The Oklahoma State Penitentiary, McAlester, employs a dentist on a full-time basis. The Oklahoma State Reformatory, Granite; Boys' Town, Stringtown; Girls' Town, Tecumseh; State Training School for Negro Boys, Boley; the Hospital for the Negro Insane, and the Consolidated Negro Institution, Taft, offer only part-time dental services for inmates, limited to extractions and fillings.

Dr. Willis C. Reed, Vinita, in a letter dated April 13, 1950, explained the nature of his practice at the local institution: "The Eastern Oklahoma Hospital for Insane has 2,600 patients. Dental service was started on a part-time basis in 1925. I go out one morning each week for the male patients and one morning each week for the female patients. Some restorative work is done although most is emergency work. I am paid a monthly salary of $90.00 for this work.

"A special office is fixed-up for this work, with chair and dental engine, cabinet, etc.—very meager facilities but I have managed with what they have provided. I work in the office about an hour and a half and then go to any ward where there is to be an emergency extraction, etc., when the patient is too violent or infirm to bring to the office."

Dr. W. L. Shamel, Sulphur, wrote, March 21, 1950, in regard to the Veterans Hospital there: "The Soldiers' Hospital was built in 1921–22, with funds provided by the state legislature, as a lasting memorial to the service men, in lieu of a bonus. It opened in November, 1922. It is state operated and accepts veterans of all wars. It has a well-equipped dental office in the administration building. I served the hospital from 1922 to 1935; Dr. John Williams of Durant, from 1935 to 1940; Dr. Dougal McKellar of Ardmore since that date. The dental position is a part-time job, ranging from one to two days a week. A straight salary is paid to cover extractions, fillings, etc., with an additional fee for each set of dentures inserted."

In 1946 a leading newspaper of the state assigned a young reporter, Mike Gorman, the task of investigating mental institutions of the state. Gorman made a thorough investigation. Then he wrote of what he saw. Article followed article in the *Daily Oklahoman* on the injustices and inhumanity toward the afflicted ones, the overcrowded dormitories, inadequate recreational facilities, and other faults and shortcomings. Thus the people of the state became aware of the "shame of Oklahoma." An aroused citizenry acted. The legislature made appropriations and created the Mental Health Board as a move toward cleaning up the mess. When appropriations proved inadequate, the people of Oklahoma responded to the pleas of Governor Roy J. Turner and in a special election September 27, 1949, approved a proposal for a bond issue for the purpose of constructing, equipping, remodeling, and repairing state buildings. Monies thus provided brought more adequate, modern housing to the inmates and personnel of the mental and eleemosynary institutions, and in 1950 Oklahoma was nationally recognized for making the greatest strides of any state toward care of mental patients within the past decade.

But Oklahoma cannot rest upon past laurels. Dr. Hayden Donahue, director, Mental Health Board, faces the problem of getting qualified dentists willing to work in the institutions for the chronically ill. He, too, will need the full co-operation of the Association in educating state legislators on the importance of dental care for inmates and of providing adequate salaries for properly trained and qualified personnel. The problem will worsen as institutional population increases. In 1900, 4 per cent of our population was 65 or over; in 1940, about 8 per cent; and it has been estimated that in 1975 the percentage will be above 11 per cent. Rest homes and institutional care for the aged will proportionately increase.

The Association has a Mental Health Committee pledged to help Dr. Donahue present institutional needs to the legislature. Present members are Noel Kaho, Claremore; T. L. Richardson and

E. A. Abernethy, Enid; Roy Gravelle, Norman; Wilbur G. White-neck, Woodward; W. L. Rhodes, Pauls Valley; Billy A. Jones, Vinita; Otto Hine, Muskogee; and Rolla C. Calkin, Guthrie. The committee looks forward to the installation of modern dental equipment in each hospital, a competent staff trained in psychosomatic dentistry, the establishment of dental internships in the mental hospitals, and a central laboratory. When Oklahoma attains these objectives, it will have made greater advances in this field than any other state.[8]

Industrial dentistry has not been entirely neglected in Oklahoma.[9] The Marland Oil Company, Ponca City, established a dental division with complete dental equipment in the 1920's, and Dr. Fred Sparks was employed on a full-time basis to administer to dental needs. All new employees were given a complete dental check-up, including X ray of teeth; permanent employees were examined annually. Later, when this company merged into the Continental Oil Company, a policy was adopted that limited detailed annual check-ups to company executives and supervisors. At present Dr. C. A. Northcutt is in charge of this practice. Records kept in this pioneer field indicate that the company made a sound investment in health of employees and man-hours saved for productive employment.

The Oklahoma Publishing Company, Oklahoma City, established in 1940 a well-equipped dental office for Dr. N. Dea Griffith, who devoted one hour a day to dental X-ray and making diagnoses for all new employees. Other employees who desire dental check-ups are likewise accorded the privilege. In all cases when dental care is suggested, employees make their own decisions in regard to remedial action and individual choice of dentist.

Thousands of Oklahomans in the armed services became aware of the importance of dental care, but industrial firms of Oklahoma have not explored its neglect as a factor in man-years lost from productive activity. Progress should be expected in this phase of preventive and corrective dentistry. Education, analysis, and action should bring a changed attitude.

[8] Noel Kaho to Harry Sorrels, July 24, 1954, in the Files of the Central Office, Oklahoma State Dental Association.

[9] "History of Industrial Dentistry in Oklahoma," prepared by Dr. L. A. Lucas, December 8, 1949. This manuscript is in the files of the Central Office, Oklahoma State Dental Association.

The Council on Dental Health in a report, "The Role of Dentistry in Chronic Illness," in the June, 1954, issue of the *Journal of the American Dental Association,* page 692, summarized this point of view: "Most dental diseases can be prevented from becoming chronic. Malocclusion caused by premature loss of teeth and undesirable habits can be prevented, and malocclusion that is hereditary in origin usually can be controlled. Dental fluorosis can be prevented by a change in the water supply or through a treatment process to remove the excess fluorides from the water. Chronic gingivitis can be prevented through hygienic measures and the removal of predisposing factors.

"Advanced periodontal disease, at least that which is local in origin, can be prevented, largely through proper control during early stages. Because of the lack of information about the etiology of periodontosis, however, preventive measures are not well defined.

"The chronic phases of Vincent's disease can be prevented through early and complete treatment of the acute condition. Growth patterns that result in malocclusion, even those that are of a hereditary nature, can be interrupted and changed at the appropriate time and with proper treatment need not become 'chronic.' Many of the changes related to senescence that result in loss of function can be prevented or largely alleviated by timely and adequate treatment so that the changes need not necessarily contribute to a chronic condition. It is obvious that dental conditions resulting from occupational situations can be prevented through proper precautions in the working environment.

"Dental caries can be prevented to a significant extent through the use of fluorides and restrictions of sweets in the diet and can be controlled by early restorations of carious teeth. The prevention of dental caries will result in prevention of pulpitis and periapical infection with the minor exception of pulp and periapical disease resulting from traumatic exposure of the pulp or to embolic infection by way of the blood stream."

One of the most active professional organizations in Oklahoma is the Oklahoma Medical, Dental, and Pharmaceutical Association. This Association of Negroes interested in the healing arts was founded in 1908, and as of September, 1953, included the following dentists in active practice: Drs. H. W. Williamson, Idabel; P. W. Sawyer, Lawton; E. L. Leech, McAlester; F. O. Smith,

H. E. Tollett, D. E. Wallace, Muskogee; Byron Biscoe, Frank B. Cox, J. M. Littlepage, W. L. Moore, H. S. Palmore, T. J. Randolph, V. Tomkins Dowell, Oklahoma City; S. E. Kimbrough, J. J. McKeever, W. L. Harrison, James F. Deal, Tulsa; A. C. Sales, Wewoka; R. B. Taylor, Sr., and R. B. Taylor, Jr., Okmulgee. State meetings are held during the second week of May, in turn at Oklahoma City, Tulsa, Okmulgee, and Muskogee, and, since professional and scientific ability is not limited by race, outstanding lecturers and clinicians of both races appear on programs.

The father-son combination of the Drs. Taylor practicing at Okmulgee is not unusual. All over Oklahoma a tradition of family practice has developed. Sons—and sometimes, daughters—have followed fathers into the profession and in many instances they have practiced together: the Bonnells, oldest continuous name in dentistry in Oklahoma, Muskogee and the Creek Nation; the Williamses, Chickasha and the Chickasaw Nation; the Williamses, Durant, and the Choctaw Nation; and the Entrikens, Enid, oldest continuous name from Oklahoma Territory. There are many others who likewise are building a fine tradition of family service which will be carried on by succeeding generations. The late Dr. L. M. Kennedy, Elk City, who practiced dentistry more than forty years and had five sons follow his profession, often remarked there had been a direct line of dentists in the Kennedy family for more than one hundred years. Similar family traditions are developing in Oklahoma dentistry.

There are other traditions of peculiar significance to the Association. This year a precedent was set when Albert Bonnell, Jr., the son of a brilliant father and former president of the organization, was honored by elevation to the presidency; two brothers have occupied the chair, Drs. T. W. and Harry Sorrels; both are former presidents of the Southwestern Society of Orthodontists. Dr. W. E. Flesher, his son Marion, the late Dr. Oren A. McCarthy, Tulsa, and Dr. Forris Woodring, Tulsa, also have served as presidents of this orthodontic society. Drs. Dean Robertson, Sumner Russman and Ben D. Caudle have held the principal office of the Southwestern Society of Pedodontists. On the national scene, Dr. W. E. Flesher has presided over the American Society of Orthodontists; the late Dr. J. B. Herring, over the American Full Denture Society; Dr. Frank Bertram, the American Association of Public

Health Dentists; and Dr. L. A. Lucas, the American Association of Endodontists. Oklahoma, too, has had three vice-presidents of the American Dental Association: Drs. A. E. Bonnell, C. R. Lawrence, and H. O. Warrick. The Association is proud of their honors, the recognition accorded them, and the examples of high achievement set.

Another branch of service that should gain in stature is that rendered by the Board of Governors, in 1955 composed of William E. Cole, president; Fred D. Entriken, first vice-president; Fred D. Riddle, second vice-president; Robert P. Keidel, secretary-treasurer; and L. K. Turnbull, Lacy H. Bell, and Norman T. Enmeier, members. Oklahoma dentistry won its long, upward fight toward the enactment of one of the better dental laws of the nation and its right to select members of the regulatory body. Dental laws are not enacted to benefit the dentist alone; if they were, they would constitute class legislation and be invalid in Oklahoma. The spirit, if not the letter, of the Oklahoma dental act is that it guarantees to the people that the future dentist shall be universally competent beyond the dentist of the past. The Board of Governors assumes this responsibility, and while under their oath of office members are first and foremost the executive officers of the dental act; they are secondarily, also, the intelligent lovers of their profession which had honored them before their selection to the regulatory agency. Personnel elected to the Board have labored to maintain high standards and make fair, equitable decisions. Dr. Richard T. Oliver, member of the Board, expressed this feeling when he addressed the Association at its annual meeting in 1954: "When you have seen members of the Board, men who have devoted years to the profession, actually break down and cry over a disciplinary necessity, or the failure of a young applicant who has recently completed six or seven years of college training, you know those men are sincere and conscientious and represent the highest type of unselfish service." Public service at the expense of a private practice is the lot of Board members and the principal award for maintaining free institutions.

Those who have witnessed changes in Oklahoma dentistry from simple efforts to relieve pain and make extractions to greater and greater skill in restoring or saving teeth and eliminating infection, know the profession has built a proud record of achievement. This has been accomplished by those loyal and hard-working members who, nameless in such a study as this, are the fibre from which has been woven a strong association. The status of a profession is not established by the brightest lights within it, but is judged by the men who belong to it, and the public concedes such respect and esteem as the standard by which it judges the conduct and performance of individual members.

This judgment factor by the public is not narrowed to professional integrity, but includes civic responsibility as well. Oklahoma dentistry has scored high in this respect. There have been men such as Dr. V. A. Boucher, Bartlesville, who served in both world wars; Dr. Boucher completed thirty-one years as an active reserve officer in September, 1945. When the Forty-fifth division, Oklahoma National Guard, was formed in 1921, Dr. W. S. Williams, Durant, was appointed division dental surgeon with the rank of major. He served until he reached retirement age in 1939, when he was given the honor of receiving the troops as they passed in review at Fort Sill and was presented a gold saber in recognition of his years of service. Dr. A. B. Rivers served on the State Pardon and Parole Board, Drs. I. M. Lightner, R. T. Oliver, O. R. Whiteneck, W. P. Morrison, Fred Seids, and S. S. Mayfield in the state legislature; and others have served on state boards and committees. Many, like Dr. Louis F. Dulany, have been mayors of cities—Dr. I. M. Lightner, Guymon, is dean in this respect, having served twelve years; many have served as city councilmen and on school boards, and have presided over civic organizations such as Rotary, Lions, Kiwanis and Chamber of Commerce groups.

In order to inspire interest in public and civic affairs, the H. H. Kaho award, named for an early-day dentist at Claremore, was offered for the first time in 1954. His son, Dr. Noel Kaho, was selected as first recipient in appreciation of his work in behalf of the Will Rogers Memorial, Claremore, and his efforts to save the Gilcrease Museum for Oklahoma.

Dr. R. O. Hirschi explained in an interview in the summer of 1954 how early leaders in the profession brought their gold to the territories. The doctor was using a figure of speech. True, they brought their gold, small supplies for delicate and artistic and permanent reconstructions, but he referred to their malleable adaptation to pioneer conditions and pure, unalloyed determination to improve their profession, the refinement of better dental laws in the crucible of Oklahoma politics, the perseverance of high ideals which led to the Oklahoma Way and a rich heritage for younger members.

These attitudes can be illustrated in many ways: consider accomplishments of the Association during recent administrations—the efforts of Charles A. Hess to serve the organization while more than 25 per cent of the membership served the country at war; the aid given by J. B. Ratliff to returning veterans; the general reorganization of the Association during H. O. Warrick's tenure as president; Max G. Armstrong's tact and ability in budgeting and fiscal affairs; the establishment of the central office by Dave Matteson; Bob Dunn's establishment of insurance programs; Fred Pitney's work in behalf of the Medical Research Foundation; Harry Wagner's bank payment plan for the purchase of dentistry; William Ringo's preventive dentistry program through fluoridation; Rolla Calkin's over-all administrative ability and mental health program; Albert Bonnell's hard-working zeal in advancing these programs.

In looking ahead toward the advancement of dentistry in Oklahoma, three examples of past accomplishments illustrate the spirit which should assure progress. The Socio-Economics Committee, of the School of Dentistry, University of Kansas City, in 1949 prepared a pamphlet on "An Inquiry Into The Socio-Economics of Dentistry."[10] The committee, composed of five members who had been in active practice twenty-five years or more, included David W. Matteson and Harry H. Sorrels of Oklahoma. The report takes the form of a series of letters written as a senior, near graduation, to an elder brother who has conducted a successful practice for twenty-five years and who responds to queries raised. Perplexing problems that face the young graduate are posed as questions in his letters. Practical, adequate answers are provided by the older brother on a broad range of subjects, such as state boards, location needs or places with low dentist-population ratios, financing the new office, fees, ratio of gross income to operating budget, hygienists, secretary-assistants, etc. Dr. Harry Sorrels, editor of the series, has served as guest lecturer at the University since the demand for in-

[10] See also "Orthodontic Economics," by Harry H. Sorrels, in the *American Journal of Orthodontics*, Volume XXXV, No. 11 (November, 1949), 858–76.

struction in these practical relationships was pointed up six years ago.

The second example comes from an item buried in news from the South Central District by Dr. E. B. Strickler which appeared in the January, 1952, issue of the *Journal:* "Dr. T. H. Williams really visits the night spots when he is in the large cities. Recently while in Chicago, Dr. and Mrs. Williams went to the Edgewater Beach Hotel, where Hildegarde is the current entertainer. She asked if he were present, and when she received an affirmative reply, Hildegarde asked him to come forward. He was questioned and he told all. Some of the answers being that he had practiced dentistry for 57 years and still had all his teeth, which he proved by showing them to her. At this the orchestra played, 'The Yanks Are Coming.' Dr. Williams couldn't keep from dancing and as he danced solo, Hildegarde started dancing with him and before the spectators knew what was happening they were witnessing one of the best dance teams of the season. It was so good the applause was deafening."

The final example relates to the career of Dr. A. L. Walters, lecturer at dental colleges, nationally known clinician, leader in nutrition, preventive dentistry, and prophylaxis, who keeps abreast of every development of dentistry. Dr. A. E. Bonnell, Jr., in reference to him in the summer of 1954 said: "Younger dentists still run over to Al Walters to find out what is new in dentistry." These twenty-four-carat attitudes—the spirit of co-operation among the profession, a youthful approach to life and duties, the motivation toward increased knowledge—should assure Oklahoma dentistry a proud record of achievement.

Bibliography

NOTE: The Oklahoma State Dental Association, since 1926, has collected items relating to the dental profession in Oklahoma: news items, newspaper clippings, biographical sketches of members, personal reminiscences, reports of committees, special studies, and pictures. Dr. C. R. Lawrence, Enid, was able to collect many items relating to territorial and early statehood activities; Dr. A. C. Seids, Oklahoma City, stimulated the interest of all the members in adding to the collection, and Dr. Harry Sorrels, Oklahoma City, has made this a major project of the Association.

Sources outside the state have been tapped for information relating to Oklahoma dentistry. Dr. Ralph W. Edwards, member of the faculty, College of Dentistry, University of Kansas City, made typewritten copies of all articles on the subject that appeared in the *Western Dental Journal* and *Hettinger News* in the early 1900's; Dr. Sorrels has repeatedly solicited and obtained additional information from the American Dental Association and other sources. Hundreds of items, properly catalogued, are in the collection.

In 1953, wire recordings were made of interviews which supplement with first-hand information written and printed narratives on pioneer conditions and recent achievements. In 1911 the Association started a quarterly which has been issued regularly; since 1907 complete minutes have been kept of all general sessions and meetings of the Executive Council of the Association; from the inception of the regulatory agency in 1891, minutes of every meeting of the territorial—later, the state—board have been preserved. With the exception of the minutes of the state board, retained by the state agency, all other items are in the Central Office of the Oklahoma State Dental Association. The collection has recently been supplemented with questionnaires answered by fifty of the older practitioners. Selected bibliographical items are listed below.

I. *Interviews*

(Taped recordings were made during the summer of 1953 with the following named individuals. Typed copies of the transcriptions are on file in the Central Office, Oklahoma State Dental Association, and the Library, University of Oklahoma, Norman.)

Frank P. Bertram, Oklahoma City; L. M. Doss, Oklahoma City; H. L. Entriken, Enid; William E. Flesher, Oklahoma City; R. O. Hirschi, Guthrie; C. H. Kibler, Oklahoma Dental Laboratory Society, Oklahoma City; Everett Lain, Oklahoma Medical Association, Oklahoma City; I. M. Lightner, Guymon; L. A. Lucas, Oklahoma City; R. H. Pendleton, Norman; A. A. Pfeiffer, Muskogee; F. J. Reichmann, Oklahoma City; E. E. Sanger, Oklahoma City; A. F. Sebert, Clinton; Fred E. Sims, Tulsa; Mrs. L. G. Smith, Women's Auxiliary, Tulsa; T. W. Sorrels, Oklahoma City; R. B. Taylor, Oklahoma Medical, Dental, and Pharmaceutical Association, Okmulgee; A. B. Walker, Norman; A. L. Walters, Tulsa; J. A. Wells, Shawnee; R. C. West, Oklahoma City; and T. H. Williams, Chickasha.

II. *Letters*

(In Central Files, Oklahoma State Dental Association.)

Bringhurst, Theo P., to J. S. Clark, May 6, May 20, 1954.
Bringhurst, Theo P., to Harry Sorrels, May 12, 1954.
Doughty, A. A., to R. H. Pendleton, February 17, 1908.
Flesher, W. E., to J. S. Clark, March 3, 1954.
Goaz, Paul W., to Harry Sorrels, October 27, 1953.
Kaho, Noel, to Harry Sorrels, July 24, 1954.
Lucas, Margaret F., to Harry Sorrels, March 4, 1951.
Peoples, D. A., to R. L. Pearson & Co., July 6, 1891. *Western Dental Journal*, Vol. V (Kansas City, 1891).
Walker, A. B., to Harry Sorrels, December 9, 1953.
Walters, A. L., to J. S. Clark, September 24, 1953; January 12, 1954.
Williams, Phillip E., to Harry Sorrels, June 4, 1954.

III. *Manuscripts*

(In Central Files, Oklahoma State Dental Association.)

Flesher, W. E. "History of Our Dental Laws." 1950.

Glass, J. N. "Southwestern Oklahoma District Dental Society." 1949.

Jewett, Clay. "Hettinger Bros. Mfg. Co." December 16, 1953.

Lucas, L. A. "Industrial Dentistry In Oklahoma." December 8, 1949.

Rinehart, R. J. "Address Before the Oklahoma State Dental Association," Tulsa, April 17, 1950.

Seids, A. C. "Oral Hygiene." N. d.

Shaffer, Ward L. "History of Dental Library, Oklahoma School of Medicine." March 27, 1950.

Smith, Mrs. L. G. "History of Women's Auxiliary to the Oklahoma State Dental Society." 1949.

Thompson, B. C. "Correspondence Covering the Work of the Committee on Institutions." April 14, 1950.

(Author unknown) "The Salvation Army Children's Clinic." N. d.

IV. *Other Primary Sources*

Constitution of the State of Oklahoma, including all Amendments and Revisions as of July 4, 1950.

Constitution and By-Laws of the Oklahoma Dental Association, adopted June 18, 1907. (Central Office Files, OSDA.)

Constitution and By-Laws of the Oklahoma State Dental Society, adopted April 1, 1914. (Central Office Files, OSDA.)

Constitution and By-Laws of the Oklahoma State Dental Association, adopted April 14, 1947. (Central Office Files, OSDA.)

Constitution of the Women's Auxiliary to the Oklahoma State Dental Society. N. d. (Central Office Files, OSDA.)

Minutes, Northern Dental Association of Oklahoma, March 11, 1909, to November 20, 1917. (Central Office Files, OSDA.)

Minutes, Northwestern Oklahoma Dental Society, March 4, 1909, to January 16, 1913. (Central Office Files, OSDA.)

Minutes, Oklahoma State Dental Association, June 8, 1907, to December 15, 1935. (Central Office Files, OSDA.)

Minutes, South Central Oklahoma Dental Society, November 10, 1914 to November 20, 1929.

Minutes, Southwestern Dental Society, December 5, 1914 to March 3, 1933.

Official Proceedings of the Oklahoma Board of Dental Examiners, 1891–1919. (In office of the secretary-treasurer of the Board of Governors of the Registered Dentists of Oklahoma, Dr. Robert P. Keidel, Muskogee, Oklahoma.)

Program, Twelfth Annual Meeting of the Oklahoma Dental Association, Guthrie, May 6, 7, 1902. (Central Office Files, OSDA.)

Program, Indian Territory Dental Association, Muskogee, May 6, 1904. (Central Office Files, OSDA.)

Program, Fourteenth Annual Meeting of the Oklahoma Dental Association, Shawnee, May 10, 11, 1904. (Central Office Files, OSDA.)

Program, Joint Meeting of Indian Territory and Oklahoma Territory Dental Associations, Oklahoma City, June 17–19, 1907. (Central Office Files, OSDA.)

Program, Oklahoma Dental Association, Muskogee, June 8–10, 1908. (Central Office Files, OSDA.)

The Eleventh Annual Report of the Oklahoma Board of Dental Examiners, 1901–1902. Guthrie, State Capitol Company, 1902.

V. *Legislative Proceedings*

Journals of the Council Proceedings for Legislature Assemblies, Territory of Oklahoma, 1890–1905.

Journals of the Proceedings of the House of Representatives for Legislature Assemblies, Territory of Oklahoma, 1890–1905.

Journals of the House of Representatives for Regular and Extraordinary Sessions, State of Oklahoma, 1907–53

Journals of the Senate for Regular and Extraordinary Sessions, State of Oklahoma, 1907–53.

Session Laws, enacted by Legislatures, Territory of Oklahoma, 1890–1905.

Session Laws, enacted by Legislatures, State of Oklahoma, 1907–53.

VI. *Court Decisions*

1. *Cases determined in the Supreme Court of the State of Oklahoma:*

Bancroft v. *Board of Governors of the Registered Dentists of Oklahoma.* Vol. 202, *Oklahoma Reports.*

Board of Governors of the Registered Dentists of Oklahoma v. *Brown.* Vol. 203, *Oklahoma Reports.*

Curtis v. *Registered Dentists of Oklahoma.* Vols. 193 and 201, *Oklahoma Reports.*

Dowell et al. v. *City of Tulsa et al. Journal of the Oklahoma Bar Association,* Vol. xxv, No. 24 (June 19, 1954).

Griesel, Ex'r. v. *Fabian.* Vol. 184, *Oklahoma Reports.*

State Board of Dental Examiners et al. v. *Pollock.* Vol. 125, *Oklahoma Reports.*

State ex rel. Board of Governors of Registered Dentists of Oklahoma v. *Rifleman.* Vol. 203, *Oklahoma Reports.*

2. *Other Court Decisions:*

Curtis v. *State.* Vol. 78, *Oklahoma Criminal Reports.* Criminal Court of Appeals for the State of Oklahoma.

Semler v. *Oregon State Board of Dental Examiners.* Vol. 294, *United States Supreme Court Reports.*

VII. *Government Publications*

Bureau of the Census. *Fifteenth Census of the United States,* Vol. I, *Population, Number and Distribution of Inhabitants.* Washington, 1933.

Directory of Registered Dentists, Specialists and Dental Hygienists in Oklahoma. Issued 1953 by the Board of Governors of Registered Dentists of the State of Oklahoma.

Public Health Bulletin, No. 226. U. S. Treasury Department, Public Health Service. Washington, D. C., May, 1936.

VIII. *Books*

Anonymous. *A Century of Service to Dentistry, 1844-1944.* Philadelphia, S. S. White Dental Mfg. Co., 1944.

Bremner, M. D. K. *The Story of Dentistry.* 2nd edition. Brooklyn, Dental Items of Interest Publishing Co., 1946.

Brill, H. E. *Story of Oklahoma City University and Its Predecessors.* Oklahoma City, University Press, 1938.

Dale, Edward Everett, and Rader, Jesse Lee. *Readings in Oklahoma History.* New York, Row, Peterson and Company, 1930.

Debo, Angie. *Oklahoma: Foot-loose and Fancy-free.* Norman, University of Oklahoma Press, 1949.

Foreman, Carolyn Thomas. *Oklahoma Imprints.* Norman, University of Oklahoma Press, 1936.

Foreman, Grant. *Muskogee: the Biography of an Oklahoma Town.* Norman, University of Oklahoma Press, 1943.

Jacobs, Joseph F., *History of the University of Kansas City School of Dentistry, Kansas City-Western Dental College.* Kansas City, 1949.

Jeffs, Irvin. *The First Eight Months of Oklahoma City.* Oklahoma City, McMaster Printing Co., 1890.

Morrison, G. Archanna. *In the Dentist's Office.* Philadelphia, J. P. Lippincott & Co., 1948.

Polk's Dental Register and Directory of the United States and Canada. 6th edition, 1904–1905. Chicago, R. L. Polk & Co., 1905.

Price, Weston A. *Nutrition and Physical Degeneration.* California, Redlands, 1939.

Corden, Seth K., and Richards, W. B. *Oklahoma Red Book,* Vols. I and II. Oklahoma City, 1912.

IX. *City Directories*

A Complete General and Business Directory, Oklahoma City, 1898. Compiled by John W. Nicely.

Burkhart's Tulsa & West Tulsa Directory for 1909. Tulsa, Burkhart's Printing and Stationery Co.

Business and Resident Directory, Guthrie & Logan County, Oklahoma, for the year commencing September 1, 1892. Guthrie, Frank G. Pronty, Publisher.

Daily Oklahoman Almanac and Industrial Record of 1908. Oklahoma City, Daily Oklahoman Publishing Co.

Hoffine's Tulsa, Oklahoma Directory for 1910. Tulsa, Hoffine Directory Co., Compilers and Publishers.

Moore's Directory of the City of Muskogee, Indian Territory, 1903, 1904, 1905, 1906.

Moore's Directory of the City of Muskogee, Oklahoma, 1908, 1910.

X. *Periodicals And Other Publications*

An Inquiry Into the Socio-Economics of Dentistry. The Socio-Economic Committee, University of Kansas City School of Dentistry. Multilithed, 1949.

Bulletin of the Oklahoma State Dental Association. Issued quarterly, January, April, July, October. June, 1911–April, 1914; July, 1947–April, 1951. Oklahoma City.

Bulletin of the Oklahoma State Dental Society. June, 1914–April, 1947.
Oklahoma City.

Dental Brief (Souvenir Edition). September, 1904. Philadelphia,
L. D. Caulk.

Information Bulletin, American Dental Association. May, 1954.
Chicago.

Journal of the American Dental Association. June, 1954. Chicago.

Journal of the National Dental Association. January, 1917–September,
1918. Chicago.

Journal of the Oklahoma State Dental Association. July, 1951–October, 1954. Oklahoma City.

News Letter, Oklahoma State Dental Association. August 1, 1954.
Oklahoma City.

Transactions of the Fourth International Dental Congress. 3 vols.,
Philadelphia, Press of the "Dental Cosmos" (The S. S. White
Dental Mfg. Co.), 1905.

XI. *Articles*

Anonymous. "The Oklahoma Dental Association," *Western Dental
Journal,* Vol. XXI (Kansas City, 1907).

Coleman, P. D. "Concerning the Practice of Dentistry in Oklahoma,"
Western Dental Journal, Vol. XXII (Kansas City, 1908).

Holmes, F. C. "Reminiscences of an Early Dental Practitioner in Western Oklahoma," *The Bulletin,* Vol. XXIX (October, 1940);
Vol. XXIX (January, 1941) Oklahoma City.

Lain, Everett S., and Caughron, G. Sherrill. "Electrogalvanic Phenomena of the Oral Cavity Caused by Dissimilar Metallic
Restorations," *Journal of the American Dental Association,*
Vol. XXIII (Chicago, 1936).

Raper, Howard R. "Notes on the Early History of Radiodontia,"
Oral Surgery, Oral Medicine, and Oral Hygiene, Vol. VI,
No. 1 (St. Louis, January, 1953).

Sorrels, Harry H. "Orthodontic Economics," *American Journal of
Orthodontics,* Vol. XXXV, No. 11 (St. Louis, November,
1949).

Walters, A. L. "The Indian Territory Dental Association; Its Organization, History and Mission," *Western Dental Journal,*
Vol. XXI (Kansas City, 1907).

White, C. L. "The Oklahoma and Indian Territory Legal Conditions,"
Western Dental Journal, Vol. XXI (Kansas City, 1907).
———. "The Organization of the New Oklahoma State Dental Asso-
ciation, June 17–19, 1907," *Western Dental Journal*, Vol. XXI
(Kansas City, 1907).

XII. *Newspapers*

Blackwell Morning Tribune. Blackwell, Oklahoma, 1931.
Indian Journal. Eufaula, Indian Territory, 1889.
Kingfisher Free Press. Kingfisher, Oklahoma, 1949.
Lexington Leader. Lexington, Oklahoma Territory, 1891.
Muskogee Democrat. Muskogee, Indian Territory, 1904, 1905.
Muskogee Evening Times. Muskogee, Indian Territory, 1901, 1902.
Muskogee Daily Phoenix. Muskogee, Indian Territory, 1888, 1891,
1893, 1894, 1899.
Muskogee Times. Muskogee, Indian Territory, 1897.
Muskogee Times Democrat. Muskogee, Oklahoma, 1906, 1907, 1908,
1909, 1911.
Oklahoma City Times. Oklahoma City, Oklahoma, 1923, 1924, 1925.
Oklahoma City Times Journal. Oklahoma City, Oklahoma, 1903,
1907.
South McAlester Capitol (weekly). South McAlester, Indian Terri-
tory, 1905.
The Daily Oklahoman. Oklahoma City, Oklahoma, 1896, 1898, 1901,
1907, 1910, 1912, 1913, 1914, 1919, 1923, 1925, 1928, 1930,
1938, 1954.
The Shawnee Daily Herald. Shawnee, Oklahoma, 1907.
The Shawnee Herald. Shawnee, Oklahoma, 1902.
Tulsa Tribune. Tulsa, Oklahoma, 1923, 1932.
Tulsa World. Tulsa, Oklahoma, 1908, 1926, 1929, 1946.
Vinita Weekly Chieftain. Vinita, Indian Territory, 1903.
Weekly Times Democrat. Oklahoma City, Oklahoma Territory, 1903.

Roster of Licensed Dentists of Oklahoma since Statutory Law Regulating
Practice in 1891 (May, 1891, through January, 1955). Each entry contains the name of the dentist, the year in which his license was issued, and
his license number.

Abbott, Rufus, 1901	92	Ames, A. B., 1905	392
Abernathy, J. G., 1909	509	Ames, Burnham B., 1919	1329
Abernethy, E. A., Jr., 1945	2238	Ammons, Earl Fay, 1916	1143
Adams, Aaron Emerson, 1891	16	Ammons, Ally C., 1926	1616
Adams, Clarence W., 1921	1439	Anderson, E. O., 1916	1126
Adams, E. C., 1913	1076	Anderson, G. W., 1928	1757
Adams, Edwin Brown, 1916	1147	Anderson, H. L., 1919	1266
Adams, Wiley John, 1925	1604	Anderson, J. A., 1908	510
Adler, R. V., 1908	646	Anderson, Lloyd E., 1951	2459
Ahrens, Donald P., 1933	1976	Anderson, P. F., 1908	511
Albert, Arthur Clinton, 1916	1139	Anderson, R. E., 1905	451
Aldridge, Warren C., 1951	2484	Anderson, Rawles, 1908	515
Alexander, C. H., 1930	1921	Andree, G. W., 1908	851
Alexander, Clay Shelton, 1923	1525	Andrews, Barrett Reid, 1951	2460
Alexander, L. D., 1928	1766	Andrews, Max R., Jr., 1912	1025
Alexander, O. E., 1908	513	Andrews, Ulysses S., 1926	1665
Alfholder, Irvin Ernest, 1925	1589	Ardrey, Joseph Cliff, 1927	1697
Allen, F. E., 1905	397	Armstrong, Jack James, 1953	2547
Allen, Fred B., 1901	105	Armstrong, Max George, 1920	1405
Allen, H. M., 1908	512	Arthurs, Jas. Lucien, 1940	2132
Allen, Neil C., 1950	2443	Asbury, J. M., 1907	497
Allen, Wm. J., 1931	1954	Ashby, Alva L., 1911	684
Allender, F. C., 1900	79	Ashby, Alva L., Jr., 1926	1653
Alley, James M., Jr., 1951	2458	Ashby, E. T., 1929	1833
Allinder, Bert Brice, 1953	2546	Atkins, John Henry, 1941	2165
Allingham, Geo. Robert, 1926	1656	Atkins, Walter D., 1950	2402
Allison, C. N., 1903	191	Atkinson, Clarence M., 1950	2444
Almquist, Carl K., 1954	2575	Atterbury, Chester Wesley, 1900	72
Alquist, Frank L., 1945	2237	Ault, Glenn S., 1920	1390
Alsbach, Geo. C., 1926	1619	Ault, Glenn S., Jr., 1946	2290
Amburgy, C., 1905	268	Auspach, F. G., 1904	241
Amburgy, G. C., 1909	907	Austbo, M. O., 1929	1831
Amend, Joseph Sheridan, 1924	1566	Austerman, Jack B., 1954	2586
Amend, Verl F., 1932	1963	Austin, A. L., 1900	242
Amend, Wm. Leslie, 1913	1080	Azbill, C. F., 1912	1026

Black, B. E., 1903	166	Bowling, G. W., 1909	908
Black, Emery H., 1908	653	Bowyer, Scott P., 1922	1507
Black, Marcus D., 1908	635	Boyd, Clyde A., Jr., 1952	2507
Black, Merle T., 1920	1428	Boyd, W. W., 1908	813
Black, O. E., 1908	660	Boyer, O. W., 1919	1315
Black, R. E., 1908	518	Boynton, J. F., 1903	175
Black, Wm. Campbell, 1927	1709	Bradfield, S. G., 1908	661
Black, Wm. Harvey, 1923	1548	Bradford, William R., 1949	2395
Blackburn, C. H., 1905	381	Bradley, A. M., 1908	652
Blackford, Corbin Hess, 1899	54	Bradshaw, R. Russell, 1913	1083
Blackly, H. L., 1916	1135	Brady, Earl M., 1915	1124
Blackly, R. M., 1912	1027	Brady, James, 1928	1748
Blackmer, Jerry W., 1952	2533	Bragg, Jubie Barton, Jr., 1953	2539
Blair, Frank P., 1933	1983	Brandenburg, F. J., 1921	1480
Blair, W. M., 1917	1198	Brandt, Emmons G., 1927	1680
Bland, Oscar, 1904	221	Branham, Wm. Clement, 1908	651
Blankenship, Eugene M., 1943	2193	Branin, Dan E., 1950	2440
Blood, John McConnell, 1899	55	Branson, Leon L., 1917	1204
Blum, Chas. J., 1929	1834	Breedlove,	
Bocock, Alman E., 1940	2141	Walton Willoughby, 1928	1781
Bodine, Ray L., 1930	1876	Brenneman, Daniel M., 1902	136
Boggs, George P., 1954	2587	Brentair, E. G., 1931	1940
Boland, J. M., 1944	2230	Bridges, Ford E., 1924	1565
Bolinger, Geo. F., Jr., 1945	2240	Brigham, F. W., 1902	148
Bolt, H. R., 1908	662	Bright, Elmer Clarence, 1916	1144
Bolte, John N., 1908	657	Bright, Wayne Cordell, 1950	2405
Bond, Ira T., 1908	519	Brimacombe, Wm. T., 1908	523
Bond, J. M., 1909	843	Brimer, Eugene Lee, Jr., 1946	2291
Bond, S. H., 1909	844	Bringhurst, Theodore P., 1906	457
Bond, S. M., 1908	521	Brissy, Cleo Chas., 1928	1764
Bond, Victor G., 1912	1062	Bristol, W. G., 1902	124
Bonifield, Geo. T., 1919	1280	Brithour, W. A., 1902	129
Bonifield, John H., 1940	2131	Britt, Robert L., 1908	524
Bonnell, Albert E., 1908	506	Broaddus, Henry Dave, 1899	63
Bonnell, Albert E., Jr., 1929	1838	Broaddus, H. D., 1902	137
Bonnette, Paul C., 1937	2054	Broadfoot, Wm. J., 1892	18
Bonncy, Sam Brainard, 1926	1627	Brock, Eugene W., 1946	2276
Boone, James Wallace, Jr., 1954	2576	Bronnough, J. M., 1901	243
Borchers, F., 1906	460	Bronson, J. F., 1935	2012
Born, Harold S., 1931	1945	Brooks, Arthur Eugene, 1908	655
Bosonetto, J. M., 1920	1429	Brown, C. T., 1919	1279
Boswell, James Herman, 1913	1088	Brown, Charles M., 1954	2588
Boucher, Vernon A., 1919	1293	Brown, Earl C., 1929	1837
Boudinot, H. E., 1908	647	Brown, Jas. A., 1917	1190
Boudreaux, Paul W., 1950	2406	Brown, Jas. E., Jr., 1941	2156
Bourdier, Jno. Wm., 1905	251	Brown, James Edward, 1918	1229
Bowen, Marion Scott, 1953	2535	Brown, James Vining, 1905	247
Bowers, Royal Glenn, 1953	2548	Brown, John Hinton, 1919	1366
Bowlby, G. S., 1909	854	Brown, John McKenzie, 1954	2589
Bowles, H. J., 1908	649	Brown, Kenneth L., 1943	2192

Brown, Norman Porter, 1919	1318	Buxton, W. V., 1909	853
Brown, Paul J., 1919	1300	Byam, Chas. Wm., 1908	805
Brown, Silas Lesley, 1908	648	Byam, R. P., 1908	806
Brown, W. K., 1911	967	Byrd, O. J., 1908	516
Brown, Wm. P., 1929	1835	Byrnes, G. W., 1908	654
Brown, Wm. Raymond, 1919	1289	Cage, A. D., 1899	60
Brownfield, Ralph A., 1920	1401	Cagle, Robert W., 1937	2053
Broyles, Isaac Earnest, 1927	1684	Cain, C. W., 1908	532
Brumbaugh, P. G., 1905	369	Cain, S. B., 1898	53
Brungardt, Adolph John, 1935	2031	Caldwell, Clyde F., 1905	387
Brunton, John Porter, 1902	138	Caldwell, F. J., 1908	528
Bruton, Robert O., 1914	1092	Caldwell, J. G., 1905	263
Bruxton, R. R., 1902	150	Caldwell, Jack B., 1936	2045
Bryan, Wm. Wear, 1908	507	Calhoun, Herbert S., 1917	1201
Bryant, B. F., 1908	517	Calkin, Rolla Chas., 1928	1785
Bryant, Joe Stanley, 1951	2448	Call, A. B., 1905	256
Bryant, Lewis Jackson, 1951	2447	Calland, James F., 1954	2609
Bryant, Wm. E., 1943	2208	Callicott, Theldred C., 1954	2567
Buchanan, F. W., 1920	1416	Calloway, C. P., 1905	255
Buchanan, H. A., 1909	823	Calmes, J. B., 1891	5
Buck, F. N., 1908	520	Calvert, Woodford B., 1917	1208
Buck, F. N., 1928	1821	Campbell, Billy J., 1946	2277
Buckley, J. E., 1905	252	Campbell, D. D., 1905	431
Buford, R. B., 1908	659	Campbell, J. L., 1912	1029
Buikstra, Albert Elliott, 1927	1720	Campbell, W. L., 1927	1734
Buikstra, Lloyd P., 1926	1655	Canby, Clarence Price, 1927	1694
Bull, Maurice Paul, 1952	2488	Cannon, Meryle Dallas, 1927	1702
Bullock, E. E., 1903	201	Caplin, Abraham W., 1918	1225
Burch, Richard J., 1931	1955	Caplin, Morris Harry, 1917	1207
Burch, Wm. Paul, Jr., 1947	2323	Carl, Geo. Dan, 1908	526
Burdick, Frank A., Jr., 1950	2409	Carl, Roy Glen, 1926	1658
Burhans, P. A., 1905	244	Carlson, Edward G., 1930	1880
Burket, G. E., 1923	908	Carmichael, J. B., 1946	2292
Burkett, E. R., 1905	423	Carnes, Wm. Clyde, 1917	1173
Burkett, W. G., 1902	157	Carpenter, Albert M., 1914	1096
Burnham, T. J., 1931	1932	Carr, Leonard Erwin, 1927	1687
Burns, Harry A., 1920	1369	Carrick, C. C., 1905	399
Burris, Alfred L., 1947	2341	Carson, Henry G., 1905	367
Burris, Otis Edgar, 1919	1323	Carson, Jas. W., 1946	2293
Burris, Thos. G., 1947	2346	Carson, John Evan, 1941	2166
Burris, Wallace M., 1923	1524	Carter, Carl Clayton, 1919	1313
Burrow, John Wallace, 1954	2565	Carter, Robert P., 1934	1990
Burton, O. F., 1902	152	Carter, Wm. Jay, 1946	2294
Busby, W. E., 1908	658	Carter, Wm. Lee, 1945	2241
Bush, Oren Dallmer, 1952	2520	Cartwright, Dale J., 1954	2602
Bush, W. F., 1905	253	Cartwright, H. R., 1931	1936
Butcher, Antis M., Jr., 1954	2600	Carver, Sidney Clyde, 1925	1609
Butcher, J. Marion, 1931	1959	Casey, Earnest Young, 1917	1206
Buxton, Arthur Henry, 1919	1321	Casford, Arthur Jefferson, 1919	1328
Buxton, Joseph Frederick, 1919	1282	Cater, T. T., 1905	259

Cates, Frank William, 1925	1601	Clock, Quentin Wesley, 1950	2429
Cathey, Charles M., 1949	2373	Clond,	
Cathey, Robert J., 1952	2518	Kenneth Lee Edward, 1954	2569
Caudle, Benj. D., 1945	2242	Cloyd, John M., 1911	970
Caudle, R. P., 1946	2295	Clugston, Frank A., 1920	1385
Caughron, Geo. Sherrill, 1929	1839	Coates, Charles L., 1949	2398
Caughron, J. R., 1905	260	Cochran, Richard G., 1954	2590
Caughron, Jack Randel, 1930	1910	Cochrell, Kenneth Leland, 1919	1301
Cavanaugh, Vincent Paul, 1934	1988	Cockerill, H. S., 1927	1735
Cave, J. F., 1901	85	Coe, J. H., 1904	218
Caywood, Albert C., 1950	2410	Coffield, Floyd D., 1938	2082
Caywood, Elmer S., 1912	1055	Coffin, A. B., 1905	262
Chamberlain, H. A., 1902	144	Coggins, Luther D., 1935	2029
Chambers, A. E., 1905	429	Coil, C. D., 1899	61
Chandler, Clarence D., 1903	214	Coil, Isaac B., 1894	30
Channell, L. W., 1925	1580	Cole, C. M., 1901	91
Chapman, A. D., 1904	217	Cole, James C., 1952	2501
Chapman, Edwin M., 1905	265	Cole, John B., Jr., 1936	2041
Chapman, John Harrison, 1923	1540	Cole, Leon Lorenzo, 1928	1774
Chapman, Judge C., 1942	2177	Cole, Wm. Edgar, 1934	1991
Chapman, Loren Edmond, 1919	1307	Coleman, Paul D., 1908	531
Cheek, Leonard Wm., 1927	1696	Collier, C. C., 1931	1961
Chester, Carter Justen, 1926	1660	Collier, Jesse Claude, 1908	670
Childs, Casey, 1937	2058	Collins, C. A., 1909	910
Childs, Vernon S., 1935	2017	Collins, Frank B., 1912	1057
Childs, Jacob William, 1919	1341	Collins, H. B., 1945	2232
Chitwood, John Luckett, 1928	1803	Collins, T. J., 1905	416
Christiansen, Geo. Daniel, 1919	1355	Colter, C. J., 1911	969
Church, L. E., 1919	1268	Colter, F. H., 1903	188
Clark, Albert W., 1905	366	Coltharp, Edward K., 1954	2577
Clark, Brent Elmer, Jr., 1949	2383	Colwick, John Cameron, 1927	1676
Clark, E. W., 1905	261	Comer, Thurman W., 1954	2578
Clark, Howard J., 1908	530	Compton, H. L., 1930	1882
Clark, L. E., 1925	1583	Conger, Robert W., 1906	459
Clark, Wm. Carl, 1918	1234	Conger, Robert Watkins, 1928	1761
Clarke, A. G., 1906	458	Conger, S. M., 1905	370
Clarke, Chas. E., 1909	857	Conine, R. C., 1911	1004
Clarke, Clarence C., 1923	1539	Connell, G. D., 1905	435
Clarke, J. J., Jr., 1931	1941	Connole, C. V., 1905	446
Clarke, John J., 1915	1110	Connor, W. H., 1905	258
Clayton, B. W., 1908	669	Cook, H. H., 1909	968
Clements, Charles C., 1922	1506	Cook, J. C., 1908	527
Clements, G. L., 1931	1931	Cook, R. T., 1917	1216
Clements, Wilbur A., 1909	887	Cooper, Aubrey H., 1947	2329
Cleveland,		Cooper, Ralph Dewey, 1950	2441
Lawrence Clayton, 1908	667	Cooper, Tim E., 1923	1100
Cleveland, W. W., 1908	666	Cooper, Walter R., Jr., 1952	2517
Clifford, T. F., 1899	62	Cooper, Wm. Hardy, 1928	1755
Clifford, T. F., 1905	371	Cooper, Wm. Mark, 1919	1304
Clinton, Jno. M., 1939	2123	Copus, J. A., 1908	529

Deatheridge,		Doss, Chas. M., 1927	1744
Harvey Horace, 1926	1645	Doss, L. M., 1906	533
Deaver, H. M., 1909	860	Dott, Geo. Meredith, 1915	1116
Deaver, J. J., 1902	807	Doty, Frederick H., 1921	1461
DeFoe, G. S., 1909	888	Dougherty, F. H., 1920	1432
Delhotal, Jack R., 1945	2243	Douglas, Bert Brown, 1925	1611
Delk, Mack Benton, 1947	2324	Douglas, E. K., 1909	879
Delson, Leon, 1930	1916	Douglas, Hollis Bruce, 1929	1840
Denney, A. I., 1920	1415	Douglas, John Alexander, 1901	107
Denny, Clarke Andrew, 1920	1389	Douglass, Chas. Elden, 1915	1119
Dent, G. I., 1905	373	Dowell, Vivian T., 1949	2397
Dent, Harvey Lee, 1926	1636	Downey, J. W., 1905	268
DeRosa, L. A., 1905	271	Doyle, Max Melton, 1927	1701
Detrick, Archie M., 1894	27	Doyle, Wm. H., 1943	2205
Devin, J. C., 1911	973	Drake, M. E., 1902	130
Devlin, Donald Hayes, 1950	2439	Draper, S. J., 1917	1212
Devoe, C. H., 1905	434	Draughon, Arthur Eugene, 1950	2437
DeWees, H. E., 1908	534	Drescher, Albert R., 1941	2149
Dewey, Walter M., 1921	1470	Drew, Chas. Walter, 1925	1575
Deyton, Chas. D., 1924	1075	Droste, Victor R., 1919	1270
Dicken, Wm. A., 1913	1074	Ducasse, A. L., 1927	1670
Dickey, Marvin R., 1929	1841	Duckworth, T. G., 1912	1031
Dickson, Edward E., 1950	2442	Duffendack, Percy J., 1928	1792
Dickson, Floyd Everett, 1927	1686	Duggin, J. T., 1901	83
Dickson, Floyd, 1952	2531	Dulany, Louis Ford, 1927	1710
Dickson, John Henry, 1952	2526	Duncan, Charles F., 1922	1503
Dickson, Lee Olin, 1922	1508	Duncan, G. C., 1905	270
Dickson, Ross O., 1915	1123	Duncan, James M., 1929	1832
Dickson, Ruby Elton, 1920	1399	Duncan, Otho, 1929	1842
Dietz, Reuben H., 1925	1591	Duncan, Robert L., 1922	1502
Diffenbacker, J. L., 1918	1240	Duncan, Walter W., 1947	2335
Dillard, Hayden, 1952	2513	Duncanson, L. E., 1909	858
Dillard, W. L., 1910	911	Dunn,	
Dingus, K. C., 1913	1084	Robert Dean Miller, 1919	1302
Diratsouyan, M. H., 1909	889	Dunn, Thomas C., 1952	2523
Divine, Hal Gardner, 1936	2040	Dutcher, W. L., 1902	164
Dixon, Chas. Harold, 1927	1718	Eagleson, Albert Robson, 1908	816
Dixon, J. Walter, 1918	1221	Eakings, Edward, 1917	1185
Dixon, Preston F., 1921	1437	Eastep, J. Ben, 1951	2461
Dodds, J. T., 1908	791	Easterling, H. C., 1946	2319
Dodson, Geo. L., 1912	1030	Eaton, H. H., 1901	274
Doherty, J. F., 1929	1830	Eaton, J. W., 1908	792
Doherty, J. T., 1908	674	Eberhardt, H. C., 1911	1005
Doherty, L. C., 1908	673	Ebersole, Robert R., 1932	1965
Dole, F. D., 1900	70	Ebling, Chas. Albert, 1919	1311
Dolf, Frank Henry, 1947	2347	Eden, J. E., 1908	678
Doll, Ronald C., 1935	2030	Edgerton, Chas. Harold, 1919	1310
Donathan, G. D., Jr., 1945	2244	Edminston, Richard J., 1898	50
Donathan, Jack, 1943	2202	Edwards, F. T., 1905	454
Donoho, O. H., 1942	2184	Edwards, Harold J., 1914	1091

Freeman, Jack A., 1940	2134	Gibbs, Wm. Thomas, 1927	1695
Freeman, Nellie, 1901	83	Gibson, A. G., 1930	1899
Freeze, Earnest C., 1927	1737	Gibson, E. Q., 1908	548
Frenelmont, E. D., 1905	273	Giese, Alfred Geo., 1905	282
Frenelmont, L. D., 1905	272	Giesler, C. J., 1911	977
Frew, Athol Lee, Jr., 1946	2278	Gilbert, Russell D., 1928	1801
Friedman, Adolph Henry, 1919	1287	Gilfallen, Arthur Harold, 1925	1593
Friedmann, A. R., 1902	132	Gilham, Wallace, 1904	225
Fritzpatrick, Wm. J., 1909	862	Gill, A. A., 1913	1068
Frye, Dick T., 1950	2428	Gille, John P., 1908	549
Fuhr, Vernal W., 1942	2173	Gillespie, C. T., 1908	664
Fuller, Jimmie E., 1950	2408	Gillespie, James B., 1895	38
Fulton, Edgar G., 1909	861	Gilroy, L. E., 1904	220
Funke, Theo. A., 1940	2135	Gilton, Robert E., 1912	1033
Furrow, Chas. A., 1904	239	Glass, Chas. H., 1939	2124
Furrow, Marene B., 1897	47	Glass, John Fisher, 1936	2051
Furrow, Wm. E., 1891	15	Glass, J. N., 1908	690
Gaines, James Foster, 1912	1034	Glass, Lester E., 1921	1445
Gale, F. C., 1905	412	Glass, Theodore Allen, 1953	2563
Gale, Wm. Morris, 1936	2044	Glaze, George, 1908	552
Gallimore,		Glick, H. E., 1908	880
John Wallace, Jr., 1951	2445	Gloner, Sterling Rogers, 1908	685
Galt, Wm. Doak, 1954	2579	Glover, Harry Dolphin, 1928	1762
Gamble, J. Thurman, 1952	2519	Goeringer, John, 1920	1438
Gamble, Nathan A., 1908	683	Gold, B. L., 1908	818
Gardner, Arlie Bernard, 1927	1699	Golden, R. F., 1905	385
Gardner, J. E., 1908	686	Goldring, James, 1905	403
Gardner, Paul, 1918	1256	Goldsbury, W. H., 1908	687
Garland, Carl D., 1920	1409	Gonce, Robert E., 1954	2592
Garland, Charles S., 1920	1408	Goodloe, Robert Wilson, 1948	2357
Garratt, F. M., 1903	182	Goodrich, H. G., 1900	75
Garrett, Lester E., 1923	1517	Goodrich, L. H., 1906	461
Garrett, Oliver Lee, 1919	1292	Gordon, Dyer C., 1910	917
Garrett, Troy Olen, 1953	2551	Gordon, John Bruce, 1923	1527
Garrison, Edwin B., 1911	978	Gose, Findey O., 1923	1549
Garrott, V. C., 1901	82	Gossett, J. R., 1907	499
Garvey, Robt. M., 1946	2317	Gossett, J. W., 1942	2180
Gatewood, E. C., 1905	358	Gotfried, C. F., 1902	125
Gauer, Lawrence, 1937	2063	Gow, J. C., 1904	222
Gault, H. C., 1899	54	Graham, A. D., 1908	689
Gault, J. C., 1905	357	Graham, R. F., 1902	135
Gawey, Albert C., 1947	2334	Graham, Thos. O., Jr., 1939	2113
Gawey, John S., 1940	2145	Granger, Donald C., 1942	2175
Geister, Chas. Edward, 1916	1130	Granger, Edward, 1909	863
Gentile, Ernest J., 1952	2502	Granger, T. H., 1908	688
Georgis, E. S., 1905	284	Granger, Thos. R., 1938	2076
Gerard, Jno. G., 1939	2112	Granot, H. B., 1920	1424
Gervin, Elijah H., 1927	1726	Grant, James Walter, 1898	52
Gettler, H. G., 1930	1914	Grant, S. E., 1905	278
Gibbens, Wm. N., 1945	2247	Grassl, Walter John, 1919	1316

Gratz, Charles Edwards, 1951	2455	Hale, Merle L., 1949	2381
Gravelle, Harold Roy, 1928	1787	Hale, N. L., 1908	798
Graves, Clarence E., 1922	1498	Hale, W. I., 1908	799
Graves, Thos. W., 1945	2270	Hall, B. Mike, 1951	2464
Gray, B. F., 1902	161	Hall, C. B., 1917	1175
Gray, C. F., 1905	281½	Hall, C. H., 1905	444
Gray, Fred A., 1905	281	Hall, Harvey D., 1954	2604
Gray, Porter E., 1918	1233	Hall, J. A., 1905	293
Gray, Wm. Clinton, 1937	2059	Hall, James A., 1926	1651
Green, Chas. H., 1901	119	Hall, Jas. Donald, 1943	2200
Green, Edward M., 1919	1277	Hall, Joseph R., 1945	2269
Green, Everett Ray, 1927	1721	Hall, Lester A., 1946	2284
Green, Gilbert J., 1917	1205	Hall, Ralph Raymond, 1919	1317
Green, Jack Lee, 1944	2216	Hall, Victor N., 1924	1552
Green, James P., 1952	2492	Hallen, F. C., 1901	97
Green, John Wilbur, 1927	1712	Halliday, H. H., 1926	1621
Greenan, Edward, 1925	1582	Halliday, W. A., 1908	694
Greenburg, Jno., 1910	949	Halm, Chas. J., Jr., 1931	1944
Greenburg, Max, 1911	976	Halterman, H. W., 1952	2524
Greene, F. R., 1908	547	Haltermann, Isaac L., 1920	1402
Greer, E. F., 1908	553	Hamilton, J. L., 1905	294
Greever, Joseph W., 1945	2248	Hamilton, Robert G., 1949	2384
Gregg, Harry W., 1920	1367	Hammer, William H., 1922	1494
Gregory, B. F., 1912	1032	Hammond, C. Howard, 1907	494
Gregory, Thos. G., 1921	1457	Hammons, R. W., 1905	447
Griffin, E. B., 1905	283	Hampton, E. B., 1905	440
Griffith, C. R., 1908	551	Hampton, E. B., 1920	1440
Griffith, Joseph K., 1908	820	Hampton, Garland, 1908	692
Griffith, Nathaniel Dee, 1929	1844	Hampton, Glenn Dolland, 1927	1719
Griffith, W. H., 1908	698½	Hampton, H. A., 1903	199
Griggs, L. F., 1908	554	Hampton, Hobson Earle, 1925	1590
Griswold, A. F., 1908	550	Hanes, Sampson S., 1920	1430
Gritz, Elmer C., 1945	2249	Hanks, Claude Benjamin, 1902	159
Gromer, Wm. Ray, 1930	1885	Hanratty, Thomas J., 1929	1846
Groom, Hal E., 1954	2603	Hansen, G. R., 1907	480
Gross, Forrest A., 1947	2330	Hansen, J. C., 1907	501
Grove, Arthur William, 1924	1568	Hanson, Alden Dewey, 1927	1717
Gruebbel, Robert August, 1927	1722	Haradjian, N. S., 1905	286
Grundy, Geo. B., 1923	1516	Hardestry, R. R., 1910	952
Grupe, Harold E., 1932	1966	Hardiman, Eugene Wald, 1919	1216
Gsell, H. H., 1908	819	Hardin, John Calvin, 1927	1698
Gum, E. S., 1908	691	Hardin, William Joseph, 1949	2390
Guptill, Arthur E., 1905	277	Hardy, J. Ed., 1899	65
Guthrie, G. R., 1905	279	Hargrove, Geo. H., 1899	57
Hack, H. W., 1905	289	Harlan,	
Haddock, John Newton, 1924	1563	Yantis Harrington, 1926	1648
Haddock, Thos. R., 1937	2052	Harlin, A. R., 1921	1463
Hadley, E. E., 1910	919	Harmon, Arthur Garfield, 1919	1349
Hairston, Everett Lee, 1921	1473	Harmon, T. F., 1908	821
Haldeman, W. O., 1905	290	Harnden, Leo, Jr., 1947	2322

Harness, Lewis Conrad, 1919	1326	Heard, Woodson N., 1920	1407
Harp, Don S., 1951	2473	Hedge, Dan Albert, 1927	1690
Harrington, Ambrose A., 1920	1383	Hedges, J. T., 1911	979
Harris, Ada, 1913	1078	Hedrick, S. N., 1909	867
Harris, C. P., 1905	295	Heerwald, Edgar W., 1916	1132
Harris, David S., Jr., 1941	2158	Hefley, Harvey Wesley, 1950	2430
Harris, Edgar Raymond, 1905	421	Hefley, Theo Lester, 1942	2178
Harris, George G., Jr., 1954	2580	Heflin, E. E., 1905	291
Harris, J. M., Jr., 1937	2060	Heivly, J. H., 1901	113
Harris, Vernon Frank, 1916	1151	Heidtman, O. C., 1909	865
Harris, Warren B., 1912	1035	Heller, David E., 1946	2316
Harrison, Forest DeWitt, 1919	1297	Hellums, H. D., 1908	557
Harrison, Frank Harold, 1919	1281	Helm, J. J., 1905	393
Harrison, Lawrence M., 1919	1359	Helmy, Isaac Morris, 1925	1586
Harrison, Mildred, 1925	1579	Helmig, C. F., 1931	1939
Harrison, R. R., 1946	2315	Henderson, B. O., 1905	424
Harrison, Thos. F., Jr., 1943	2198	Henderson, Russell L., 1920	1404
Harrison, W. A., 1908	560	Hendricks, W. B., 1907	479
Harrison, W. L., 1921	1476	Hendrix, Paul, 1918	1236
Harrison, William, 1908	555	Henry, Dale Samuel, 1915	1114
Harrison, Wm. H., 1905	846	Henson, James O., 1915	1117
Hart, Clinton T., 1896	42	Henson, Perkins Fentiss, 1916	1146
Hart, E. H., 1910	918	Henson, Robert E., 1912	1036
Hart, Geo. Crigler, 1915	1122	Herald, William C., 1952	2506
Hart, Jas. D., 1910	951	Herd, Richard M., 1945	2261
Hart, Jas. O., Jr., 1946	2296	Herring, Herbert Russell, 1925	1598
Harter, C. W., 1905	292	Herring, J. B., 1908	561
Hartsfield, Jno. D., 1908	695	Herring, W. A., 1894	35
Hartzog, Allen G., 1928	1756	Herron, J. C., 1901	109
Hartzog, Alva L., 1929	1824	Hess, Chas. A., 1912	1037
Harvey, L. A., 1938	2081	Hess, E. R., 1926	1623
Harville, Roy Joseph, 1916	1138	Hiatt, James G., 1950	2434
Hauser, Irving Mathew, 1928	1793	Hiatt, William Reed, 1950	2438
Havely, C. K., 1910	950	Hickman, J. J., 1908	693
Hawkins, Edna Love, 1920	1410	Hickman, Carlos Stephen, 1925	1577
Hawkins, J. B., 1910	920	Higgins, Marion L., 1901	102
Hawkins, R. E., 1924	1201	Hilbarn, E. N., 1900	76
Hawthorne,		Hill, Alva J., 1947	2337
Dorwin Eugene, 1953	2564	Hill, Carle Estes, 1920	1387
Hayden, D. J., 1905	288	Hill, V. E., 1911	1009
Hayes, Alice C., 1917	1215	Hill, Wm. Lorenze, 1927	1692
Hayes, Clinton L., 1907	500	Hillman, Hector, 1909	866
Hayes, Ralph E., 1903	168	Hine, Otto Lewis H., 1915	1102
Haymes, Ben Franklin, 1941	2159	Hine, Ted S., 1952	2508
Haynes, Wm. B., 1932	1974	Hines, G. B., 1908	696
Hays, Hugh Gordon, 1926	1642	Hines, J. B., 1905	285
Hays, Merle Dale, 1951	2465	Hiniker, Nicholas L., 1934	1993
Hays, Russell V., 1918	1259	Hinson, P. F., 1916	1146
Hazen, W. D., 1905	384	Hirschi, Robt. G., 1945	2272
Heard, Elmer, Jr., 1954	2593	Hirschi, R. O., 1901	88

Hirth, Charles E., 1905	287	Huffman, J. W., 1902	127
Hitchcock, I. D., 1908	800	Huggler, Judson E., 1951	2479
Hixon, A. C., 1898	51	Hughes, D. A., 1911	1008
Hobbs, John Richard, 1928	1769	Hughes, Geo. A., 1894	28
Hocker, Chas. Richard, 1922	1499	Hull, Edgar Griffin, 1923	1518
Hodge, E. L., 1912	1038	Humphries, P. V., 1908	822
Hodge, G. R., 1910	921	Hunter, W. Ralph, 1929	1845
Hodges, E. A., 1907	487	Hurt, Wm. J., 1938	2084
Hodhapp, Raymond J., 1928	1800	Husband, R. O., 1927	1733
Holden, H. B., 1905	405	Huston, Benjamin M., 1923	1532
Holder, Harry A., 1918	1261	Huston, E. J., 1905	374
Holdreith, Virgil C., 1935	2022	Hutcheson, Verl Estel, 1932	1969
Hollabough, Glyn Lamar, 1954	2570	Ice, J. E., 1910	922
Holliday, E. O., 1902	162	Ice, T. J., 1908	562
Holliday, Herman H., 1926	1621	Ingalls, P. E., 1911	980
Holloman, Jas. H., 1939	2103	Ingram, G. G., 1931	1942
Holloway, C. J., 1908	558	Ingram, George, 1949	2399
Holm, Chas. J., Jr., 1931	1944	Ingram, John S., 1921	1474
Holman, Donald C., 1948	2358	Ingram, M. L., 1908	697
Holmes, Avery Giles, 1930	1925	Ingram, R. B., 1920	1417
Holmes, A. J., 1901	84	Ingram, Robert Paul, 1934	1994
Holmes, Fred C., 1900	68	Irby, Garland C., 1943	2194
Holt, Arvil B., 1950	2415	Ireland, Leon, 1950	2401
Holt, C. A., 1901	87	Irion, V. K., 1927	1672
Holum, Mrs. G. N., 1916	1140	Ishmael, Don M., 1944	2228
Hooper, Clifford Leon, 1951	2446	Jack, Albert S., 1914	1097
Hooper, James Leroy, 1951	2486	Jackson, James Robert, 1916	1166
Hope, B. N., 1904	223	Jackson, Kenneth Lionel, 1925	1613
Hopkins, Henry Panton, 1925	1602	Jackson, W. D., 1950	2426
Hopkins, Wm. C., 1945	2250	Jacobi, H., 1912	1039
Hopkinson, Walker, 1918	1258	Jacobs, A. C., 1916	1160
Hopper, Chas. L., 1918	1253	Jacobs, G. Dyas, 1920	1395
Horton, H. B., 1908	559	Jacobs, Gulford T., 1929	1847
House, C. H., 1901	113	Jacobs, Harley Fred, 1919	1283
Howard, Fay G., 1920	1436	Jacobs, Wm. T., 1908	565
Howard, Mervin Cecil, 1928	1790	Jacobsen, Elwood, 1903	177
Howard, M. R., 1906	462	James, Don R., 1946	2297
Howard, W. H., 1920	1419	James, Wm. Richard, 1920	1370
Howard, Walter Joseph, 1926	1641	Janney, Warner M., 1891	4
Howe, Michael James, 1954	2566	Jedlicka, H. C., 1923	1544
Howell, I. B., 1921	1487	Jenkins, E. C., 1905	297
Howell, Thomas W., 1893	23	Jenkins, Fairy Dailey, 1921	1450
Howell, Wm. A., 1917	1191	Jenkins, Henry L., 1908	568
Howell, Wm. D., 1925	1578	Jenkins, Joseph B., 1918	1238
Hozen, Calvin Edward, 1901	87	Jenkins, J. H., 1908	567
Hrabe, Anton, 1904	233	Jenks, E. C., 1903	200
Hudson, Andrew H., 1909	892	Jepson, Don G., 1939	2114
Hudson, Truman Aldine, 1936	2049	Jernigan, G. C., 1927	1738
Huff, C. V., 1908	556	John, Herbert, 1925	1610
Huffhines, Seaf Edward, 1930	1886	Johns, Glover, 1929	1871

Johnson, A. J., 1916	1164	Keim, C. P., 1908	573
Johnson, A. S., 1905	375	Keim, Geo. H., 1903	203
Johnson, Edward Felix, 1917	1183	Keisling, F. C., 1918	1220
Johnson, E. H., 1910	940	Keith, A. P., 1902	154
Johnson, George, 1908	701	Keith, Robert E., 1916	1141
Johnson,		Keith, W. W., 1915	1063
George Raymond, 1954	2572	Kelly, Clarence E., 1953	2552
Johnson, Henry Beeson, 1920	1392	Kelly, Bernice E., 1904	226
Johnson, H. J., 1908	703	Kelsey, Lucius A., 1895	37
Johnson, Norman Floyd, 1925	1583	Kemp, L. S., 1904	238
Johnson, U. G., 1908	702	Kennebeck, George R., 1926	1625
Johnson, W. B., 1909	868	Kennedy, Alfred Frazier, 1905	448
Johnston, David F., 1908	566	Kennedy, Barney, 1931	1933
Johnston, Joe Kelso, 1927	1705	Kennedy, Fay H., 1948	2367
Johnston, Joseph E., 1921	1448	Kennedy, J. L., 1929	1849
Johnston, Lee H., 1913	1086	Kennedy, L. M., 1908	572
Johnston, Richard A., 1908	563	Kennedy, Lynden M., 1941	2151
Jones, Austin Lex, 1926	1614	Kennedy, L. S., 1929	1848
Jones, Beverly, 1906	473	Kennedy, M. A., 1917	1219
Jones, Billy A., 1952	2514	Kennedy, Thomas H., 1933	1978
Jones, C. S., 1912	1040	Kennedy, Wm. Arthur, 1919	1336
Jones, Charley Lee, 1919	1303	Kennerdall, C. J., 1905	301
Jones, E. L., 1908	700	Kennon, W. K., 1911	983
Jones, Georgia D., 1921	1449	Kerby, Warren H., 1934	2010
Jones, Harold Paul, 1927	1704	Kermott, O. L., 1909	847
Jones, Hilliard S., 1908	700	Kersey, Clarence C., 1935	2027
Jones, Jesse, 1911	981	Kessler, Walter Burnell, 1925	1585
Jones, J. B., 1908	699	Key, Ted Woodrow, 1947	2328
Jones, Joseph Nathaniel, 1909	881	Keyes, Edward Frazier, 1916	1127
Jones, J. W., 1902	142	Kibler, Richard C., 1908	824
Jones, J. W., 1914	1090	Kidd, Howard Ray, 1919	1263
Jones, R. B., 1908	698	Kiddo, Clyde Howard, 1927	1689
Jones, Robert Gerald, 1949	2392	Kieser, Clifford V., 1909	982
Jones, Thomas A., 1905	455	Kilboun, Grant R., 1927	1715
Jones, U. S., 1908	564	Killiam, F. Q., 1926	1661
Jones, Volney Victor, 1926	1646	Kimball, G. G., 1925	1606
Jones, W. B., 1905	414	Kimbrough, E. Judson, 1903	195
Jordan, Cyrus Augustus, 1900	74	Kimbrough, Sylvester E., 1918	1227
Juhl, Lee K., 1931	1949	King, Frank, 1908	706
Kagey, David Franklin, 1919	1308	King, M. D., 1905	300
Kaho, Harry Howard, 1908	569	Kinzy, Leo H., 1919	1312
Kaho, N. Noel, 1930	1912	Kippenberger, Louis H., 1929	1851
Kalb, John Estes, 1920	1400	Kirkpatrick, E. E., 1894	25
Kalon, W. G., 1908	574	Kirkpatrick, F. K., 1921	1442
Karch, Ralph Raymond, 1923	1523	Kirkpatrick, O. A., 1908	707
Keel, C. W., 1905	299	Klabzuba, Edward E., 1926	1654
Keener, Jno. LeRoy, 1942	2172	Klabzuba Frank B., 1927	1713
Keidel, Robert P., 1943	2203	Klapacs, Victor P., 1923	1531
Keifer, F. O., 1908	571	Klein, Glenn W., 1952	2505
Keifer, Harry Lee, 1932	1968	Klein, Louis F., 1954	2605

Long, S. A., 1904	216	McConaghie,	
Longwell, W. T., 1918	1231	Vernon David, 1923	1551
Loomis, Edgerton Fay, 1908	709	McConn, Jas. F., 1913	1071
Lord, D. D., 1931	1937	McConn, Martin L., 1895	41
Lott, Wayne H., 1950	2417	McConnell, Leon G., 1934	1999
Louwien, Gus, 1907	481	McCoy, Elijah, 1894	33
Love, Buz Lee, 1919	1325	McCracken, Charles E., 1937	2056
Love, Robert S., 1905	417	McCracken, Gerald A., 1933	1977
Loveless, Sam G., 1949	2400	McCreary, W. B., 1901	86
Lovell, M. C., 1901	118	McCrory, J. J., 1945	2253
Lo Vellette, Roy E., 1919	1342	McCrum, Thomas B., 1930	1929
Lo Vellette, William E., 1952	2528	McCue, C. M., 1921	1452
Lowes, G. G., 1905	303	McCue, W. E., 1919	1340
Lowrie, Austin M., 1921	1438	McCullough, Thos. M., 1945	2266
Lucas, Howard T., 1917	1177	McCutchan, James F., 1920	1386
Lucas, L. A., 1930	1918	McCutchen, Don P., 1938	2079
Ludlow, C. E., 1938	2086	McDonald, Clyde Baker, 1934	1997
Luellen, Samuel Vance, 1898	49	McDonald, J. C., 1908	592
Luthcotte, Clifford, 1930	1889	McDonald, Wm. H., 1916	1142
Lyman, Chas. W., 1917	1223	McDonough, J. C., 1908	796
Lyman, Sam Warner, 1926	1637	McDonough, W. W., 1908	713
Lynn, A. L., 1930	1919	McElhinney, Wilmer W., 1927	1706
Lyon, C. W., 1908	825	McElwaine, L. P., 1945	2273
McAdoo, C. C., 1908	732	McEwen, Earl Drake, 1920	1394
McAdoo, H. L., 1908	726	McGee, L. C., 1929	1858
McAfee, J. A., 1908	717	McGill, Thomas W., 1914	1098
McAllister, D. B., 1938	2087	McGouirk,	
McAllister, H. A., 1902	123	Glenn Chandler, 1951	2452
McAnally, Geo. D., 1927	1746	McGreevy, Wm. H., 1902	141
McAnally, Jas. D., 1943	2199	McGregor,	
McAnerny, F. A., 1946	2300	Winton George, 1927	1708
McAnnally, Wm. M., 1918	1242	McHenry, John Henry, 1927	1691
McAtee, Von Rue, 1940	2144	McInnis, Harry B., 1939	2110
McAuley, F. A., 1905	321	McKay, Sidney Earl, 1923	1537
McBride, George Ivan, 1928	1763	McKee, V. M., 1908	727
McBride, Geo. L., 1947	2342	McKeehan, Alfred B., 1903	186
McCall, Douglas T., 1951	2467	McKeever, Joseph J., 1913	1087
McCarthy, E. T., 1905	317	McKellar, Dougal A., 1917	1187
McCartney, O. E., 1905	315	McKelvey, E. C., 1908	728
McCarty, Ira E., 1906	463	McKelvy, W. L. B., 1909	883
McCarty, Joseph L., 1921	1446	McKennon, Parma D., Jr., 1938	2095
McCarty, O. H., 1905	377	McKenzie, A. E., 1908	801
McCathron, John G., 1891	9	McKenzie, P. S., 1908	590
McClain, Cecil Ray, 1952	2516	McKenzie, W. H., 1908	718
McClintic, Geo. V., 1921	1456	McKeown, Howard A., 1915	1108
McClintock, E. C., 1905	323	McKinley, T. W., 1908	587
McClure, Harry M., 1921	1466	McLarty, Charles, 1908	729
McClure, J. W., 1905	320	McLarty, Todd, 1929	1859
McClurg, J. A., 1909	793	McLaughlin, F. J., 1904	227
McCollum, Glen W., 1934	1998	McLaughlin, G. I., 1939	2101

Miles, Robert Lewis, 1947	2349	Moore, John, 1908	585
Miles, T. H., 1893	24	Moore, Lewis Raymond, 1934	1995
Miley, Earl L., 1923	1536	Moore, Max R., 1952	2495
Miley, Tom H., 1942	2181	Moore, Milton L., 1939	2117
Miller, A. W., 1907	483	Moore, Robt. Louis, 1940	2136
Miller, C. S., 1901	104	Moore, W. C., 1942	2182
Miller, Don L., 1954	2594	Moore, Willard L., 1921	1467
Miller, E. E., 1903	187	Moorman, Jesse Adams, 1908	593
Miller, Ernest L., 1940	2128	Moran, M. J., 1904	231
Miller, Frank L., 1923	1547	Morgan, Chas. Maurice, 1928	1802
Miller, F. Werner, 1934	1996	Morgan, D. H., 1903	171
Miller, J. A., 1906	464	Morgan, H. A., 1908	586
Miller, James Raymond, 1936	2043	Morgan, M. J., 1915	1111
Miller, Jno. Alvin, 1946	2282	Morgan, S. A., 1909	848
Miller, John Taylor, 1908	828	Morris, Burdette, 1938	2073
Miller, Keith R., 1950	2419	Morris, E. W., 1908	810
Miller, Norman E., 1908	723	Morris, J. T., 1908	731
Miller, Ronnie H., 1931	1943	Morris, R. E., 1908	584
Miller, T. J., 1908	588	Morrison, Carl J., 1928	1765
Miller, V. A., 1920	1421	Morrison, David G., 1931	1946
Milligan, W. S., 1908	578	Morrison, O. M., 1908	591
Mills, E. James, 1905	313	Morrison, Wm. P., 1914	1089
Mills, Jack H., 1952	2496	Morrow, J. A., 1905	312
Mills, James Dillard, 1928	1772	Morrow, J. D., 1930	1903
Mills, S. B., 1910	923	Mose, Jno. D., 1943	2212
Millsap, John Wm., 1908	827	Moseley, W. V., 1912	1043
Mindeman, George E., 1951	2466	Motley, Eric L., 1953	2554
Minter, R. M., 1905	401	Moulder, Earl Y., 1929	1857
Mitcham, Francis Marion, 1908	715	Mullen, David Cline, 1905	420
Mitchell, E. E., 1903	172	Mullen, Joseph Henry, 1903	204
Mitchell, James O'Neal, 1929	1854	Mundy, Henry H., 1921	1482
Mitchell, Jno. Lee, 1944	2219	Munger, M. W., 1905	316
Mitchell, Kenneth A., 1928	1786	Murdock, T. F., 1908	725
Mitchell, Leonard G., 1903	184	Murdock, Thomas John, 1950	2420
Mitchell, M. L., 1943	2211	Murphy, H. L., 1905	310
Mitchell, Rupert C., 1938	2077	Murphy, Jas. M., 1939	2109
Mitchell, W. C., 1909	871	Murray, Carl Morrison, 1917	1210
Moe, Erik, 1920	1397	Murray, Moses W., 1908	508
Montgomery, Gaston, 1903	170	Musgrave, Everett, 1911	1012
Montgomery, T. A., 1908	721	Musgrave, J. D., 1904	229
Moon,		Myers, T. A., 1902	156
Edward Crawford, Jr., 1948	2368	Nauman, B., 1906	465
Moon, Joseph D., 1917	1174	Neal, Cecil D., 1928	1788
Moore, David R., 1905	411	Neal, James Pierson, 1915	1118
Moore, Edward Lee, 1905	314	Nease, William J., 1952	2498
Moore, E. W., 1908	580	Neel, Bert, 1908	595
Moore, Frank Clifford, 1900	67	Neel, Wilbur E., 1954	2611
Moore, G. B., 1908	577	Neighbors, E. H., 1926	1620
Moore, Inez C., 1908	579	Neiman, W. H., 1909	899
Moore, Jack D., 1939	2116	Neissel, Verner Peter, 1924	1571

Pearson, Alvin Wendell, 1934	2008	Potter, Wm. Lewis, 1908	606
Peet, S. T., 1908	744	Potts, E. W., 1946	2303
Pelky, W. H., 1907	496	Potts, J. R., 1917	1195
Pendleton, Ben, 1908	745	Potts, L. L., 1908	830
Pendleton, Daniel F., 1922	1505	Pounds, A. A., 1929	1860
Pendleton, R. H., 1901	98	Powell B. F., 1908	604
Penick, O. R., 1926	1639	Powell, Benjamin F., Jr., 1953	2544
Penley, Walter Elmo, 1953	2540	Powell, J. B., 1908	797
Pennell, W. S., 1908	600	Powell, John L., 1940	2138
Pennington, Dee C., 1938	2089	Powhatan, L. C., 1908	607
Penrose, W. C., 1905	406	Poynor, Oscar Q., 1913	1073
Peoples, David A., 1891	2	Poynor, Wm. Lee, 1917	1182
Perkins, E. R., 1903	197	Prather, R. M., 1905	408
Perry, Clifton C., 1907	495	Presgrove, Russell J., 1952	2497
Perry, James T., 1933	1985	Pressley,	
Peters, Alphonso, 1908	746	Thomas Jefferson, 1926	1659
Peterson, Clarence W., 1951	2483	Pretty, Wm. H., 1937	2065
Peterson, D. N., 1905	325	Price, Everett Alfred, 1949	2379
Peterson, Ludwic Elmer, 1918	1252	Price, E. H., 1918	1235
Petit, S. H., 1908	599	Price, T. A., 1911	989
Petty, Evan W., 1933	1979	Price, Wm. B., 1909	900
Pfeiffer, A. A., 1908	743	Pringle, G. A., 1908	803
Phelan, Patrick, 1937	2069	Proctor, G. R., 1912	1044
Phillips, Donald K., 1933	1982	Proffitt, J. H., 1905	326
Phillips, W. S., 1908	742	Pruett, Chas. Lewis, 1947	2350
Phipps, Chas. E., 1945	2271	Pruitt, Luke Wendell, 1927	1728
Pickens, R. O., 1923	1545	Pruner, A. F., 1910	925
Pickhardt, L. H., 1919	1346	Pryor, Jesse Henry, 1919	1343
Piercy, Harvey J., 1926	1647	Pugh, Wm. Henry, 1905	409
Pigford, Jack D., 1946	2320	Putman, J. C., 1910	924
Pinkner, Joe, Jr., 1939	2106	Pyatt, Clarence E., 1928	1754
Pippin, Bascum C., Jr., 1952	2504	Quast, Ed Christian, 1934	2000
Pisiel, Joseph Pos, 1903	174	Quimby, Dale Maurice, 1949	2382
Pitney, Fred Owen, 1926	1638	Quinn, J. Harry, 1908	608
Plath, R. E., 1905	330	Raak, Kenneth D., 1950	2427
Pletcher, J. W., 1906	469	Raffington, W. T., 1927	1736
Plowman, Paul E., 1954	2595	Ragland, A. G., 1910	942
Poindexter, Wm., Jr., 1945	2262	Rainwater, W. E., 1912	1046
Polhamus, Elvin R., 1914	1099	Ralls, R. L., 1921	1456
Pollock, Adolph A., 1917	1184	Ralph, H. B., 1912	1047
Pollock, Harold Raymond, 1953	2536	Rambo, M. E., 1908	618
Pollock, Leo, 1911	1014	Ramseur, Roy, 1923	1534
Pollock, S., 1908	602	Ramsey, P. H., 1908	831
Pomeroy, L. M., 1905	407	Ramsey, R. H., 1905	436
Pool, Wm. Leroy, 1954	2585	Rand, T. H., 1905	331
Porth, Edgar, 1920	1381	Randall, Owen Heath, 1919	1332
Portwood, R. S., 1908	605	Randolph, Josh Douglas, 1953	2538
Potter, A. B., 1902	121	Randolph, T. J., 1909	901
Potter, A. B., 1917	1172	Raney, Frank O., 1919	1294
Potter, J. W., 1911	988	Rankin, E. B., 1912	1045

Rookstool, Farris L., 1934	2001	Sanger, E. E., 1907	491
Rookstool, Wendell D., 1933	1984	Sanger, G. L., 1938	2090
Rookwood, Thomas C., 1917	1180	Sanger, Sunshine F. C., 1948	2356
Rose, B. L., 1910	927	Sankey, Wm. E., 1920	1423
Rose, C. N., 1905	333	Sapper, E. J., 1908	794
Rose, Elton A., Jr., 1946	2305	Sather, Wm., 1919	1284
Rose, William H., 1952	2512	Saubert, Walter John, 1925	1576
Rosenburg, H. D., 1908	832	Saul, E. B., 1943	2204
Rosnick, John C., 1927	1703	Saunders, L. P., 1902	153
Ross, R. S., 1913	1070	Saunders, W. R., 1905	340
Ross, Wm. W., 1944	2223	Sawyer, P. W., 1939	2111
Rossington, W. A., 1908	753	Sayler, J. E., 1905	342
Roush, W. T., 1911	1015	Schaffer, Lee Harrison, 1911	1016
Rowe, C. A., 1907	503	Schiefelbusch, Max, 1908	755
Rowe, H. C., 1908	617	Schley, C. E., 1908	767
Rowe, Lloyd F., 1937	2071	Schlicht, Otto H., 1936	2047
Rozen, Meyer, 1930	1915	Schmid, William L., 1950	2433
Rozen, Ralph David, 1927	1724	Schneider, J. G., 1905	419
Ruble, James B., 1931	1947	Schock, John L., 1930	1875
Rudd, Kenneth D., 1948	2363	Schoeni, Theodore Elliott, 1938	2074
Ruddell, George, 1899	64	Schow, Carl E., 1947	2336
Ruhlen, Chas. A., 1911	992	Schowengerdt, W. O., 1910	930
Rumsey, Dwight Wilson, 1942	2171	Schrader, Lee B., 1922	1510
Rush, T. J., 1893	22	Schroeder, Arthur E., 1905	432
Rush, W. D., 1908	750	Schultz, J. J., 1901	115
Russell, Albert E., 1923	1541	Schwartz, P. W., 1912	1048
Russell, Clyde G., 1937	2068	Scimeca, Hilde Irene, 1951	2472
Russell, E. W., Jr., 1947	2331	Scism, Norman A., 1919	1322
Russell, Grady Pease, 1919	1320	Scott, Albert Dandy, 1953	2559
Russell, James B., 1948	2355	Scott, Clark Oren, 1919	1357
Russell, Jay D., 1891	6	Scott, L. W., 1905	307
Russell, Leon H., 1927	1683	Scott, Taylor B., 1946	2306
Russman, Sumner A., 1938	2096	Scott, W. C., 1908	622
Rutherford, G. C., 1910	957	Scranton, H. S., 1910	934
Ryan, E. P. R., 1908	611	Scrivener, J. A., 1929	1862
Ryan, Louis J., 1934	2009	Scroggin, Jess Walker, 1922	1495
Ryan, Martin C., 1908	610	Scruton, W. J., 1912	1059
Ryan, W. V., 1908	834	Seagrave, C. W., 1908	838
Sadtler, G. H., 1908	621	Seaman, F. G., 1908	769
Saffarans, H. T., 1908	760	Seamands, Charles W., 1951	2487
Sales, A. C., 1939	2125	Searl, Ronald Francis, 1925	1594
Salsbury, G. R., 1908	759	Sears, J. W., 1908	619
Salyer, John W., 1947	2339	Seaton, Benjamin H., 1894	34
Salzberg, B. A., 1909	903	Sebert, Alvin F., 1910	932
Sampeck, Adrian J., 1950	2403	Sebert, C. A., 1943	2206
Sanchez, Francisco Javier, 1950	2418	Sebora, Earl Lloyd, 1919	1331
Sanders, Wm. Earl, 1936	2048	Seeds, Robert Rowe, 1920	1375
Sandlin, Harold G., 1944	2222	Seesaran, Herman R., 1952	2529
Sandlin, James Claude, 1919	1305	Segur, F. D., 1908	624
Sanger, Edw. B., 1946	2283	Seids, Arthur C., 1905	365

Smith, Thomas Sylvester, 1928	1783	Stewart, C. F., 1902	146
Smith, Wade Henry, 1928	1780	Stewart, Frank William, 1950	2413
Smith, Wayne K., 1948	2354	Stewart, Jack Lauren, 1952	2511
Smith, William E., Jr., 1952	2525	Stewart, John W., 1920	1373
Smith, Wm. Pryor, 1941	2161	Stewart, Kenneth F., 1954	2596
Smith, W. S., 1907	489	Stewart, O. A., 1908	766
Smoot, James Lawrence, 1919	1338	Stewart, Robt. Emment, 1916	1129
Smoot, Robert E., 1921	1471	Stickel, F. A., Jr., 1902	151
Smyser, John Ward, 1899	58	Stiffler, Francis G., 1903	183
Smyth, Cyril Quinn, 1916	1125	Stigler, Harold T., 1942	2170
Sneed, J. L. T., 1910	482	Stiles, L. E., 1906	474
Snider, R. D., 1927	1732	Stilley, V. A., Jr., 1921	1481
Snider, W. H., 1902	163	Stilwell, R. F., 1908	628
Snodgrass, R. C., 1908	625	Stinson, Jimmie Lue, 1952	2499
Snyder, Oscar P., 1930	1877	Stivison, W. M., 1908	836
Sollis, H. V., 1903	185	Stone, Elmo R., 1922	1489
Sorrels, Harry Harold, 1925	1607	Stone, Earl Vincent, 1926	1644
Sorrels, Tullie Wallace, 1915	1120	Stone, F. P., 1910	933
Spann, S. E., Jr., 1942	2179	Stone, J. R., 1905	449
Sparks, E. F. K., 1896	44	Stooksbury, J. H., 1905	341
Sparks, Fred D., 1901	114	Storm, Bruce D., 1927	1700
Sparks, James Vincent, 1921	926	Stotts, W. Harvey, 1934	2003
Spears, Robt. Eli., 1947	2343	Stowell, G. R., 1911	1017
Spencer, Sheldon, 1930	1901	Strake, Frank Albert, 1927	1723
Spettel, L. J., 1908	757	Strand, Collins W., 1934	2004
Spicer, James A., 1916	1158	Stratton, A. C., 1905	396
Spyres, Ray M., 1946	2289	Strawn, W. Irving, 1917	1203
Stacy, Farris Alvin, 1924	1553	Streck, Warren F., 1945	2268
Stafford, H. E., 1945	2234	Strickler, C. D., 1930	1906
Stafford, Thomas S., 1913	1064	Strickler, Elmer Bon, 1924	1564
Stalford, F. D., 1901	96	Stroughton, Frank R., 1931	1953
Standfield, L. E., 1908	808	Stuart, A. E. I., 1931	1934
Standley, Cade B., 1919	1275	Stuart, E. G., 1899	59
Stanfield, C. Mac., 1915	1113	Stubblefield, E. A., 1908	768
Stanke, E. F., 1908	761	Stubbs, J. S., 1906	468
Stanwood, H. D., 1907	488	Suesskind, Henry, 1908	620
Staples, J. M., 1908	756	Suffield, Harry F., 1909	876
Stapleton, C. L., 1909	904	Sullivan, Edgar L., 1939	2120
Stapp, J. M., 1908	765	Sullivan, Lars Ruben, 1919	1306
Stebbins, Edward L., 1954	2599	Sullivan,	
Stebbins, E. W., 1921	1443	Martin Frederick, 1934	2002
Steckel, Geo. Wm., 1925	1589	Sullivan, O. Gordon, 1949	2380
Steelyl, W. L., 1908	626	Sullivan, Robert H., 1941	2154
Steinbeck, C. H., 1905	391	Sundberg, I., 1905	336
Stembo, Edward, 1909	874	Sutton, F. W., 1905	418
Stephenson, C. E., 1905	339	Swafford, Munroe, 1901	80
Stevens, P. N., 1910	935	Swander, Claude Ray, 1916	1131
Stevenson, C. R., 1909	850	Swanson, A. E., 1903	189
Stevenson, G. E., 1908	762	Swartz, Wm. B., 1945	2260
Stevison, W. M., 1908	836	Sweet, W. S., 1901	79

Swift, Lionel Vance, 1919	1271	Tiller, William D., 1908	632
Swigert, Geo. Orton, 1919	1350	Tingay, Lynn H., 1930	1879
Swihart, S. S., 1903	208	Tinsley, K. C., 1930	1907
Synowski, Richard C., 1952	2493	Tipton, Albert C., Jr., 1954	2581
Taft, O. H., 1903	211	Tischauner, A. A., 1930	1893
Taggart, Chas. O., 1908	795	Tisdal, Victor C., 1940	2130
Talbutt, Dillard E., 1920	1368	Tissier, T. M., 1921	1458
Talbutt, J. B., 1905	363	Titterington, James L., 1916	1152
Talley, Olin J., 1938	2091	Titterington, Richard M., 1916	1153
Talley, Rex W., 1937	2066	Tobey, Ronnal Lloyd, 1953	2561
Tanner, S. W., 1905	344	Todd, Earl V., 1921	1468
Tarpley, Thomas D., 1954	2598	Tollett, H. E., 1924	1569
Tate, Oscar B., 1937	2062	Toma, Thos. J., 1947	2351
Taubman, Arthur I., 1948	2365	Tomlin, Bryce D., 1954	2597
Taubman, Milton S., 1939	2121	Tourtellot, T. J., 1906	478
Taylor, Carlyle, 1916	1159	Townsend, J. A., 1902	149
Taylor, E. D., 1902	128	Townsend, Money M., 1928	1759
Taylor, Geo. E., 1908	772	Travis, Floyd P., 1928	1816
Taylor, Herbert H., 1933	1980	Travis, Plato H., 1916	1167
Taylor, J. N., 1909	885½	Travis, Wm. Clinton, 1919	1319
Taylor, Ray M., 1944	2220	Traw, E. C., 1916	1169
Taylor, Robert B., 1920	1422	Trawick, Jim Steen, 1926	1662
Taylor, Robert B., Jr., 1953	2537	Treadwell, Thos. J., 1916	1145
Taylor, Wallace H., 1950	2404	Trimble, A. R., 1917	1186
Taymon, G. H., 1908	631	Trimble, Aaron R., Jr., 1943	2187
Teaff, Joe Aaron, 1943	2188	Trimble, Chas. I., 1919	1339
Teall, Gordon L., 1934	2011	Trimble, Joe T., 1928	1820
Temples, John M., 1908	771	Trindle, Floyd W., 1952	2515
Tennis, Lesley Emerson, 1934	2005	Triplett, R. L., 1944	2225
Thacker, T. T., 1918	1230	Trotter, L. C., 1940	2139
Thelin, Alfred Lewis, 1920	1376	Trotter, Virgil H., 1946	2309
Thomas, C. C., 1905	345	Troupe, A. B., 1917	1181
Thomas, F. E. L., 1908	634	Trusler, Frank S., 1917	1213
Thomas, Ira J., 1918	1241	Tschauner, A. A., 1930	1893
Thomas, Jas. A., 1943	2260	Tull, Aaron B., 1901	93
Thomas, James P., 1941	2164	Turk, Alonzo Benjamin, 1919	1314
Thomason, Hugh Dewitt, 1938	2075	Turnbaugh,	
Thomasson, K. W., 1946	2308	Franklin Edward, 1919	1288
Thompson, Ben Chester, 1919	1269	Turnbull, Adam, 1901	89
Thompson, C. A., 1908	633	Turnbull, Cecil Wayne, 1928	1776
Thompson, Clyde C., 1919	1335	Turnbull,	
Thompson, J. D., 1908	770	Leonard Kenneth, 1935	2025
Thompson, Jas. Mayer, 1926	1640	Turnbull, Ralph P., 1929	1865
Thompson, Jno. M., Jr., 1922	1491	Turner, Fred A., 1919	1324
Thompson, Oren A., 1935	2020	Turner, G. F., 1929	1828
Thompson, W. H., 1905	346	Turner, Geo. L., 1919	1327
Thompson, Walter M., 1954	2608	Turner, Howard Leroy, 1920	1396
Thurman, W. E., 1930	1908	Turner, J. A., 1910	960
Tibbetts, Z. H., 1921	1486	Turner, N. E., 1919	1347
Tibbs, Russell V., 1930	1892	Turner, R. L., 1946	2321

Turner, Wilbur R., 1921	1459	Ward, Max E., 1939	2105
Tyler, Chas. Day, 1942	2169	Ward, Thomas Acquinas, 1928	1799
Tyler, Theresa M. (Hunt), 1902	134	Warden, Ezra F., 1946	2311
Umholtz, B. M., 1903	209	Warden, Thomas, 1911	1018
Unverferth,		Warder, Lloyd Emery, 1927	1675
Albert Harmon, 1919	1264	Ware, Prentiss E., 1937	2055
Vammen, Reuel E., 1951	2477	Warner, C. P., 1905	355
Vammen, W. L., 1944	2232	Warner, Dale D., 1915	1115
Vandas, Geo. James, 1912	1049	Warner, M. W., 1904	234
Van Duzer, Robt. Missin, 1913	1077	Warren, E. C., 1911	1002
Vann, Geo. S., 1926	1624	Warren, F. G., 1908	789
Vann, Roy H., 1937	2057	Warren, F. W., 1910	938
VanSant, Jas. P., 1939	2107	Warrick, H. O., 1921	1451
Vaughan, J. B., 1909	877	Warrick, Thurman W., 1935	2026
Vaughan, Wm. S., 1910	936	Warwick, Walter Allen, 1917	1211
Vaught, C. S., 1905	348	Washington, D. E., 1946	2314
Venk, Ralph Earl, 1951	2478	Washington, F. Q., 1930	1922
Vincent, Ernest C., 1953	2542	Waters, Feron G., 1949	2375
Vincent, W. S., 1905	347	Waters, Tom Rogers, 1950	2412
Vinette, W. J., 1908	636	Watkins, A. T., 1905	386
Voelkle, A. R., 1944	2218	Watkins, E. C., 1904	240
Waddell, John Quigley, 1893	20	Watkins, H. R., 1907	484
Wadlin, John Albert, 1924	1561	Watkins, James H., 1921	1453
Wadlin, Jno. Albert, 1943	2185	Watson, A. T., 1908	777
Wagner, Harry N., 1921	1469	Watson, Luther Perry, 1951	2481
Wagoner, J. B., 1905	356	Watson, Martha, 1908	778
Wahl, Lewis F., 1937	2061	Wauson, A. R., 1916	1128
Wait, W. L., 1902	140	Weatherford, J. L., 1908	637
Walker, A. B., 1903	210	Weaver, H. O., 1913	1072
Walker, A. J., 1921	1483	Webb, J. W., 1911	1001
Walker, David, 1905	349	Webber, Geo. R., 1945	2263
Walker, E. A., 1903	179	Weeks, Horace A., 1908	773
Walker, H. M., 1908	788	Wehrheim, Francis Wm., 1928	1794
Walker, H. T., 1908	774	Weiler, Eugene Joseph, 1949	2386
Walker, L. L., 1938	2092	Weinberger, Jules A., 1940	2148
Walker, Richard Page, 1950	2422	Weir, W. A., 1903	180
Walker, W. E., 1905	395	Weir, Wm. J., 1943	2209
Wall, Thomas P., 1908	782	Weiss, Samuel George, 1920	1406
Wallace, Austin Welton, 1924	1570	Welch, Harhl H., 1930	1878
Wallace, David Emett, 1918	1246	Welch, Joe, 1915	1112
Wallace, G. C., 1902	143	Wells, Chas. Byron, 1920	1384
Wallace, J. R., 1917	1214	Wells, Chas. Wesley, 1918	1249
Wallack, D. L., 1901	101	Wells, H. J., 1904	232
Walters, Aaron, 1917	1176	Wells, James Alfred, 1899	56
Walters, A. L., 1908	640	Wertz, Duane Forest, 1925	1603
Walters, R. A., 1908	785	West, Arthur, 1903	193
Walters, R. S., 1911	998	West, Arthur J., 1906	470
Waltrip, P. W., 1911	997	West, C. E., 1908	779
Waltzen, L. D., 1909	905	West, H. Ralston, 1900	66
Waltzer, Ross E., 1946	2310	West, R. C., 1908	811

Westenhaver, Earl H., 1905	352	Williams, Phillip Earl, 1926	1628
Westerberg, Milton L., 1948	2366	Williams, R. L., 1910	962
Wetzell, D. P., 1902	150	Williams, T. H., 1894	36
Wheeler,		Williams, W. S., 1905	351
Norton Lawrence, 1925	1588	Williamson, John Albert, 1926	1652
Wheeler, Paul Crayton, 1927	1711	Williamson, R. W., 1921	1478
Wheeler, V. R., 1910	961	Williamston, H. W., 1920	1425
Wheeler, W. A., 1912	1050	Willis, L. Leroy, 1934	2007
Whitby, A. Baxter, 1906	476	Willis, Walter Wolf, 1949	2377
White, Carlton B., 1920	1414	Wills, L. L., 1913	1069
White, Charles E., 1919	1285	Wilson, Chas. V., 1941	2155
White, Charles Lincoln, 1901	106	Wilson, Clarence D., 1908	643
White, Chester Arthur, 1908	781	Wilson, Drury, 1925	1595
White, Clem, 1907	504	Wilson, E. D., 1902	155
White, F. G., 1930	1923	Wilson, Edwin Lee, 1946	2313
White, H. B., 1912	1053	Wilson, Lyle C., 1935	2034
White, Harry E., 1921	1455	Wilson, Nolen E., 1927	1673
White, Lillian M., 1929	1866	Wilson, Otto Benny, 1920	1388
White, Paul Roy, 1928	1795	Wilson, Robert, 1892	19
White, Stuart N., 1946	2312	Wilson, R. J., 1908	644
White, Wm. Barton, 1912	1019	Wilson, Stephen D., 1908	775
White, W. M., 1920	1433	Wilson, W. E., 1917	1199
White, W. N., 1908	784	Wilson, Wilburn H., 1927	1688
White, Wm. D., 1928	1809	Wilson, W. M., 1908	645
Whiteneck,		Windes, Kenneth W., 1927	1677
Otho Raymond, 1934	2006	Winfrey, W. G., 1909	878
Whiteneck, Wilbur G., 1936	2050	Winkler, E. G., 1905	354
Whiteside, Everett Earl, 1949	2389	Winslow, E. B., 1905	350
Whitfield, J. H., 1905	389	Winston, M. L., 1944	2226
Whitlock, Lowell D., 1951	2475	Winter, Marion Ernest, 1952	2489
Whitman, Paul S., 1943	2186	Wise, Eugene W., 1923	1528
Whitton, Randel F., 1945	2264	Withers, A. C., 1906	471
Wicker, Wm. Frank, 1923	1521	Witherspoon, T. L., 1930	1928
Wikoff, C. H., 1897	1½	Wolfe, Harold Richard, 1916	1133
Wilborn, Jno. C., 1944	2231	Wolfe, Ray, 1905	388
Wilcox, H. S., 1908	839	Wolfe, Thomas W., 1929	1868
Wilkinson, I. S., 1920	1426	Wolfe, W. C., 1901	108
Wilkinson, Jay Bernard, 1924	1562	Wood, Chas. F., 1921	1479
Williams, A. J., 1901	116	Wood, Eugene V., 1918	1257
Williams, Chas. Roper, 1919	1291	Wood, Nathanial Clark, 1906	787
Williams, Chas. Victor, 1949	2393	Wood, Rhame Paul, 1951	2471
Williams, Elmer O., 1907	493	Wooderson, Robert M., 1912	1052
Williams, Felix Cameron, 1925	1587	Wooding, John L., 1908	642
Williams, Geo. Hewitt, 1922	1497	Woodring, Emory F., 1912	1051
Williams, G. R., 1908	786	Woods, Wallace W., 1947	2332
Williams, J. Edward, 1919	1363	Woodward, E. J., 1908	639
Williams, J. M., 1908	638	Woodward, Martin A., 1908	776
Williams, Jas. R., 1906	780	Woodward, Robt. Samuel, 1910	943
Williams, L. A., 1921	1484	Wooldridge, H. R., 1945	2257
Williams, Melvin R., 1929	1867	Wooldridge, Mervin H., 1918	1232

Woolomes, C. R., 1908	809	Wyllis, L. T., 1907	505
Woolwine, R. V., 1905	362	Wynn, Jas. O., 1947	2338
Woolwine, Rowland W., 1910	937	Yancey, G. E., 1908	840
Wooten, J. A., 1905	413	Yarbrough, Caesar A., 1912	1054
Wooten, J. W., 1901	110	Yarnell, Edgar Peyton, 1919	1345
Workman, C. B., 1905	415	Yates, Wm. C., 1928	1804
Workman,		Yeager, Douglas A., 1941	2162
Harry Leonard, 1928	1750	Yeager, R. J., Jr., 1945	2258
Worley, Chas. T., 1909	906	Yoast, Herman M., 1917	1178
Worley, J. B. D., 1897	48	Yonker, Donald H., 1946	2318
Worthen,		York, Jno. C., 1938	2080
Rodney LaDuane, 1951	2454	Youmans, C. C., 1904	230
Worwag, John M., 1927	1681	Young, Jennie M., 1908	796
Wright, Frank John, 1919	1298	Young, Noel S., 1929	1826
Wright, J. E., 1908	641	Young, Wm. O., 1922	1511
Wright, L. D., 1939	2104	Youngblood,	
Wright, Millard C., 1911	999	Stafford Rufus, 1925	1574
Wright, Robt. E., 1946	2280	Yulue, Arthur Harry, 1930	1894
Wright, W. E., 1945	2235	Zell, A. L., 1928	1806
Wright, Wilfred Clay, 1952	2491	Zell, A. L., 1911	1003
Wyatt, Geo. W., 1905	353	Zinn, Geo. Edwin, 1908	841
Wyatt, Olin Edison, Jr., 1953	2562	Zivell, Wm. Lee, 1939	2122
Wyche, John C., 1936	2038	Zurbuck, W. W., 1908	842
Wyche, Thos. Geo., 1940	2143	Zyskowski, John Kizer, 1928	1789
Wykoff, Jas. Ervin, 1942	2167		

APPENDIX B

Delegates and Alternates Representing Oklahoma State Dental Association at annual sessions of the national association: The National Dental Association, 1914–1922, the American Dental Association, 1923–1954.

1914
Delegates:
A. B. Potter, Oklahoma City
B. L. Shobe, Tulsa
Alternates:
J. R. Caughron, Oklahoma City
T. H. Williams, Chickasha
1915
No roll call published

1916
Delegates:
L. G. Mitchell, Oklahoma City
C. L. White, Oklahoma City
Alternates:
B. L. Shobe, Tulsa
A. B. Potter, Oklahoma City
1917
Delegates:
C. R. Lawrence, Enid

A. E. Bonnell, Muskogee
L. G. Mitchell, Oklahoma City
Alternates:
N. C. Wood, Ardmore
G. G. Lowes, Lawton
1918
Delegates:
C. R. Lawrence, Enid
J. M. Temples, 301 Robinson Arcade,
Tulsa
Alternates:
T. H. Williams, Chickasha
A. L. Walters, Checotah
1919
Delegates:
C. R. Lawrence, Enid
W. E. Flesher, 516 Colcord Bldg.,
Oklahoma City
A. E. Bonnell, 402 Surety Bldg.,
Muskogee
Alternates:
C. A. Furrow, Tulsa
E. E. Overmyer, Muskogee
1920
Delegates:
C. R. Lawrence, Enid.
J. Q. Waddell, Kingfisher
A. E. Bonnell, 402 Surety Bldg.,
Muskogee
Alternates:
W. E. Flesher, 516 Colcord Bldg.,
Oklahoma City
A. L. Walters, Tulsa
J. R. Caughron, Lee Bldg.,
Oklahoma City
1921
Delegates:
C. R. Lawrence, 212 Stephenson Bldg.,
Enid
A. E. Bonnell, 402 Surety Bldg.,
Muskogee
W. E. Flesher, 208 Colcord Bldg.,
Oklahoma City
Alternates:
None
1922
Delegates:
C. L. White, Oklahoma City
C. S. Foster, Chickasha
L. L. Barnes

Alternates:
None
1923
Delegates:
C. R. Lawrence, 212 Stephenson Bldg.,
Enid
C. L. White, Oklahoma City
L. L. Barnes, Oklahoma City
Alternates:
None
1924
Delegates:
C. R. Lawrence, 212 Stephenson Bldg.,
Enid
C. L. White, Oklahoma City
L.L. Barnes, Oklahoma City
Alternates:
A. E. Bonnell, 402 Surety Bldg.,
Muskogee
C. A. Ruhlen, Cushing
A. B. Walker, Norman
1925
Delegates:
A. E. Bonnell, 402 Surety Bldg.,
Muskogee
C. L. White, 1205 Medical Arts Bldg.,
Oklahoma City
Alternates:
J. M. Temples, Tulsa
C. A. Ruhlen, Cushing
A. B. Walker, Norman
1926
Delegates:
A. E. Bonnell, 402 Surety Bldg.,
Muskogee
C. R. Lawrence, Enid
W. T. Jacobs, 205½ Barnes Bldg.,
Muskogee
Alternates:
C. L. White, Medical Arts Bldg.,
Oklahoma City
S. A. Long, McAlester
Fred D. Sparks, Ponca City
1927
Delegates:
A. E. Bonnell, Surety Bldg., Muskogee
C. L. White, Medical Arts Bldg.,
Oklahoma City
Alternates:
S. A. Long, McAlester

Fred D. Sparks, Ponca City

1928

Delegates:

C. R. Lawrence, Enid

A. E. Bonnell, Surety Bldg., Muskogee

E. L. Miley, Medical Arts Bldg.,
Oklahoma City

Alternates:

Charles A. Furrow, Atlas Life Bldg.,
Tulsa

Ira Malone, Sapulpa

H. O. Warrick, Enid

1929

Delegates:

C. R. Lawrence, Enid

A. E. Bonnell, Surety Bldg., Muskogee

E. L. Miley, Medical Arts Bldg.,
Oklahoma City

Alternates:

A. F. Sebert, Clinton

C. A. Furrow, Atlas Life Bldg., Tulsa

H. O. Warrick, Enid

1930

Delegates:

A. E. Bonnell, Surety Bldg., Muskogee

C. R. Lawrence, Enid

F. J. Reichmann, Medical Arts Bldg.,
Oklahoma City

Alternates:

A. F. Sebert, Clinton

T. W. Sorrels, Medical Arts Bldg.,
Oklahoma City

C. L. White, Medical Arts Bldg.,
Oklahoma City

Substitutes:

G. L. Dodson, Muskogee

H. H. Sorrels, Medical Arts Bldg.,
Oklahoma City

1931

Delegates:

A. E. Bonnell, 420 Surety Bldg.,
Muskogee

C. R. Lawrence, American Nat'l. Bank
Bldg., Enid

F. J. Reichmann, Medical Arts Bldg.,
Oklahoma City

Alternates:

L. F. Foster, Guthrie

T. W. Sorrels, Medical Arts Bldg.,
Oklahoma City

C. L. White, Medical Arts Bldg.,
Oklahoma City

1932

Delegates:

C. R. Lawrence, American Bank Bldg.,
Enid

J. A. Wells, Shawnee

Alternates:

L. L. Barnes, Medical Arts Bldg.,
Oklahoma City

G. L. Dodson, Muskogee

1933

Delegates:

C. R. Lawrence, American Bank Bldg.,
Enid

J. A. Wells, Shawnee

Alternates:

L. L. Barnes, Medical Arts Bldg.,
Oklahoma City

G. L. Dodson, Muskogee

1934

Delegates:

A. L. Walters, Medical Arts Bldg.,
Tulsa

A. E. Bonnell, Surety Bldg., Muskogee

F. J. Reichmann, Medical Arts Bldg.,
Oklahoma City

Alternates:

O. F. Sinks, Medical Arts Bldg., Tulsa

J. B. Jenkins, Medical Arts Bldg.,
Oklahoma City

G. A. Roelke, Medical Arts Bldg., Tulsa

1935

Delegates:

A. L. Walters, Medical Arts Bldg.,
Tulsa

A. E. Bonnell, Surety Bldg., Muskogee

F. J. Reichmann, Medical Arts Bldg.,
Oklahoma City

Alternates:

O. F. Sinks, Medical Arts Bldg., Tulsa

G. A. Roelke, Medical Arts Bldg., Tulsa

E. L. Miley, Ramsey Tower, Oklahoma
City

1936

Delegates:

A. L. Walters, Medical Arts Bldg.,
Tulsa

F. J. Reichmann, Medical Arts Bldg.,
Oklahoma City

Alternates:
O. F. Sinks, Medical Arts Bldg., Tulsa
G. A. Roelke, Medical Arts Bldg.,
Tulsa
E. L. Miley, Ramsey Tower,
Oklahoma City
Substitute:
John N. Glass, Medical Arts Bldg.,
Tulsa

1937
Delegates:
C. B. Ball, Frederick
L. V. Swift, Osler Bldg., Oklahoma
City
F. J. Reichmann, Medical Arts Bldg.,
Oklahoma City
Alternates:
A. B. Rivers, Okmulgee
A. F. Sebert, Clinton
Substitutes:
C. R. Lawrence, Bass Bldg., Enid
T. H. Granger, Ada

1938
Delegates:
John N. Glass, Tulsa
G. L. Dodson, Muskogee
F. J. Reichmann, Medical Arts Bldg.,
Oklahoma City
Alternates:
A. F. Sebert, Clinton
R. H. Dietz, Pawnee
O. F. Sinks, Medical Arts Bldg., Tulsa

1939
Delegates:
C. R. Lawrence, Bass Bldg., Enid
Max G. Armstrong, Beacon Life Bldg.,
Tulsa
John N. Glass, National Mutual Bldg.,
Tulsa
George L. Dodson, Muskogee
Alternates:
F. J. Reichmann, Medical Arts Bldg.,
Oklahoma City
A. F. Sebert, Clinton
O. F. Sinks, Dental Arts Bldg., Tulsa
R. H. Dietz, Pawnee

1940
Delegates:
George L. Dodson, Muskogee

Wm. E. Flesher, Medical Arts Bldg.,
Oklahoma City
J. Ben Herring, Oklahoma City
Alternates:
A. E. Bonnell, Jr., Surety Bldg.,
Muskogee
John N. Glass, National Mutual Bldg.,
Tulsa
O. F. Sinks, Dental Arts Bldg., Tulsa
Ben C. Thompson, McAlester

1941
Delegates:
George L. Dodson, Muskogee
W. E. Flesher, Medical Arts Bldg.,
Oklahoma City
O. W. Boyer, Perry
Alternates:
John N. Glass, National Mutual Bldg.,
Tulsa
B. C. Thompson, McAlester
R. M. Dunn, Medical Arts Bldg., Tulsa

1942
Delegates:
Charles A. Hess, Durant
H. O. Warrick, Broadway Tower, Enid
Eugene W. Wise, Medical Arts Bldg.,
Tulsa
Alternates:
Frank P. Bertram, Okla. Dept. of
Health, Oklahoma City
Fred C. Seids, Perry
Jack D. Moore, Ada
Substitute:
George E. Roland, Medical Arts Bldg.,
Oklahoma City

1943
Delegates:
Charles A. Hess, Durant
H. O. Warrick, Enid
Eugene W. Wise, Medical Arts Bldg.,
Tulsa
Alternates:
Frank P. Bertram, State Dept. of Health,
Oklahoma City
Fred C. Seids, Perry
Geo. E. Roland, Medical Arts Bldg.,
Oklahoma City

1944
Delegates:
H. O. Warrick, Enid

J. B. Ratliff, Hobart
Eugene W. Wise, Medical Arts Bldg.,
Tulsa
Fred C. Seids, Perry
Alternates:
Robert M. Dunn, Medical Arts Bldg.,
Tulsa
Fred O. Pitney, Medical Arts Bldg.,
Oklahoma City
Charles A. Hess, Durant

1945
No meeting of the House of
Delegates was held.

1946
Delegates:
A. E. Bonnell, Jr., Surety Bldg.,
Muskogee
Fred O. Pitney, Medical Arts Bldg.,
Oklahoma City
H. O. Warrick, Enid
Eugene W. Wise, Medical Arts Bldg.,
Tulsa
Alternates:
Frank P. Bertram, 3400 N. Eastern St.,
Oklahoma City
R. M. Dunn, Medical Arts Bldg., Tulsa
Charles A. Hess, Durant
J. B. Ratliff, Hobart

1947
Delegates:
Albert E. Bonnell, Jr., Muskogee
Fred O. Pitney, Oklahoma City
H. O. Warrick, Enid
Eugene W. Wise, Tulsa
Alternates:
Frank P. Bertram, Oklahoma City
R. M. Dunn, Tulsa
Charles A. Hess, Durant
J. B. Ratliff, Hobart

1948
Delegates:
Fred O. Pitney, Oklahoma City
H. O. Warrick, Enid
F. J. Reichmann, Oklahoma City
Frank P. Bertram, Oklahoma City
Alternates:
Charles A. Hess, Durant
R. M. Dunn, Tulsa
J. B. Ratliff, Hobart

1949
Delegates:
F. J. Reichmann, Oklahoma City
F. P. Bertram, Oklahoma City
Fred O. Pitney, Oklahoma City
H. O. Warrick, Enid
Alternates:
J. B. Ratliff, Hobart
C. A. Hess, Durant
R. M. Dunn, Tulsa

1950
Delegates:
F. O. Pitney, Oklahoma City
H. O. Warrick, Enid
F. J. Reichmann, Oklahoma City
A. E. Bonnell, Jr., Muskogee
Alternates:
C. A. Hess, Durant
R. M. Dunn, Tulsa
J. B. Ratliff, Hobart
H. N. Wagner, Henryetta

1951
Delegates:
F. J. Reichmann, Oklahoma City
A. E. Bonnell, Jr., Muskogee
Fred O. Pitney, Oklahoma City
H. O. Warrick, Enid
Alternates:
J. B. Ratliff, Hobart
H. N. Wagner, Henryetta
C. A. Hess, Durant
D. W. Matteson, Oklahoma City

1952
Delegates:
Fred O. Pitney, Oklahoma City
H. O. Warrick, Enid
F. J. Reichmann, Oklahoma City
A. E. Bonnell, Jr., Muskogee
Alternates:
C. A. Hess, Durant
D. W. Matteson, Oklahoma City
C. E. McCracken, Tulsa
H. N. Wagner, Henryetta

1953
Delegates:
Fred O. Pitney, Oklahoma City
H. O. Warrick, Enid
F. J. Reichmann, Oklahoma City
A. E. Bonnell, Jr., Muskogee

Alternates:
C. A. Hess, Durant
D. W. Matteson, Oklahoma City
C. E. McCracken, Tulsa
H. N. Wagner, Henryetta

1954
Delegates:
Fred O. Pitney, Oklahoma City

H. O. Warrick, Enid
F. J. Reichmann, Oklahoma City
H. N. Wagner, Henryetta
Alternates:
C. A. Hess, Durant
L. D. Wright, Oklahoma City
C. E. McCracken, Tulsa
Rolla C. Calkin, Guthrie

APPENDIX C

Licensed in Limited Practice since Statutory Law of 1935. Numbers preceding names are the license numbers.

Exodontists
1 Ira E. McCarty
2 Scott P. Bowyer
3 E. K. Mabry (deceased)
4 Francis J. Reichmann
5 Homer L. Leathers (deceased)
6 H. N. Magee (deceased)
7 Phillip E. Williams
8 Paul C. Bonnette (navy)
9 Howard Emery Stafford
10 William Burke Swartz
11 Athol Lee Frew, Jr.
12 Mack B. Delk
13 Robert G. Hirschi
14 Tom H. Miley
15 George E. Reynolds
16 Edward A. Abernethy
17 J. P. Lansden (deceased)
18 A. I. Taubman
19 Frank W. Stewart
20 Carl E. Schow
21 Dan Edward Brannin
22 Dorwin E. Hawthorne
23 Charles V. Wilson
24 Donald H. Devlin
Orthodontists
1 T. Wallace Sorrels
2 William E. Flesher

3 E. Forris Woodring
4 O. H. McCarty (deceased)
5 H. B. Bolt
6 Harry H. Sorrels
7 Elmer B. Strickler
8 Carl D. Strickler
9 John G. Leftwich
10 Frank P. Bertram
11 Wm. Eugene Overmyer
12 Fred E. Sims (deceased)
13 Joe T. Reece
14 Roger C. Meyer
15 Marion Allen Flesher
16 L. C. Trotter (deceased)
17 Hugh Austin Sims
18 Earl Richard Cunningham
19 George Robert Webber
20 James D. Hall
21 W. N. Flesher
22 Harold Samuel Born
23 Lester L. Merrifield
24 Warren K. Ormon
25 Raymond Caudle
26 Robert Hayden Knarr
27 Barrett R. Andrews
Periodontists
1 Harry A. Burns
2 Earl L. Miley

3   Earl D. Sillers (deceased)
4   William H. Cooper
5   Douglas A. Yeager
6   Ross Eugene Waltzer
    Prosthodontists
1   J. Ben Herring (deceased)
2   William Jacobs (deceased)
3   O. E. Sloan

4   U. S. Andrews
5   Gustav A. Roelke
    Pedodontists
1   Joseph Dean Robertson
2   Ben Davis Caudle
3   Sumner A. Russman
4   Arthur L. Olson
5   John Emmett Lewis

APPENDIX D

Dental Hygienists Licensed since Statutory Law in 1919. Numbers preceding names are license numbers. Non-active members are designated by an asterisk.

1   Nettie R. Turley
7   Mrs. J. C. Weiterson
9   Veronica L. Matton*
10 Doris B. Barrett
11 Lila Lee Brown*
12 Donna McDaniel Duncan*
13 Jamie L. Cooper*
15 Mary D. Bassman*
17 Celia A. West*
18 Francis R. Riddle
19 Mildred L. Smith
20 Betty V. Warden*
21 Fay H. Wallingford*
22 Helen Virginia Hunter*
23 Helen Olga O'Brien
24 Virginia Hogee
25 Mrs. Leo A. Rogers*
26 Alice Sarah Holbert*
27 M. Helene Barry
28 Martha Wilder*
29 Geneva A. Knight
30 Mildred Maxine Clark
31 Jessie Mae Butts
32 Marjorie DeVorss*
33 Muriel E. Bjorniberg*
34 Irene P. Welch*

35 Bonnie Jean Walker*
36 Verla Mae Covalt*
37 Mrs. Richard Wright
38 Sue LeFlore Marshall
39 Bertha H. Brown
40 Mrs. Robert Bass
41 Ruth Irene Kelly
42 Connie Lue Rector*
43 Mrs. Kordack*
44 Gertrude McKay*
45 Alice Marie Kelley
46 Kathryn E. Tennis*
47 Floydine M. Williams
48 Mary Monica Burke
49 Mrs. Judson E. Huggler
50 Barbara Ann Schaefer
51 Mrs. Margaret Halpine
52 Phyllis Inez Mummery
53 Mary G. Sloanaker*
54 Joan Selph Chambers
55 Charlotte Isabel Kelley
56 Loretta N. Hurley
57 Barbara H. Smith
58 Mrs. Elizabeth Roach
59 Mrs. Mariann Boggs

Officers of Oklahoma Dental Organizations
1. *Oklahoma Territory Dental Association* (*organized* 1891)

1891–1892

President	J. S. Nicholson	El Reno
Vice-President	W. E. Furrow	Guthrie
Secretary	D. A. Peoples	Guthrie
Corres. Secretary	G. F. Dean	Oklahoma City
Treasurer	M. L. McConn	Purcell

1892–1893

President	J. S. Nicholson	El Reno
Vice-President	W. E. Furrow	Guthrie
Secretary	Laura Davis	Oklahoma City
Treasurer	J. B. Calmes	Guthrie

1893–1894

Apparently the 1892–1893 officers served through this year also.

1894–1895

President	M. L. McConn	Purcell
Vice-President	E. S. Rinehart	Oklahoma City
Secretary-Treasurer	D. A. Peoples	Guthrie
Corres. Secretary	W. E. Furrow	Guthrie

1895–1896

President	E. E. Kirkpatrick	Oklahoma City
Vice-President	G. A. Hughes	Guthrie
Secretary-Treasurer	L. A. Kelsey	Chandler
Corres. Secretary	W. E. Furrow	Guthrie

1896–1897

President	J. B. Gillespie	Woodward
Vice-President	G. A. Hughes	Guthrie
Secretary-Treasurer	E. E. Kirkpatrick	Oklahoma City
Corres. Secretary	W. L. Maupin	Oklahoma City

1897–1898

President	No Record	
Vice-President	No Record	
Secretary-Treasurer	E. E. Kirkpatrick	Oklahoma City

1898–1899

President	J. B. Gillespie	Woodward
Vice-President	No Record	
Secretary-Treasurer	E. E. Kirkpatrick	Oklahoma City

1899–1900

President	E. E. Kirkpatrick	Oklahoma City
Vice-President	T. F. Clifford	El Reno
Secretary-Treasurer	A. D. Cage	Stillwater
Corres. Secretary	M. L. McConn	Shawnee

1900–1901

President	E. E. Kirkpatrick	Oklahoma City
Vice-President	T. F. Clifford	El Reno
Secretary-Treasurer	A. D. Cage	Stillwater
Corres. Secretary	M. L. McConn	Shawnee

1901–1902

President	G. A. Hughes	Guthrie
Vice-President	C. A. Hazen	Newkirk
Secretary-Treasurer	R. H. Pendleton	Norman

1903–1904

President	J. A. Wells	Shawnee
Vice-President	F. D. Stalford	Perry
Secretary-Treasurer	R. H. Pendleton	Norman

1904–1905

President	F. H. Colter	Oklahoma City
Vice-President	R. H. Pendleton	Norman
Secretary-Treasurer	Theo P. Bringhurst	Shawnee

1905–1906

President	Theo P. Bringhurst	Shawnee
Vice-President	E. N. Hilburn	McLoud
Secretary-Treasurer	C. L. White	Oklahoma City

1906–1907

President	A. A. Doughty	Oklahoma City
Vice-President	A. T. Cramer	El Reno
Secretary-Treasurer	C. L. White	Oklahoma City
Executive Committee:	F. H. Colter	Oklahoma City
	R. S. Parsons	Oklahoma City
	G. A. Nichols	Oklahoma City

333

2. *Indian Territory Dental Association (organized* 1903)

1903–1904

President	J. E. Wright	So. McAlester
Vice-President	C. W. Day	Vinita
Secretary	J. G. Abernethy	Ardmore
Treasurer	S. A. Long	So. McAlester

1904–1905

President	C. W. Day	Vinita
Vice-President	A. E. Bonnell	Muskogee
Secretary	F. A. Stickel, Jr.	Muskogee
Treasurer	S. A. Long	So. McAlester

1905–1906

President	A. E. Bonnell	Muskogee
Vice-President	S. A. Long	So. McAlester
Secretary	F. A. Stickel, Jr.	Muskogee
Treasurer	A. L. Walters	Checotah

1906–1907

President	S. A. Long	So. McAlester
Vice-President	A. E. Adams	Ardmore
Secretary	F. A. Stickel, Jr.	Muskogee
Treasurer	A. L. Walters	Checotah

3. *Oklahoma State Dental Association (organized* 1907)

1907–1908

President	C. L. White	Oklahoma City
1st Vice-President	C. W. Day	Vinita
2nd Vice-President	R. O. Hirschi	Guthrie
Secretary	F. A. Stickel, Jr.	Muskogee
Treasurer	C. L. Nicholson	El Reno

1908–1909

President	A. L. Walters	Tulsa
1st Vice-President	G. C. Wallace	Shawnee
2nd Vice-President	N. C. Wood	Ardmore
Secretary	E. P. R. Ryan	Muskogee
Treasurer	L. G. Mitchell	Oklahoma City

1909–1910

President	Fred D. Sparks	Ponca City
1st Vice-President	J. M. Staples	Atoka
2nd Vice-President	Earl Westenhaver	Enid

334

Secretary	A. L. Walters	Checotah
Treasurer	S. A. Long	McAlester

1910–1911

President	B. L. Shobe	Tulsa
1st Vice-President	C. W. Day	Vinita
2nd Vice-President	R. S. Parsons	Oklahoma City
Secretary	A. L. Walters	Checotah
Treasurer	N. C. Wood	Ardmore

1911–1912

President	C. R. Lawrence	Enid
1st Vice-President	C. W. Day	Vinita
2nd Vice-President	Ira Malone	Sapulpa
Secretary	A. L. Walters	Checotah
Treasurer	N. C. Wood	Ardmore

1912–1913

President	S. A. Long	McAlester
1st Vice President	G. C. Wallace	Shawnee
2nd Vice-President	A. A. Pfeiffer	Muskogee
Secretary	A. L. Walters	Checotah
Treasurer	N. C. Wood	Ardmore

1913–1914

President	R. S. Parsons	Oklahoma City
1st Vice-President	N. C. Wood	Ardmore
2nd Vice-President	A. B. Potter	Oklahoma City
Secretary	C. R. Lawrence	Enid
Treasurer	A. B. Walker	Fairview

1914–1915

President	J. M. Temples	Tulsa
Vice-President	J. H. Sims	Watonga
Secretary	C. R. Lawrence	Enid
Treasurer	A. B. Walker	Fairview

1915–1916

President	W. E. Flesher	Frederick
Vice-President	C. W. Day	Tulsa
Secretary	C. R. Lawrence	Enid
Treasurer	A. B. Walker	Fairview

1916–1917

President	C. N. Wood	Ardmore
Vice-President	J. H. Sims	Watonga

335

Secretary	W. E. Flesher	Frederick
Treasurer	A. B. Walker	Fairview

1917–1918

President	T. H. Williams	Chickasha
President-Elect	J. A. Morrow	Carmen
Secretary	W. E. Flesher	Frederick
Treasurer	A. B. Walker	Fairview

1918–1919

President	J. A. Morrow	Carmen
President-Elect	A. E. Bonnell	Muskogee
Secretary	W. E. Flesher	Frederick
Treasurer	A. B. Walker	Fairview

1919–1920

President	A. E. Bonnell	Muskogee
President-Elect	C. W. Day	Tulsa
Secretary	J. A. Morrow	Enid
Treasurer	A. B. Walker	Fairview

1920–1921

President	C. W. Day	Tulsa
President-Elect	A. B. Walker	Fairview
Secretary	J. A. Morrow	Enid
Treasurer	T. W. Sorrels	Oklahoma City

1921–1922

President	A. B. Walker	Norman
President-Elect	L. M. Doss	Oklahoma City
Secretary	F. C. Reisling	Tulsa
Treasurer	T. W. Sorrels	Oklahoma City

1922–1923

President	L. M. Doss	Oklahoma City
President-Elect	Charles A. Ruhlen	Cushing
Secretary	A. B. Walker	Fairview
Treasurer	J. B. Jenkins	Oklahoma City

1923–1924

President	Charles A. Ruhlen	Cushing
President-Elect	A. F. Sebert	Clinton
Secretary	A. B. Walker	Fairview
Treasurer	J. B. Jenkins	Oklahoma City

1924–1925

President	A. F. Sebert	Clinton
President-Elect	W. T. Jacobs	Muskogee

Secretary	A. B. Walker	Norman
Treasurer	J. B. Jenkins	Oklahoma City

1925–1926

President	W. T. Jacobs	Muskogee
President-Elect	T. W. Sorrels	Oklahoma City
Secretary	C. L. White	Oklahoma City
Treasurer	C. A. D. Beer	Enid

1926–1927

President	T. W. Sorrels	Oklahoma City
President-Elect	Charles A. Furrow	Tulsa
Secretary	Roy H. Ellis	Okmulgee
Treasurer	C. A. D. Beer	Enid

1927–1928

President	C. A. Furrow	Tulsa
President-Elect	W. J. Scruton	Oklahoma City
Secretary	Roy H. Ellis	Okmulgee
Treasurer	C. A. D. Beer	Enid

1928–1929

President	W. J. Scruton	Oklahoma City
President-Elect	Roy H. Ellis	Okmulgee
Secretary	E. E. Sanger	Yukon
Treasurer	C. A. D. Beer	Enid

1929–1930

President	Roy H. Ellis	Okmulgee
President-Elect	C. A. D. Beer	Enid
Secretary	E. E. Sanger	Yukon
Treasurer	C. B. Ball	Frederick

1930–1931

President	C. A. D. Beer	Enid
President-Elect	Oren H. McCarty	Tulsa
Secretary	E. E. Sanger	Yukon
Treasurer	C. B. Ball	Frederick

1931–1932

President	Oren H. McCarty	Tulsa
President-Elect	A. C. Seids	Oklahoma City
Secretary	E. E. Sanger	Yukon
Treasurer	C. B. Ball	Frederick

1932–1933

President	A. C. Seids	Oklahoma City

President-Elect	E. E. Overmyer	Muskogee
Secretary	F. J. Reichmann	Oklahoma City
Treasurer	C. B. Ball	Frederick

1933–1934

President	E. E. Overmyer	Muskogee
President-Elect	J. A. Wells	Shawnee
Secretary	F. J. Reichmann	Oklahoma City
Treasurer	C. B. Ball	Frederick

1934–1935

President	J. A. Wells	Shawnee
President-Elect	C. B. Ball	Frederick
Secretary	F. J. Reichmann	Oklahoma City
Treasurer	W. S. Phillips	McAlester

1935–1936

President	C. B. Ball	Ardmore
President-Elect	A. B. Rivers	Okmulgee
Secretary	F. J. Reichmann	Oklahoma City
Treasurer	W. S. Phillips	McAlester

1936–1937

President	A. B. Rivers	Okmulgee
President-Elect	W. S. Phillips	McAlester
Secretary	O. W. Boyer	Perry
Treasurer	O. F. Sinks	Tulsa

1937–1938

President	W. S. Phillips	McAlester
President-Elect	F. J. Reichmann	Oklahoma City
Secretary	O. W. Boyer	Perry
Treasurer	O. F. Sinks	Tulsa

1938–1939

President	F. J. Reichmann	Oklahoma City
President-Elect	O. F. Sinks	Tulsa
Vice-President	H. W. Smith	Lawton
Secretary	O. W. Boyer	Perry
Treasurer	W. C. Travis	Chickasha

1939–1940

President	O. F. Sinks	Tulsa
President-Elect	H. H. Sorrels	Oklahoma City
Vice-President	George Shimoon	Muskogee
Secretary	O. W. Boyer	Perry
Treasurer	W. C. Travis	Chickasha

1940–1941

President	H. H. Sorrels	Oklahoma City
President-Elect	Scott P. Bowyer	Tulsa
Vice-President	C. S. Ferner	Tulsa
Secretary	O. W. Boyer	Perry
Treasurer	W. C. Travis	Chickasha

1941–1942

President	Scott P. Bowyer	Tulsa
President-Elect	G. E. Rowland	Oklahoma City
Vice-President	J. D. Hart	Wewoka
Secretary	E. W. Wise	Tulsa
Treasurer	W. C. Travis	Chickasha

1942–1943

President	G. E. Roland	Oklahoma City
President-Elect	G. A. Roelke	Tulsa
Vice-President	J. H. Crockett	Durant
Secretary	E. W. Wise	Tulsa
Treasurer	W. C. Travis	Chickasha

1943–1944

President	G. A. Roelke	Tulsa
President-Elect	C. A. Hess	Durant
Vice-President	I. E. Cordrey	Blackwell
Secretary	E. W. Wise	Tulsa
Treasurer	W. C. Travis	Chickasha

1944–1945

President	C. A. Hess	Durant
President-Elect	J. B. Ratliff	Hobart
Vice-President	Earl Miley	Edmond
Secretary	E. W. Wise	Tulsa
Treasurer	W. C. Travis	Chickasha

1945–1946

President	J. B. Ratliff	Hobart
President-Elect	H. O. Warrick	Enid
Vice-President	F. D. Dole	Lawton
Secretary	E. W. Wise	Tulsa
Treasurer	W. C. Travis	Chickasha

1946–1947

President	H. O. Warrick	Enid
President-Elect	Max G. Armstrong	Tulsa
Vice-President	T. W. McKinley	Stigler

Secretary	E. W. Wise	Tulsa
Treasurer	W. C. Travis	Chickasha

1947–1948

President	Max G. Armstrong	Tulsa
President-Elect	David W. Matteson	Oklahoma City
Vice-President	Fred Seids	Perry
Secretary-Treasurer	E. W. Wise	Tulsa
Executive Secretary	R. H. Tunnicliff	Oklahoma City

1948–1949

President	David W. Matteson	Oklahoma City
President-Elect	R. M. Dunn	Tulsa
Vice-President	W. C. Carnes	Henryetta
Secretary-Treasurer	F. H. Binkley	Hennessey
Executive Secretary	H. Leon Snow	Oklahoma City

1949–1950

President	R. M. Dunn	Tulsa
President-Elect	Fred O. Pitney	Oklahoma City
Vice-President	Fred E. Sims	Tulsa
Secretary-Treasurer	F. H. Binkley	Hennessey
Executive Secretary	H. Leon Snow	Oklahoma City

1950–1951

President	Fred O. Pitney	Oklahoma City
President-Elect	H. N. Wagner	Henryetta
Vice-President	T. A. Jones	Oklahoma City
Secretary-Treasurer	Rolla C. Calkin	Guthrie
Executive Secretary	H. Leon Snow	Oklahoma City

1951–1952

President	H. N. Wagner	Henryetta
President-Elect	William P. Ringo	Bartlesville
Vice-President	W. C. Travis	Chickasha
Secretary-Treasurer	Rolla C. Calkin	Guthrie
Executive Secretary	H. Leon Snow	Oklahoma City

1952–1953

President	William P. Ringo	Bartlesville
President-Elect	Rolla C. Calkin	Guthrie
Vice-President	William D. Rush	Tulsa
Secretary-Treasurer	Dean Robertson	Oklahoma City
Executive Secretary	Bill Howard	Oklahoma City

1953–1954

President	Rolla C. Calkin	Guthrie
President-Elect	Albert E. Bonnell, Jr.	Muskogee
Vice-President	Joseph D. Moon	Mangum
Secretary-Treasurer	Dean Robertson	Oklahoma City
Executive Secretary	Bill Howard	Oklahoma City

1954–1955

President	Albert E. Bonnell, Jr.	Muskogee
President-Elect	Douglas L. Rippeto	Oklahoma City
Vice-President	Glenn S. Ault	Hobart
Secretary-Treasurer	Sumner A. Russman	Oklahoma City
Executive Secretary	Bill Howard	Oklahoma City

APPENDIX F

Secretaries of the Oklahoma State Dental Association

F. A. Stickel, Jr.	1907–1908	Roy H. Ellis	1926–1928
E. P. R. Ryan	1908–1909	E. E. Sanger	1928–1932
A. L. Walters	1909–1913	F. J. Reichmann	1932–1936
C. R. Lawrence	1913–1916	O. W. Boyer	1936–1941
W. E. Flesher	1916–1919	Eugene W. Wise	1941–1948
J. A. Morrow	1919–1921	Floyd H. Binkley	1948–1950
F. C. Reisling	1921–1922	Rolla C. Calkin	1950–1952
A. B. Walker	1922–1925	Dean Robertson	1952–1954
C. L. White	1925–1926	Sumner A. Russman	1954–

Executive Secretaries

June 1, 1947–July–1948	Richard Tunnicliff
August 1, 1948–April 30, 1952	H. Leon Snow
May 1, 1952–	Bill B. Howard

APPENDIX G

Editors of the Oklahoma State Dental Association *Bulletin* and *Journal*

Year	Editor	City
1911	June. First issue of *Bulletin* published.	
1911	C. R. Lawrence	Enid
1912	A. L. Walters	Tulsa
1913	C. R. Lawrence	Enid
1914	C. R. Lawrence	Enid
1915	C. R. Lawrence	Enid
1916	W. E. Flesher	Frederick
1917	W. E. Flesher	Frederick
1918	W. E. Flesher	Frederick
1919	J. A. Morrow	Enid
1920	F. C. Reisling	Tulsa
1921	C. R. Lawrence	Enid
1922	F. C. Reisling	Tulsa
1923	A. B. Walker	Fairview
1924	A. B. Walker	Fairview
1925	C. L. White	Oklahoma City
1926	F. J. Reichmann	Oklahoma City
1927	F. J. Reichmann	Oklahoma City
1928	F. J. Reichmann	Oklahoma City
1929	E. E. Sanger	Yukon
1930	F. J. Reichmann	Oklahoma City
1931	F. J. Reichmann	Oklahoma City
1932	F. J. Reichmann	Oklahoma City
1933	F. J. Reichmann	Oklahoma City
1934	F. J. Reichmann	Oklahoma City
1935	F. J. Reichmann	Oklahoma City
1936	O. W. Bowyer	Perry
1937	O. W. Bowyer	Perry
1938	O. W. Bowyer	Perry
1939	O. W. Bowyer	Perry
1940	O. W. Bowyer	Perry
1941	Eugene W. Wise	Tulsa
1942	Eugene W. Wise	Tulsa
1943	Eugene W. Wise	Tulsa
1944	Eugene W. Wise	Tulsa

1945	Eugene W. Wise	Tulsa
1946	Eugene W. Wise	Tulsa
1947	Eugene W. Wise	Tulsa
1948	J. Millard Robertson	Oklahoma City
1949	Wm. C. Hopkins	Oklahoma City
1950	Wm. C. Hopkins	Oklahoma City
1951	Albert R. Drescher	Oklahoma City
1952	Albert R. Drescher	Oklahoma City
1953	Albert R. Drescher	Oklahoma City
1954	Albert R. Drescher	Oklahoma City

APPENDIX H

Program Essayists Appearing before the Oklahoma State Dental Association.

March 25–30, 1912, Oklahoma City, *fifth annual meeting.*
   Speakers: J. P. Buckley, Ph.G., D.D.S., Chicago; F. Ewing Roach, D.D.S., Chicago; G. Walter Dittmar, D.D.S., Chicago.
March 24–29, 1913, Oklahoma City, *sixth annual meeting.*
   Speakers: Martin Dewey, D.D.S., Kansas City; J. V. Conzett, D.D.S., Dubuque; Thos. P. Hinman, D.D.S., Atlanta.
March 30–April 4, 1914, Oklahoma City, *seventh annual meeting.*
   Speakers: Jos. Eby, D.D.S., and Thos. P. Hinman, D.D.S., Atlanta.
March 15–19, 1915, Oklahoma City, *eighth annual meeting.*
   Speakers: Drs. J. H. Prothero, W. H. G. Logan, Chicago; Drs. J. G. Hollingsworth, C. C. Allen, H. Wilson Allen, Kansas City.
March 20–26, 1916, Kansas City, Mo. *ninth annual meeting:* (Tri-State).
   Speakers: Thos. P. Hinman, D.D.S., Atlanta; Forrest H. Orton, D.D.S., St. Paul; M. L. Rhein, M.D., D.D.S., New York; C. N. Johnson, M.A., L.D.S., D.D.S., Chicago; J. P. Buckley, Ph.G., D.D.S., Chicago; Richard H. Riethmuller, Ph.D., D.D.S., Philadelphia; Weston A. Price, M.S., D.D.S., Cleveland.
March 26–30, 1917, Oklahoma City, *tenth annual meeting.*
   Speakers: Wm. E. Harper, D.D.S., Chicago; W. E. Cummer, L.D.S., D.D.S., Toronto; Arthur E. Smith, D.D.S., Chicago.

343

April 1–6, 1918, Tulsa, *eleventh annual meeting.*
  Speakers: Elmer S. Best, D.D.S., Minneapolis; Rupert E. Hall, D.D.S., Chicago; F. Ewing Roach, D.D.S., Chicago; Arthur E. Smith, D.D.S., Chicago; James Mark Prime, D.D.S., Omaha; Mrs. Iva Mae Hover, Omaha.

March 3–8, 1919, Oklahoma City, *twelfth annual meeting.*
  Speakers: Thos. B. Hartzell, D.M.D., M.D., Minneapolis; M. L. Rhein, D.D.S., M.D., New York; M. M. House, D.D.S., Indianapolis; F. Ewing Roach, D.D.S., Chicago; Willis A. Coston, D.D.S., Topeka; A. W. Starbuck, D.D.S., Denver; Arthur E. Smith, D.D.S., M.D., Chicago.

March 15–20, 1920, Tulsa, *thirteenth annual meeting.*
  Speakers: Dayton Dunbar Campbell, D.D.S., Kansas City; Clyde McClelland, D.D.S., Kansas City; Thomas B. Hartzell, D.M.D., M.D., Minneapolis; Arthur E. Smith, D.D.S., M.D., Chicago; F. E. Roach, D.D.S., Chicago; T. W. Maves, D.D.S., Minneapolis.

March 14–19, 1921, Oklahoma City, *fourteenth annual meeting.*
  Speakers: J. M. Temples, D.D.S., Tulsa; A. L. Walters, D.D.S., Tulsa.

April 10–14, 1922, Kansas City, Mo., *fifteenth annual meeting:* (Tri-State).
  Speakers: Otto U. King, D.D.S., F.A.C.D., Chicago; Wallace Seccombe, D.D.S., F.A.C.D., Toronto, Canada; Arthur D. Black, A. M., M.D., D.D.S., Sc.D., Chicago; C. N. Johnson, M.A., L.D.S., D.D.S., F.A.C.D., Chicago; Marcus L. Ward, D.D.S., Ann Arbor; Frederick B. Noyes, D.D.S., Chicago; Arthur E. Smith, D.D.S., M.D., Chicago; M. M. House, D.D.S., Indianapolis.

April 23–25, 1923, Oklahoma City, *sixteenth annual meeting.*
  Speakers: W. E. Flesher, D.D.S., Oklahoma City; Oren H. McCarty, D.D.S., Tulsa; E. F. Woodring, D.D.S., Tulsa; T. Wallace Sorrels, D.D.S., Oklahoma City.

April 22–25, 1924, Enid, *seventeenth annual meeting.*
  Speakers: Ira C. Brownlie, D.D.S., Denver; William L. Shearer, D.D.S., Omaha; Miller W. Rice, D.D.S., Kansas City.

April 27–May 1, 1925, Oklahoma City, *eighteenth annual meeting.*
  Speakers: Dayton Dunbar Campbell, D.D.S., Kansas City; W. Clyde McClelland, D.D.S., Kansas City; C. N. Mertz, D.D.S., Topeka; W. A. Coston, D.D.S., Kansas City; W. L. Shearer, D. D. S., Omaha.

April 27–30, 1926, Tulsa, *nineteenth annual meeting.*
  Speakers: Edward T. Hatton, D.D.S., Chicago.

April 25–28, 1927, Oklahoma City, *twentieth annual meeting.*
  Speakers: E. S. Lane, M.D.; R. R. Sesline; Justin D. Towner, D.D.S.,

344

Memphis; Jesse D. White, D.M.D., St. Louis; I. Lester Furnas, D.D.S., Cleveland; Harry M. McFarland, D.D.S., Kansas City; Miss Evelyn Schmidt.

April 30–May 3, 1928, Tulsa, *twenty-first annual meeting*.
Speakers: C. N. Johnson, D.D.S., Chicago; Boyd S. Gardner, D.D.S., Rochester; Philip R. Thomas, D.D.S., Minneapolis; James C. Mortonson, D.D.S. and Morton H. Mortonson, D.D.S., Milwaukee; Dayton D. Campbell, D.D.S., and A. L. Walters, D.D.S., Tulsa.

April 22–25, 1929, Oklahoma City, *twenty-second annual meeting*.
Speakers: George Wood Clapp, D.D.S., New York City; Charles A. Furrow, D.D.S., Tulsa; C. J. Stansberry, D.D.S., Seattle; James P. Ruyl, D.D.S., New York City; Thomas B. Hartzell, D.D.S., Minneapolis; R. J. Rinehart, D.D.S., Kansas City; Jay D. Scott, D.D.S., Kansas City.

April 21–24, 1930, Tulsa, *twenty-third annual meeting*.
Speakers: Sherman L. Davis, D.D.S.; Elmer W. Bunce, D.D.S.; Guy F. Bayly, D.D.S.; V. K. Allen, D.M.D.

April 20–23, 1931, Oklahoma City, *twenty-fourth annual meeting*.
Speakers: Geo. G. Ingham, D.D.S., New York; Wm. E. Harper, D.D.S.; Edw. J. Ryan, B.S., D.D.S., Chicago.

April 18–21, 1932, Muskogee, Oklahoma, *twenty-fifth annual meeting*.
Speakers: Herbert D. Coy, D.D.S., Hamburg, Iowa; Carl W. Hoffer, D.D.S., Nashville; Clarence O. Simpson, M.D., D.D.S., F.A.C.D., St. Louis.

April 17–20, 1933, Oklahoma City, *twenty-sixth annual meeting*.
Speakers: A. L. Walters, D.D.S., Tulsa; George W. Randell, D.D.S., Chicago; Stanley D. Tilman, D.D.S., Chicago.

May 6–9, 1934, Kansas City, Mo., *twenty-seventh annual meeting:* (Tri-State).
Speakers: Frank M. Casto, Bert L. Hooper, John B. LaDue, Milton T. Hanke, William E. Harper, Harold W. Oppice, John J. Travis, C. S. Kile, F. J. Reichmann, Willis A. Coston, John W. Kemper.

April 14–17, 1935, Enid, *twenty-eighth annual meeting*.
Speakers: L. F. Rittershofer, D.D.S., Ann Arbor; J. M. Temples, D.D.S., Joplin; A. E. Bonnell, D.D.S., Muskogee; O. W. Boyer, D.D.S., Perry, Oklahoma; C. R. Lawrence, D.D.S., Enid; Samuel M. Gordon, D.D.S., Chicago, Illinois.

August 31–September 4, 1936, Dallas, *twenty-ninth annual meeting*.
Speakers: Dr. Arthur D. Black, Chicago; Dr. Chas. S. Tuller, New Orleans; Dr. Paul Hill, Tucson; Dr. Hermann Becks, San Francisco; Dr. Edward H. Cary, Dallas; Dr. F. W. Rounds, Boston; Dr. Wil-

345

fred Terrell, Pasadena; Dr. A. W. Sears, Jacksonville; Dr. Dickson
G. Bell, San Francisco.

April 4–7, 1937, Tulsa, *thirtieth annual meeting*.
Speakers: W. Clyde Davis, D.D.S., A.M., M.D., Lincoln; Leon R.
Kramer, D.D.S., Topeka; Claude C. Cannon, D.D.S., Fayette, Ala-
bama; Ralph W. Edwards, D.D.S., F.A.C.D., Kansas City; Charles
Shepard Tuller, D.D.S., New Orleans; J. N. Bolte, D.D.S., Tulsa.

April 17–20, 1938, Tulsa, *thirty-first annual meeting*.
Speakers: L. R. Main, D.D.S., F.A.C.D., St. Louis; Ralph C. Cooley,
D.D.S., F.I.C.D., Houston; Walter T. McFall, D.D.S., F.I.C.D.,
Nashville

April 24–28, 1939, Oklahoma City, *thirty-second annual meeting:* (South-
west Dental Congress).
Speakers: Dr. Tom V. Connor, Dallas; Dr. Lon Morrey, Chicago; Dr.
Frank C. Cady, Washington, D. C.; Dr. Emery Morris, Battle Creek;
Dr. C. R. Lawrence, Enid; Dr. Don H. Billinger, Detroit; Dr. Joseph
E. Schaefer, Chicago; Dr. Bert L. Hooper, Lincoln; Dr. Claude C.
Cannon, Fayette, Ala.; Dr. Walter McFall, Nashville; Dr. John C.
Brauer, Iowa City; Dr. Herman Becks, San Francisco; Dr. Ralph
Sommer, University of Michigan; Dr. H. I. Coy, Richmond, Va.

April 14–17, 1940, Tulsa, *thirty-third annual meeting*.
Speakers: George M. Hollenback, D.D.S., F.A.C.D., Los Angeles;
John Kuratli, D.M.D., F.I.C.D., Portland; Herbert Ely Williams,
D.D.S., Red Bank, N.J.

April 27–30, 1941, Oklahoma City, *thirty-fourth annual meeting*.
Speakers: General Leigh C. Fairbank; Floyd E. Straith, D.D.S., Mich-
igan; Gladys M. Kinsman, Ph. D., Oklahoma A. & M.; Homer
Simpson, D.D.S., Dallas; Phillip Jay, D.D.S., M.S., Michigan.

April 19–22, 1942, Tulsa, *thirty-fifth annual meeting*.
Speakers: Oren A. Oliver, D.D.S., F.A.C.D., F.I.C.D., Nashville;
George W. Crane, Ph.D., Harold W. Oppice, D.D.S., Chicago.

April 12–14, 1943, Oklahoma City, *thirty-sixth annual meeting*.
Speakers: Don E. Woodward, D. D. S., M.S.D., Kansas City; J.
Burtch Stevens, D.D.S., F.I.C.D., Hutchinson, Kansas; Max Korn-
feld, D.D.S., F.A.C.D., St. Louis.

April 16–19, 1944, Tulsa, *thirty-seventh annual meeting*.
Speakers: O. B. Coomer, D.D.S., F.I.C.D., Louisville; William L.
Shearer, D.D.S., M.D., B.S., A.B., University of Neb.; D. A. Listiak,
D.D.S., M.S., Dallas.

October 14–17, 1945, Oklahoma City, *thirty-eighth annual meeting*.
Speakers: Edward L. Ball, D.D.S., F.A.C.D., Cincinnati; William
H. Crawford, D.D.S., University of Minnesota; Walter H. Scherer,

D.D.S., Houston; Phillip E. Williams, B.S., D.D.S., M.S., Borden's General Hospital, Chickasha, Okla.

March 31–April 3, 1946, Tulsa, *thirty-ninth annual meeting*.
   Speakers: George P. Brenner, D.D.S., Milwaukee; Captain Joseph P. Osterloh, D.D.S., San Francisco.

April 13–16, 1947, Oklahoma City, *fortieth annual meeting*.
   Speakers: Sterling V. Mead, D.D.S., Washington, D. C.; L. R. Main, D.D.S., St. Louis; G. Thaddeus Gregory, D.D.S., Indiana University; Warren Willman, D.D.S., M.S., Chicago.

April 11–14, 1948, Tulsa, *forty-first annual meeting*.
   Speakers: Miles R. Markley, D.D.S., F.A.C.D., Denver; Charles H. Kendall, D. D.S., Milwaukee; Ewell Neil, Sr., D.D.S., Oak Ridge, Ky.

April 10–13, 1949, Oklahoma City, *forty-second annual meeting*.
   Speakers: Harold Hillenbrand, D.D.S., Chicago; Willard E. Ogle, D.D.S., Dallas; Kenneth A. Easlick, D.D.S., Ann Arbor; Morris J. Thompson, D.D.S., Beverly Hills; Wallace N. Kirby, D.D.S., Downers Grove, Ill.

April 16–18, 1950, Tulsa, *forty-third annual meeting*.
   Speakers: Philip E. Adams, D.M.D., Boston; Rowe Smith, D.D.S., Texarkana, Arkansas-Texas; Lloyd H. Dodd, D.D.S., Decatur; Ford W. Stevens, D.D.S., Philadelphia.

April 15–17, 1951, Oklahoma City, *forty-fourth annual meeting*.
   Speakers: Willard Ogle, D.D.S., Dallas; Francis J. Garvey, LL.B., Chicago; John B. Ladue, D.D.S., Chicago; Ray Perschbacher, D.D.S., Denver; Melvin E. Page, D.D.S., St. Petersburg.

April 20–23, 1952, Oklahoma City, *forty-fifth annual meeting*.
   Speakers: Leroy M. Ennis, D.D.S., Philadelphia; Herbert B. Bain, Chicago (director of Bureau of Public Information of the ADA); Kenneth F. Grove, D.D.S., Denver; Hamilton B. G. Robinson, D.D.S., Columbus; Cecil H. Bliss, D.D.S., Sioux City.

April 19–22, 1953, Tulsa, *forty-sixth annual meeting*.
   Speakers: William R. Alstadt, D.D.S., F.I.C.D., Little Rock; Douglas A. Yeager, B.S., D.D.S., Oklahoma City; William E. Durbeck, D.D.S., San Antonio; S. C. Robinson, D.M.D., Portland; Charles D. Kochakian, Ph.D., Oklahoma City.

April 20–23, 1954, Oklahoma City, *forty-seventh annual meeting*.
   Speakers: Dr. Birger Nygaard-Ostby, Norway; L. A. Lucas, D.D.S., Oklahoma City; Wallas N. Kirby, B.S., D.D.S., a member of the faculty of Loyola Dental College; Dr. H. O. Warrick, vice-president, American Dental Association, Enid.

APPENDIX J

Oklahoma State Board of Dental Examiners and the Board of Governors of Registered Dentists, State of Oklahoma, since Statutory Law in 1891.

1891
G. F. Dean
J. S. Nicholson
D. A. Peoples
W. M. Janney

1892
G. F. Dean
J. S. Nicholson
D. A. Peoples
W. M. Janney
L. L. Miles

1893
G. F. Dean
J. S. Nicholson
D. A. Peoples
W. M. Janney
L. L. Miles

1894
G. F. Dean
J. S. Nicholson
D. A. Peoples
W. M. Janney
L. L. Miles

1895
G. F. Dean
J. S. Nicholson
D. A. Peoples
W. M. Janney
L. L. Miles

1896
L. A. Kelsey
R. Wilson
G. A. Hughes
W. L. Maupin
J. Q. Waddell

1897
G. A. Hughes
J. Q. Waddell
L. A. Kelsey
W. E. Furrow
E. E. Kirkpatrick

1898
D. A. Peoples
J. Q. Waddell
L. A. Kelsey
W. E. Furrow
E. E. Kirkpatrick

1899
D. A. Peoples
J. Q. Waddell
L. A. Kelsey
W. E. Furrow
E. E. Kirkpatrick

1900
J. Q. Waddell
L. A. Kelsey
R. Wilson
W. E. Furrow
E. E. Kirkpatrick

1901
J. Q. Waddell
F. D. Sparks
A. C. Hixon
A. M. Detrick
L. A. Kelsey

1902
J. A. Waddell
L. A. Kelsey
F. D. Sparks
A. C. Hixon
A. M. Detrick

1903
J. Q. Waddell
L. A. Kelsey
F. D. Sparks
A. C. Hixon
A. M. Detrick

1904
J. Q. Waddell
L. A. Kelsey
F. D. Sparks

A. C. Hixon
A. M. Detrick

1905
J. Q. Waddell
F. D. Sparks
A. C. Hixon
A. M. Detrick
R. H. Pendleton

1906
J. Q. Waddell
A. C. Hixon
A. M. Detrick
R. H. Pendleton
F. C. Seids

1907
A. C. Hixon
F. C. Seids
W. W. Bryan
M. W. Murray
A. E. Bonnell

1908
A. C. Hixon
F. C. Seids
W. W. Bryan
M. W. Murray
A. E. Bonnell

1909
A. C. Hixon
F. C. Seids
W. W. Bryan
M. W. Murray
A. E. Bonnell

1910
A. C. Hixon
F. C. Seids
W. W. Bryan
M. W. Murray
A. E. Bonnell

1911
A. C. Hixon
W. W. Bryan

A. E. Bonnell
G. W. Bowling
E. E. Heflin

1912

A. C. Hixon
W. W. Bryan
A. E. Bonnell
G. W. Bowling
E. E. Heflin

1913

A. C. Hixon
W. W. Bryan
A. E. Bonnell
G. W. Bowling
E. E. Heflin

1914

W. W. Bryan
A. E. Bonnell
E. E. Heflin
G. C. Wallace
H. Overby

1915

W. W. Bryan
A. E. Bonnell
E. E. Heflin
G. C. Wallace
H. Overby

1916

A. E. Bonnell
G. C. Wallace
H. Overby
E. E. Heflin
L. M. Doss
H. R. Watkins

1917

G. C. Wallace
H. Overby
A. B. Potter
H. R. Watkins
L. M. Doss

1918

H. Overby
L. M. Doss
H. R. Watkins
A. B. Potter
W. S. Williams

1919

L. M. Doss
H. R. Watkins

S. S. Mayfield
A. B. Potter
W. S. Williams

1920

L. M. Doss
H. R. Watkins
A. B. Potter
W. S. Williams
S. S. Mayfield

1921

W. S. Williams
A. B. Potter
John Hawkins
S. S. Mayfield
L. M. Doss

1922

W. S. Williams
Fred D. Sparks
John Hawkins
A. B. Potter
L. M. Doss

1923

W. S. Williams
Fred D. Sparks
John Hawkins
C. L. Berry
L. M. Doss

1924

W. S. Williams
Fred D. Sparks
A. B. Potter
John Hawkins
L. M. Doss

1925

W. S. Williams
Charles A. Hess
C. L. Berry
Fred D. Sparks
L. M. Doss

1926

W. S. Williams
Charles A. Hess
C. L. Berry
Fred D. Sparks
L. M. Doss

1927

W. S. Williams
Charles A. Furrow
E. E. Sanger
L. M. Doss

Charles A. Hess

1928

W. S. Williams
Charles A. Furrow
E. E. Sanger
L. M. Doss
Charles A. Hess

1929

W. S. Williams
E. E. Sanger
A. C. Seids
J. D. Moon
Charles A. Hess

1930

A. C. Seids
J. D. Moon
Charles A. Hess
W. S. Williams
E. E. Sanger

1931

A. C. Seids
J. D. Moon
Charles A. Hess
W. S. Williams
E. E. Sanger

1932

W. S. Williams
Charles A. Hess
J. D. Moon
G. W. Andree
E. E. Sanger

1933

W. S. Williams
Charles A. Hess
J. D. Moon
G. W. Andree
E. E. Sanger

1934

W. S. Williams
E. E. Heflin
Charles A. Hess
G. W. Andree
E. E. Sanger

1935

H. H. Deatherage
W. S. Phillips
J. P. Neal
C. E. Hill
W. C. Travis
Scott P. Bowyer

B. C. Singleton
L. W. Cheek
W. T. Longwell
1936
H. H. Deatherage
W. S. Phillips
J. P. Neal
C. E. Hill
W. C. Travis
Scott P. Bowyer
B. C. Singleton
L. W. Cheek
W. T. Longwell
1937
Scott P. Bowyer
Fred D. Sparks
P. E. Williams
W. T. Longwell
A. W. Grove
J. P. Neal
W. C. Travis
Lillian White
1938
Scott P. Bowyer
A. W. Grove
J. P. Neal
Fred D. Sparks
P. E. Williams
W. T. Longwell
Lillian White
N. Dea Griffith
1939
Scott P. Bowyer
J. B. Neal
W. T. Jacobs
Fred D. Sparks
N. Dea Griffith
H. Roy Gravelle
W. T. Longwell
1940
J. P. Neal
Scott P. Bowyer
N. Dea Griffith
H. Roy Gravelle
W. T. Jacobs
H. L. Entriken
W. T. Longwell
1941
Scott P. Bowyer
N. Dea Griffith

W. C. Travis
H. Roy Gravelle
W. T. Jacobs
H. L. Entriken
W. T. Longwell
1942
Scott P. Bowyer
N. Dea Griffith
W. C. Travis
H. Roy Gravelle
R. E. Stewart
H. L. Entriken
W. T. Longwell
1943
Scott P. Bowyer
W. C. Travis
H. L. Entriken
H. Roy Gravelle
R. E. Stewart
D. L. Rippeto
W. T. Longwell
1944
W. C. Travis
H. L. Entriken
H. Roy Gravelle
D. L. Rippeto
Scott P. Bowyer
R. E. Stewart
W. T. Longwell
1945
W. C. Travis
H. L. Entriken
H. Roy Gravelle
D. L. Rippeto
Scott P. Bowyer
R. E. Stewart
W. T. Longwell
1946
R. E. Stewart
Scott P. Bowyer
H. Roy Gravelle
H. L. Entriken
W. C. Travis
N. Dea Griffith
W. T. Longwell
1947
R. E. Stewart
H. Roy Gravelle
N. Dea Griffith
Scott P. Bowyer

W. C. Travis
H. L. Entriken
W. T. Longwell
1948
Scott P. Bowyer
W. C. Travis
John B. Cole
E. J. Crowder
O. D. Kutch
H. N. Wagner
N. Dea Griffith
1949
John B. Cole
H. N. Wagner
O. D. Kutch
R. T. Oliver
W. E. Davis
L. K. Turnbull
N. Dea Griffith
1950
H. N. Wagner
O. D. Kutch
L. K. Turnbull
R. T. Oliver
John B. Cole
W. E. Davis
N. Dea Griffith
1951
O. D. Kutch
John B. Cole
L. K. Turnbull
R. T. Oliver
W. E. Davis
R. P. Keidel
N. Dea Griffith
1952
O. D. Kutch
John B. Cole
L. K. Turnbull
R. T. Oliver
W. E. Davis
R. P. Keidel
W. E. Cole
1953
L. K. Turnbull
W. E. Cole
John B. Cole
O. D. Kutch
F. D. Entriken

350

R. T. Oliver	F. D. Riddle	F. D. Entriken
R. P. Keidel	O. D. Kutch	F. D. Riddle
1954	R. P. Keidel	R. P. Keidel
L. K. Turnbull	R. T. Oliver	L. H. Bell
W. E. Cole	1955	L. K. Turnbull
F. D. Entriken	W. E. Cole	N. T. Enmeier

APPENDIX K

ARTHUR C. SEIDS MEMORIAL CLINIC AWARD

Scott P. Bowyer	1933	T. A. Jones	1947
H. O. Warrick	1934	R. T. Oliver	1948
John H. Smiley	1935	G. A. Roelke	1949
C. L. Jones*	1936	W. B. Kessler	1950
F. J. Reichmann	1937	John C. Wilborn ⎫	
John A. Wadlin*	1938	Ralph L. Triplett ⎬	1951
J. D. Hart	1939	John N. Miles ⎭	
Joe K. Johnston*	1940	G. A. Roelke	1952
L. A. Lucas	1941	V. C. Tisdale, Jr. ⎫	
L. A. Lucas	1942	C. A. Sebert ⎬	1953
L. A. Lucas	1943	L. J. Bryant ⎭	
Cup retired to Lucas		V. C. Tisdale, Jr. ⎫	
Norton L. Wheeler	1944	C. A. Sebert ⎬	1954
Norton L. Wheeler	1945	L. J. Bryant ⎭	
Norton L. Wheeler	1946		
Cup retired to Wheeler		* Deceased	

APPENDIX L

THE SHOBE MEMORIAL HONOREES

TO THE MEMORY OF

B. L. SHOBE D.D.S.

Founder of the
OKLAHOMA STATE DENTAL SOCIETY

Post-Graduate Course

This tablet is dedicated as a memento to Dr. Shobe and to others who may subsequently Thus Be Honored as a Token of Esteem from the Members of the Oklahoma State Dental Society.

B. L. Shobe	C. R. Lawrence
1863–1917	1879–1940
Charles W. Day	C. L. White
1869–1934	1877–1941
Albert E. Bonnell	Arthur C. Seids
1865–1936	1881–1947

ERECTED 1931
Place: Medical and Dental Arts Building, Tulsa, Oklahoma

APPENDIX M

THE HARRY H. KAHO MEMORIAL AWARD

FOR

DISTINGUISHED SERVICE
(in civic work)

Awarded annually by Public Relations Committee
Oklahoma State Dental Association

WINNERS

1954   Noel Kaho, D.D.S.   Claremore, Oklahoma

THOMAS A. JONES AWARD
BEST CLINIC DENTAL ASSISTANTS SOCIETY
Awarded Annually

WINNERS

1953   Phyllis Terry

1954   Wanda George

Silver Certificate Holders

(The men listed below have been awarded a Silver Certificate for twenty-five consecutive years of membership in the Oklahoma State Dental Association.)

1932

W. E. Furrow

C. L. White

C. W. Day

R. O. Hirschi

W. S. Williams

C. B. Ball

L. L. Barnes

A. M. Bradley

L. M. Doss

H. L. Entriken

J. H. Mullins

T. A. Meyers

E. E. Overmyer

A. A. Pfeiffer

J. A. Wells

T. H. Williams

A. B. Walker

A. E. Bonnell, Sr.
Ira McCarty
Oren McCarty
A. J. Beatty
J. A. Townsend
G. R. Smith
A. L. Walters

1933
George L. Dodson
C. S. Ferner
W. E. Flesher
J. R. Gossett
W. T. Jacobs
R. S. Parsons
A. B. Potter
W. S. Phillips
Fred Sparks
A. C. Seids
R. M. VanDuzan

1934
George Andree
H. J. Baker
H. G. Carson
C. R. Lawrence
G. C. Wallace
J. T. Miller

1935
L. H. Lanier
E. K. Mabry
D. R. Moore
A. C. Render
George Shimoon
J. M. Temples

1939
C. A. D. Beer

1942
J. D. Moon
W. D. Rush
A. B. Rivers
C. A. Hess
J. W. Millsaps
R. E. Stewart
John Glass
Forris Woodring
Fred Lenhart
J. M. Asbury
H. W. Smith
C. R. Swander
J. C. Devin
O. F. Sinks

F. E. L. Thomas
F. D. Dole
O. L. H. Hine
L. E. Duncanson
C. P. Keim
T. W. Sorrels

1943
J. O. H. Niemann
F. A. Niemann
H. B. Bolt
T. F. Harmon

1944
O. W. Boyer
L. E. Crume
R. E. LoVellette
R. M. Dunn
L. G. Smith
C. A. Ruhlen
J. B. Ratliff

1945
H. R. Kidd
J. A. Brown
Lloyd E. Church
W. C. Travis
H. O. Warrick
W. C. Carnes
A. F. Sebert
M. G. Armstrong
Fred Seids

1947
C. S. Omohundro
V. A. Boucher
C. I. Trimble
C. H. Edgerton
B. C. Thompson
M. H. Wooldridge
Fred A. Turner

1948
Roy Ellis
J. E. Brown, Sr.
Scott P. Bowyer
H. N. Wagner
C. I. Cunningham
R. E. Smoot
R. L. Duncan
L. M. Harrison
E. E. Ogle

1949
F. J. Reichmann
P. C. Hendrix

355

I. M. Lightner
B. W. Fesler
E. E. Sanger
E. L. Miley
C. H. Hammond

1950
J. L. Mayfield
H. H. Sorrels
A. W. Wallace
O. B. Wilson
E. D. Sillers
T. W. McKinley
Roy A. Smith
G. S. Ault
Roger C. Meyer

1951
J. S. Trawick
L. A. Lingelbach
Fred O. Pitney
David W. Matteson
D. L. Rippeto
V. V. Jones
W. W. Reese
W. B. Kessler
E. B. Strickler
C. V. Kieser
W. M. McAnally
(posthumously)

1952
Wiley J. Adams
A. E. Buikstra
Floyd H. Binkley
A. C. Crose
Ralph Huber Cully
Ralph R. Karch

1953
Rolla Calkin
Robert Conger
Harry D. Glover
Mervin C. Howard
William Overmyer

1954
Allen George Hartzog
George Sherill Caughron
Hugh G. Hayes
Max Knarr
Prentiss G. Ledbetter
Albert E. Bonnell, Jr.
Ward L. Shaffer
Bruce D. Storm
Melvin Randall Williams
Wilburn H. Wilson
Wilbert J. Scruton
Myers W. Lockard
Wilmer McElhinney

APPENDIX P

Gold Certificate Holders

(The men listed below have been awarded a Gold Certificate for fifty years of service in the practice of dentistry, twenty-five years of which have been spent consecutively as members of the Oklahoma State Dental Association.)

1947
C. S. Ferner
R. H. Pendleton
Fred Sparks
F. C. Seids
C. I. Trimble

T. H. Williams
W. S. Williams

1948
Roy Ellis
W. T. Jacobs

1949
A. A. Pfeiffer
J. A. Wells
R. S. Parsons
1950
H. L. Entriken
R. O. Hirschi
L. M. Doss
F. D. Dole

1951
A. L. Walters
1952
A. M. Bradley
A. B. Walker
1953
J. H. Mullin
1954
G. R. Smith

APPENDIX Q

Oklahoma Dentists in the Armed Forces. The symbols following the ranks indicate service in: *World War I; †World War II; and ‡ the Korean War.

1. *United States Army and Air Force*

Adams, Wiley J.	Col.*† (Line)	Bonifield, J. H.	Maj.‡
Albert, A. C.	Lt.*	Bonnell, A. E., Jr.	Maj.†
Ammons, Earl T.	Lt.*	Born, H. S.	Capt.†
Arthurs, James L.	Maj.†	Boucher, V. A.	Maj.*†
Atkins, Walter D.	Lt. Col.† (Line)	Boyer, O. W.	Capt.†
Ault, Glenn S.	Col.†	Brandenberg, F. J.	Lt. Col.†
Ault, Glenn S., Jr.	Capt.‡	Brown, Charles M.	Capt.‡
Badeen, Samuel	Capt.†	Brown, J. A.	Lt.*
Baker, Bill R.	Lt.‡	Brown, James E., Jr.	Capt.†
Baker, Geo. H.	Capt.‡	Bruner, Fred W.	Lt.‡
Baker, R. W.	Maj.†	Caldwell, Jack B.	Col.†
Barnes, Emery R.	Capt.†	Carl, Roy G.	Capt.†
Barnes, Paul C.	Capt.†	Carmichael, J. B.	Capt.†
Barnetti, Paul C.	Capt.†	Carson, J. W.	Capt.‡
Barrett, S. Max	Capt.†	Carter, Robert P.	Capt.†
Beattie, R. E.	Lt.*	Cartwright, Dale J.	Lt.‡
Beatty, A. J. T.	Maj.*	Caudle, R. P.	Capt.†
Beauchamp, R. O.	Maj.†	Cheek, L. W.	Capt.†
Beer, C. A. D.	Maj.†	Childs, Casey	Col.†
Bell, G. E.	Lt.‡	Chiles, J. W.	Capt.*
Bell, Lacy H.	Lt. Col.†	Clinton, J. M.	Capt.†
Berry, C. L.	Maj.*	Clock, Quenton W.	Lt.‡
Biscoe, Byron	Capt.†‡	Coggins, L. D.	Capt.†
Blum, Charles	Maj.†‡	Cole, Leon L., Jr.	Col.†
Boone, J. W., Jr.	Capt.‡	Collier, C. C.	Capt.†

357

Collins, Homer B.	Capt.†‡	Granger, Thomas R.	Maj.†
Conger, R. W.	Capt.†	Graves, Thomas W.	Capt.‡
Cooper, Aubrey H.	Capt.†	Grey, P. E.	Lt.†
Cornett, J. J.	Lt. Col.*†	Gross, Forest A.	Capt.†
Cornish, Paul A.	Maj.†‡	Groves, Arthur W.	Maj.†‡
Cox, Frank B.	Lt.‡	Haddock, T. R.	Maj.†
Crawford, J. J.	Capt.†	Hall, J. D.,	Capt.†
Crowder, Ansel M.	Capt.*	Hall, Joseph R.	Capt.‡
Cruzan, W. V.	Lt. Col.†‡	Hall, Lester A.	Capt.†‡
Cully, Ralph H.	Maj.†	Hamilton, Robert	Capt.†
Cunningham, E. R.	Capt.†	Hanson, C. A.	Lt.*
Cunningham, W. E., Jr.	Capt.†	Harden, W. J.	Lt.†
Dailey, F. M.	Capt.†	Harris, J. M.	Lt. Col.†
Dallke, Walter O.	Lt.*	Harrison, Richard R.	Capt.‡
Danne, A. J.	Lt.‡	Hart, James	Maj.‡
Davis, C. E.	Capt.†	Hauser, Irving M.	Lt.†
Davis, W. C.	Capt.†	Hays, H. G.	Maj.†
Deal, James F.	Capt.†	Hendrix, Paul	Lt.*
Dean, J. E.	Lt.*	Henry, Dale S.	Lt.*
Dean, Jack F.	Lt.†	Henson, R. E.	Lt.*
Doherty, J. T.	Lt.*	Hess, Charles A.	Capt.*
Dolf, Frank H.	Capt.‡	Hiatt, W. R.	Lt.†
Doll, Ronald C.	Maj.†	Hill, Alva J.	Capt.‡
Dolt, George M.	Lt.*	Hine, Otto L. H.	Capt.*
Donathan, Grady D., Jr.	Capt.†‡	Holdreith, V. C.	Capt.†
Donathan, Jack N.	Capt.†	Holloman, J. H.	Maj.†
Donoho, Otis H.	Maj.‡	Howe, Michael J.	Lt.‡
Doyle, Wm. H.	Capt.†	Hudson, T. A.	Capt.†
Duffy, John W.	Maj.†	Hurt, Wm. J.	Lt.†
Duncan, W. W.	Capt.‡	Ireland, Leon	Lt.†
Eaton, Howard H.	Lt.*	Jones, F. S.	Lt.*
Ebersole, Robert R.	Maj.†	Jones, Harold S.	Lt.†
Edgerton, C. H.	Lt. Col.*†	Jones, Judge S.	Lt.*
Eirwin, Young D.	Maj.‡	Jones, Robert E.	Lt.†
Eithel, Charles M.	Maj.†	Keith, R. E.	Lt.*
Ellis, Robert L.	Capt.†	Kersey, C. C.	Capt.†
Farber, C. M.	Col.†‡	Keys, E. F.	Lt.*
Flesher, M. A.	Maj.†	Kibler, R. C.	Lt.*
Fowler, N. E.	Capt.†	Kieser, C. V.	Lt.*
Frazier, B. B.	Capt.‡	Kutch, O. D.	Maj.†
Frew, Athol L., Jr.	Maj.‡	Kuzel, L. J.	Lt.†
Frye, D. T.	Lt.†	Laird, H. B.	Lt.*
Gale, Wm. M.	Maj.‡	Lamborne, H. E.	Capt.†
Gallimore, J. W., Jr.	Lt.‡	Land, H. A.	Maj.†
Gauer, L. S.	Lt. Col.†	Lane, Raymond	Lt.†
Gawey, John S.	Capt.†	Landrum, John R.	Capt.†
Gibbens, Wm. N.	Capt.‡	Lansen, J. P.	Capt.†
Glass, Charles	Lt.†	Landsen, T. M.	Lt. Col.†
Glass, John, Jr.	Capt.†	LeHew, Clifford H.	Capt.†
Granger, Ed	Capt.*	Lewis, Eugene W.	Lt.†

Lewis, H. N.	Maj.†	Osborne, A. W.	Maj.†
Lewis, Harvey U.	Lt.*	Overmyer, Wm. E.	Capt.†
Lewis, Leon E.	Capt.‡	Owen, Robert C.	Capt.†
Lewis, R. P., Jr.	Lt.†	Owens, Clarence L.	Lt.‡
Makins, Leo A.	Maj.†	Pace, L. E.	Maj.‡
Masters, Connor M.	Capt.†	Partch, O. L.	Capt.†
Martin, E. P.	Lt.†	Patterson, L. A.	Lt.*
Mayfield, J. L.	Maj.†	Payne, Wm. L.	Lt.*
McAllister, Don B.	Maj.†	Peach, John S.	Lt.*
McAnerny, F. A.	Capt.‡	Pennington, D. C.	Lt. Col.†
McBride, George L.	Lt.†	Pigford, Jack D.	Maj.‡
McCollough, T. M.	Capt.‡	Pollack, A. A.	Lt.*
McCollum, Glenn W.	Maj.†	Pool, Wm. L.	Lt.‡
McCracken, Charles E.	Maj.†	Pretty, W. H.	Maj.†
McCutchen, Donald	Capt.†‡	Pruett, Charles L.	Lt.‡
McGee, Luther C.	Capt.†	Quast, Edward C.	Lt.†
McHenry, J. H.	Capt.†	Quimby, Dale M.	Lt.‡
McKellar, Dougal A.	Lt.*	Randall, O. H.	Maj.†
McKennon, P. D.	Capt.†	Ray, Ralph R.	Maj.†
McLarty, Todd	Capt.†	Reichmann, F. J. Brig. Gen.† (Line)	
McLaughton, G. I.	Capt.†	Renegar, Raymond L.	Capt.‡
McMurry, Wm. S.	Capt.†	Reynolds, Ray H.	Lt.‡
McReynolds, M. D.	Capt.†	Rhodes, Ray F.	Capt.†
Merrifield, L. L.	Capt.‡	Rhodes, R. P.	Capt.†
Miles, Robert L.	Capt.‡	Rhodes, Wm. L.	Capt.†
Miley, Tom H.	Maj.†	Richardson, C. D.	Maj.†
Miller, Don L.	Lt.‡	Richardson, Clarence T.	Col.†
Miller, E. L.	Maj.†	Riddle, Fred O.	Lt.†
Miller, J. A.	Capt.†	Ritchey, Charles L.	Maj.†
Mitchell, J. O.	Maj.†	Rivers, A. B.	Lt.*
Mitchell, L. G.	Maj.*	Robertson, J. Dean	Maj.†
Mitchell, R. C.	Maj.†	Robertson, J. Millard	Maj.†
Moon, J. D.	Lt.‡	Roland, George E.	Lt.*
Moore, Jack	Capt.†	Rookstool, W. D.	Maj.†
Moore, Leon M.	Maj.†	Rose, E. A.	Capt.‡
Moore, L. R.	Maj.†	Rowe, Lloyd F.	Maj.†
Moore, Milton L.	Maj.†	Ruble, J. B.	Capt.†
Moore, R. L.	Capt.†	Rush, W. D.	Lt.*
Morrison, W. P.	Lt.*	Russell, E. W., Jr.	Capt.†
Neal, C. D.	Lt.*	Russman, Sumner A.	Lt. Col.†
Newman, Robert M.	Lt.‡	Sanger, E. B.	Maj.†‡
Norris, Donald A., Jr.	Lt.‡	Sanger, E. E.	Col.†
Noss, Joe E.	Lt.‡	Saul, E. B.	Capt.†
Obert, John T.	Lt.*	Schoeni, T. E.	Capt.†
O'Brien, Charles M., Jr.	Maj.‡	Scott, Taylor B.	Capt.‡
O'Brien, James L.	Capt.‡	Scruton, W. J.	Lt. Col.*
Ogle, E. E.	Col.†‡ (Line)	Sebert, C. A.	Capt.†
Ogle, M. W.	Lt. Col.†	Shacklett, J. L.	Lt. Col.†
Olson, A. L.	Capt.‡	Shadid, R. J.	Capt.†
Orman, W. K.	Lt.†	Shaffer, W. L.	Maj.†

Shamel, W. L.	Maj.†	Toma, Thomas J.	Lt.‡
Shannon, C. B.	Lt.*	Triplett, R. L.	Capt.†
Shepard, David J.	Capt.‡	Turnbull, Ralph P.	Lt. Col.†
Sheppard, K. T.	Capt.†	Tyler, C. D.	Capt.†
Sherrod, H. B.	Lt. Col.†	Ullestad, R. J.	Lt. Col.†
Shields, B. M.	Capt.†	Wallace, A. W.	Capt.†
Shimoon, George G.	Capt.‡	Waltzer, Ross	Capt.†
Shurr, R. C.	Maj.†	Warrick, T. W.	Capt.†
Skuttee, T. S.	Capt.†	Washington, D. E.	Capt.†
Smith, C. Q.	Lt.*	Webber, George R.	Capt.‡
Smith, E. A.	Capt.†	Weir, Wm. J.	Capt.†
Smith, Wm. P.	Maj.†	White, Brandon A.	Capt.‡
Sorrels, T. W.	Lt.*	White, Stuart N.	Capt.‡
Spears, Robert E.	Lt.‡	White, Wm. D.	Col.*†‡
Stalford, F. D.	Maj.*	Whiteneck, O. R.	Capt.†
Streck, Warren F.	Capt.‡	Whiteneck, W. G.	Capt.†
Sullivan, Frederick M.	Col.†	Whiteside, E. E.	Capt.†
Sullivan, Gordon L.	Capt.†‡	Whitton, Randell F.	Capt.†
Sullivan, R. H.	Maj.‡	Wienberger, J. A.	Capt.†
Swander, C. R.	Maj.*†	Williams, C. V.	Lt.†
Swartz, P. W.	Lt.*	Williams, J. E.	Lt. Col.†
Talley, R. W.	Capt.†	Wilson, E. L.	Capt.†
Taylor, Robert B., Jr.	Lt.‡	Wolk, H. R.	Lt.*
Taylor, R. M.	Maj.†	Woods, W. W.	Capt.‡
Thomas, F. E. L.	Lt.*	Wright, R. E.	Capt.†
Thomas, J. A.	Capt.†	Wynn, J. O.	Capt.‡
Thomas, James P.	Maj.‡	Yeager, R. J.	Capt.†
Tisdale, V. C.	Lt. Col.†	York, J. C.	Capt.†
Titterington, R. N.	Lt.*		

2. *United States Navy*

Abernathy, E. A., Jr.	Lt.†	Chase, W. W.	Cdr.†
Atkins, Jack	Lcdr.†	Cole, J. B.	Lt.†
Austbo, Merritt O.	Cdr.†	Cole, William E.	Cdr.†
Austerman, J. B.	Lt. (jg)‡	Delhotal, Jack R.	Lt.†
Bates, L. F.	Lcdr.†	Delk, M. B.	Lt.†
Bell, Gerald E.	Lt.†	Dickson, F. E.	Lt.†
Bentley, Cuthbert A.	Lt.†	Dickson, R. E.	Lcdr.†
Bias, Sike J.	Lt.†‡	Divine, Hal	Lt.†
Black, W. C.	Lcdr.†	Easterling, Henry C.	Lt. †‡
Bonnett, Paul C.	Cdr.†‡	Entriken, Fred	Lcdr.†
Boudreaux, Paul W.	Lt.†	Erdman, R. F.	Cdr.†
Bradford, W. R.	Lcdr.†	Etling, L. D.	Lt.†
Brimer, Eugene L.	Lt.†	Ewton, Donald K.	Lt.†
Bryant, W. E.	Lt.†	Foster, E. W., Jr.	Lt.†
Campbell, Billy J.	Lt.†	Gerard, J. G.	Lcdr.†
Carter, W. L.	Lt.†	Goodloe, Robt. W.	Lcdr.†‡
Caudle, Benj. D.	Lt.†	Granger, Donald C.	Lcdr.†
Caughron, G. S.	Lcdr.†	Greenan, P. E.	Lcdr.†

Greever, Joseph W.	Lt.†‡	Reece, J. T.	Lt.†
Griffith, N. Dea	Cdr.†	(Coast Guard)	
Hall, J. A.	Lcdr.†	Reynolds, Geo. E.	Lt.†
Heller, D. E.	Lt.†	Ross, W. W.	Lt.†‡
Hirschi, Robt. G.	Lt.†‡	Rumsey, D. W.	Lt.†
Hopkins, Wm. C.	Lt.†‡	Scott, R. H.	Lcdr.†‡
Ingram, Robt. P., Jr.	Lt.†	Sellers, W. N.	Lt.†
Ishmael, Don M.	Lt.†	Sherrill, John T.	Lcdr.†
James, Don R.	Lt.‡	Sims, H. A.	Lt.†
Keidel, Robt. P.	Lt.†	Smith, Edward W.	Lt. (jg)‡
Lewis, John E.	Cdr.†	Talley, O. J.	Lt.†
Mabry, E. H.	Lt.†	(Coast Guard)	
Martin, W. R.	Lt.†	Taubman, Arthur I.	Lt.‡
Matteson, David W.	Cdr.†‡	Taubman, M. S.	Cdr.†
Mayfield, James W.	Lt.†‡	Teaff, J. A.	Lt.†
McCrory, J. J.	Lt.†	Thomason, H. D.	Lcdr.†
McElwaine, L. P.	Lt.†	Thompson, J. M.,	Lcdr.†
McInnis, Harry	Capt.†	Trimble, Joe	Lt.†
McReynolds, A. A.	Lt.†‡	Trotter, L. C.	Lcdr.†
Menkoff, G. B.	Lt.‡	Trotter, Virgil H.	Lt.‡
Merritt, H. J.	Lt.†	Turnborough, F. E.	Lt.*
Miles, John N.	Lt.†	Turnbull, L. K.	Lcdr.†
Mitchell, N. L.	Lt.†	Wadlin, John H., Jr.	Lt.†
Mose, J. D.	Lt.†	Whitman, Paul S.	Lt.†
Ogden, Ingram	Lcdr.†‡	Willis, L. L.	Cdr.†
Olsgard, W. A.	Lcdr.†	Windes, Kenneth	Lt.†
Pinkner, Joe, Jr.	Lcdr.†	Wooldridge, H. R.	Lt.†‡
Potts, Earnest W.	Lt.‡	Wright, L. D.	Lcdr.†
		Yeager, Douglas A.	Lcdr.†

APPENDIX R

Officers of the Women's Auxiliary, Oklahoma State Dental Association (organized 1937).

1937–1938

President	Mrs. L. G. Smith
1st Vice-President	Mrs. W. S. Phillips
2nd Vice-President	Mrs. A. J. Beatty
3rd Vice-President	Mrs. E. E. Overmyer
Corres. Secretary	Mrs. E. L. Moore
Recording Secretary	Mrs. Eugene Wise
Treasurer	Mrs. H. L. Carson

1938–1939

President	Mrs. A. C. Seids
President Elect	Mrs. Eugene Wise
Vice-President	Mrs. A. J. Beatty
Corres. Secretary	Mrs. F. J. Reichmann
Recording Secretary	Mrs. Eugene Wise
Treasurer	Mrs. H. L. Carson

1939–1940

President	Mrs. Eugene Wise
President Elect	Mrs. F. J. Reichmann
Vice-President	Mrs. F. C. Seids
Corres. Secretary	Mrs. Norton Wheeler
Recording Secretary	Mrs. A. N. Dow
Treasurer	Mrs. J. M. Robertson

1940–1941

President	Mrs. F. J. Reichmann
President Elect	Mrs. Ira McCarty
Vice-President	Mrs. Earl Sillers
Corres. Secretary	Mrs. D. W. Matteson
Recording Secretary	Mrs. Harry Sorrels
Treasurer	Mrs. H. E. Hampton

1941–1942

President	Mrs. Ira McCarty
President Elect	Mrs. D. W. Matteson
Vice-President	Mrs. Rolla Calkin
Corres. Secretary	Mrs. Fred Sims
Recording Secretary	Mrs. James Mayfield
Treasurer	Mrs. M. W. Lockard

1942–1943

President	Mrs. D. W. Matteson
	Mrs. James Mayfield (acting)
President Elect	Mrs. H. G. Carson
Vice-President	Mrs. James Mayfield
Corres. Secretary	Mrs. M. W. Lockard
Recording Secretary	Mrs. H. E. Hampton
Treasurer	Mrs. Ira Parker

1943–1944

President	Mrs. H. E. Hampton (acting)
President Elect	Mrs. M. W. Lockard

Vice-President	Mrs. H. E. Hampton
Corres. Secretary	Mrs. R. B. Ingram
Recording Secretary	Mrs. A. L. Lynn
Treasurer	Mrs. I. M. Helmey

1944–1945

President	Mrs. M. W. Lockard
President Elect	Mrs. Earl Sillers
Vice-President	Mrs. Harry Sorrels
Corres. Secretary	Mrs. Howard Anderson
Recording Secretary	Mrs. Rolla Calkin
Treasurer	Mrs. S. G. Weiss

1945–1946

President	Mrs. Earl Sillers
President Elect	Mrs. Harry Sorrels
Vice-President	Mrs. A. L. Lynn
Corres. Secretary	Mrs. N. T. Enmier
Recording Secretary	Mrs. H. L. Bannister
Treasurer	Mrs. H. H. Taylor

1946–1947

President	Mrs. Harry Sorrels
President Elect	Mrs. Fred Sims
Vice-President	Mrs. L. H. Kippenberger
Corres. Secretary	Mrs. Fred Pitney
Recording Secretary	Mrs. F. F. Fellrath
Treasurer	Mrs. U. S. Andrews

1947–1948

President	Mrs. Fred Sims
President Elect	Mrs. L. H. Kippenberger
Vice-President	Mrs. S. G. Weiss
Corres. Secretary	Mrs. R. T. Oliver
Recording Secretary	Mrs. Wm. Cole
Treasurer	Mrs. Fred Seids

1948–1949

President	Mrs. L. H. Kippenberger
President Elect	Mrs. R. M. Dunn
Vice-President	Mrs. L. W. Cheek
Corres. Secretary	Mrs. C. A. D. Beer
Recording Secretary	Mrs. Wm. Davis
Treasurer	Mrs. Howard Gettler

1949–1950

President	Mrs. R. M. Dunn
President Elect	Mrs. Frank Bertram
Vice-President	Mrs. P. G. Ledbetter
Corres. Secretary	Mrs. Albert Williamson
Recording Secretary	Mrs. T. W. Warrick
Treasurer	Mrs. B. D. Storm

1950–1951

President	Mrs. Frank Bertram
President Elect	Mrs. S. G. Weiss
Vice-President	Mrs. T. W. Warrick
Corres. Secretary	Mrs. J. M. Robertson
Recording Secretary	Mrs. G. R. Webber
Treasurer	Mrs. Norton Wheeler

1951–1952

President	Mrs. S. G. Weiss
President Elect	Mrs. Wm. B. Haynes
Vice-President	Mrs. Geo. Webber
Corres. Secretary	Mrs. R. P. Keidel
Recording Secretary	Mrs. Clyde Russell
Treasurer	Mrs. Paul Hendrick

1952–1953

President	Mrs. Wm. B. Haynes
President Elect	Mrs. Howard Anderson
Vice-President	Mrs. Rolla Calkin
Corres. Secretary	Mrs. Charles Eitel
Recording Secretary	Mrs. James Miller
Treasurer	Mrs. Clyde Russell

1953–1954

President	Mrs. Howard Anderson
President Elect	Mrs. J. Albert Williamson
Vice-President	Mrs. U. S. Andrews
Corres. Secretary	Mrs. W. H. Cooper
Recording Secretary	Mrs. H. N. Wagner
Treasurer	Mrs. Arthur Lynn

1954–1955

President	Mrs. J. Albert Williamson
President Elect	Mrs. J. H. Bannister
Vice-President	Mrs. Albert S. Jack

Corres. Secretary	Mrs. Hugh Sims
Recording Secretary	Mrs. J. E. Brown, Jr.
Treasurer	Mrs. Wilson Chase

APPENDIX S

Officers of the Oklahoma State Dental Assistants Society (organized 1926).

President	Secretary	Year
Doyle, Blanch	Turley, Nettie	1926
Rogers, Retha	Desmond, Alma	1927
Poff, Mary	Sampson, Pat	1928
Payne, Norma	Mallard, Jewell	1929
Meagher, Lillian	Rogers, Retha	1930
Comba, Lillian	Rogers, Retha	1931
Conkright, Mae	Rogers, Retha	1932
Jackson, Mary	Mahoney, Anna Mae	1933
Robinson, Tela	Ligon, Lucy	1934

(Inactive 1935 until 1939)

President	Secretary	Year
Tisdale, Helen	Blackburn, Zama	1939
Chastain, Ruth	Butts, Jessie Mae	1940
Day, Lucille	Tisdale, Helen	1941
Jackson, Mary	Miller, Mary	1942
Eagle, Lucy	Chennault, Elma	1943
Babb, Myrtle	Chennault, Elma	1944
Goad, Jackie	Elliott, Virginia	1945
Buergey, Georgie	Chennault, Elma	1946
Bilyeu, Ruby	Chennault, Elma	1947
Wachab, Mable	Terry, Evelyn	1948
Lombard, Eva	Goad, Jackie	1949
Potter, Georgia	Goad, Jackie	1950
Brown, Noveta	Morris, Chloe	1951
Jones, Martha	Jacobson, Janice	1952
Seaton, Ruby	Jacobson, Janice	1953
Grimes, Mary Lou	Jacobson, Janice	1954

Certified Dental Assistants of Oklahoma (organized 1949).

Barr, Ann	Okmulgee
Berkey, Virginia	806 Med. Arts Bldg., Oklahoma City
Bilyeu, Ruby	316 Commerce, Oklahoma City
Blissit, Bettie M.	1432 E. 35, Tulsa
Brown, Noveta E.	1315 E. 10, Tulsa
Buergey, Georgia	1143 E. Evanston, Tulsa
Castle, Ora	1843 N. W. 16, Oklahoma City
Chennault, Elma	Oklahoma City
Conner, Mary	1511 S. Trenton, Tulsa
Crities, Winona May	1206 E. Broadway, Enid
Cypert, A. Lorraine	728 E. 6, Ada
Eagle, Lucy E.	401 S. 7, Henryetta
Ebner, Mary E.	1907 Liberty Bank Bldg., Oklahoma City
George, Wanda	1104 Med. Arts Bldg., Oklahoma City
Gibson, E. Lenell	407 South Junction, Muskogee
Goad, Jackie Rambo	908 Med. Arts Bldg., Oklahoma City
Green, Claudine	V. A. Hospital, Oklahoma City
Grimes, Mary Lou	Tulsa
Groh, Luana	Tulsa
Hamm, Bessie L.	Box 546 Britton
Heintz, Norma Lee	613 W. Cherokee, Enid
Hellinghausen, Hazel K.	217 Stanolind Bldg., Tulsa
Huffman, Neva M.	Box 57, Medford
Jackson, Winifred	419 N. Beard, Ada
Jacobson, Janice	1245 E. 31, Tulsa
Jennings, Beverly	Tulsa
Kennedy, Marie	Britton
Lehenbauer, Mae C.	Oklahoma City
Lombard, Eva	Tulsa
Longan, Genevine	306 Colcord Bldg., Oklahoma City
Mallard, Jewell B.	607 S. Yale, Tulsa
Mannon, Jean	1718 N. Cincinnati Pl., Tulsa
Matthews, Betty	Tulsa
Morris, Chloe	1215 S. Denver, Tulsa
O'Banion, Frances	705 Med. Arts Bldg., Tulsa
Palmore, Alyce	908 E. 4, Ada
Pannell, Billye	1419 N. E. Park Pl., Oklahoma City
Patrick, Rosemary	104½ E. Main, Ada
Patrick, Rubye Louella	1638 Avondale, Muskogee
Potter, Georgia	1309 W. Central, Oklahoma City
Pray, Irene	811 Hales Bldg., Oklahoma City
Ray, Genevieve J.	Route 1, Box 90A–2, Oklahoma City
Reed, Ruby G.	1950 N. W. Park Pl., Oklahoma City

Robinson, Pat · 310 Pasteur Bldg., Oklahoma City
Rowley, Gladys · 824 N. Elwood, Tulsa
Rucker, Adeline J. · 1206 Med. Arts Bldg., Oklahoma City
Sadongei, Romona · Tulsa
Saltenberger, Betty Fisher · 1427 E. 2, Tulsa
Shafer, Esther · 1101 N. Bdwy V. A., Oklahoma City
Shields, Elsie · Box 523, Konawa
Stimson, Allamae · Tulsa
Strickland, Norma Jean · 509 N. W. 11, Oklahoma City
Stringer, Helen E. · 1028 S. W. 33, Oklahoma City
Taylor, Adeline · 520 N. W. 33, Oklahoma City
Terry, Phyllis · Box 765, Bethany
Thomason, Flora M. · 1601 S. Carson, Tulsa
Thompson, Audrey Elizabeth · 2300 Delaware, Muskogee
Thompson, Vella Mae · 1324 S. Gary, Tulsa
Tompkins, Irene · 925 W. Britton, Britton
Trotter, Lena · 1514½ S. Peoria, Tulsa
Van Hooser, Pauline · 2233 N. W. 41, Oklahoma City
Wachob, Mabel · 2312 Elmira, Muskogee
Walker, Perna Ringer · 1113 Med. Arts Bldg., Tulsa
Waller, Carole · 106 S. E. 37, Oklahoma City
Ward, Billye Schmitt · 1728 N. W. 16, Oklahoma City
Ward, Mary · Tulsa
Weaver, Vida Louise · 1410½ N. W. 21, Oklahoma City
White, Beulah · 662 1st Nat'l. Bank, Oklahoma City
Wood, Dorothy St. Cyr. · 1215 S. Denver, Tulsa
Yoes, Maurine · 2608 N. W. 15, Oklahoma City

APPENDIX U

Dental Department, University of Oklahoma School of Medicine and Visiting Staff of University Hospitals, Oklahoma City, Oklahoma.

Name	Appointment Date	Last Rank	Date
Reichmann, Francis J.	5–1–27	Clinical Professor	1949
Shaffer, Ward L.	9–1–30	Associate Professor	1953
Robertson, John Millard	11–12–35	Assistant Professor	1952
Bertram, Frank Pitkin	11–12–35	Assistant Professor	1950
Flesher, Marion A.	3–31–41	Assistant Professor	1953
Miller, James R.	7–2–42	Assistant Professor	1952

Drescher, Albert R.	7–1–42	Assistant Professor	1952
Wright, Leroy David	7–1–48	Instructor	1950
Frew, Athol Lee	7–1–48	Instructor	1950
Hirschi, Robert Graham	7–1–49	Instructor	1950
Yeager, Douglas A.	7–1–50	Instructor	1952
Russman, Sumner A.	7–1–50	Instructor	1952
Robertson, Dean	7–1–50	Instructor	1952
Cunningham, Earl Richard	7–1–51	Instructor	1952
Flesher, Wm. Nason	5–1–51	Instructor	1952
Reynolds, George E.	7–1–51	Instructor	1952
Miley, Thomas H.	3–1–52	Instructor	1953
Stewart, Frank W.	3–1–52	Instructor	1953
Goaz, Paul W.	9–18–53	Clinical Assistant	1953
Schow, Carl E.	9–18–53	Clinical Assistant	1953

APPENDIX V

Residents in Oral Surgery, University Hospitals, Oklahoma City from 1923 to 1954

Reichmann, Francis J.	July 1, 1923–December 1, 1925
(Resident could not be secured, so Dr. Reichmann continued on a half-time basis.)	
Ball, Alvin L.	July 1, 1927–June 30, 1928
Shaffer, Ward L.	July 1, 1928–June 30, 1929
Broyles, I. E.	July 1, 1929–June 30, 1930
Bertram, Frank P.	July 1, 1930–June 30, 1931
Juhl, Lee K.	July 1, 1931–June 30, 1932
Eure, Darden J.	July 1, 1932–August 15, 1932
Shepard, Kenneth T.	August 15, 1932–June 30, 1933
Robertson, J. Millard	July 1, 1933–June 30, 1934
Sullivan, Martin F.	July 1, 1934–June 30, 1935
Kersey, Clarence C.	July 1,1935–June 30, 1936
Bonnette, Paul C.	July 1, 1936–June 30, 1937
Haddock, Thomas P.	July 1, 1937–June 30, 1938
Erdman, Robert F.	July 1, 1938–June 30, 1939
McLaughlin, George L.	July 1, 1939–June 30, 1940

Gawey, John S.	July 1, 1940–June 30, 1941
Pace, L. E.	July 1, 1941–June 30, 1942
Wykoff, James E.	July 1, 1942–June 30, 1943
Orman, Warren K.	July 1, 1943–May 31, 1944

(From May 31, 1944, to January 1, 1946, James Miller, Albert Drescher, and Frank Bertram served on a part-time basis.)

Gimple, S.	January 1, 1946–June 30, 1946
Hirschi, Robert G.	July 1, 1946–June 30, 1947
Reynolds, George	July 1, 1947–September 30, 1949
Devlin, Donald	September 1, 1949–August 31, 1950
Miley, Thomas H.	July 1, 1950–October 31, 1951
Clark, Richard	July 1, 1951–July 1, 1952
Schow, Carl E.	March 1, 1952–April 30, 1953
Anderson, Martin F.	March 25, 1953–March 24, 1954
Williams, Ralph M.	July 16, 1953–July 15, 1954
Tipton, Albert	March 1, 1954–present
Shultz, Peter	September 1, 1954–present

APPENDIX W

Elected to Life Membership, American Dental Association. Date of election follows the name.

Dr. Henry B. Bolt, 1949
1424 W. Main St.
Enid, Okla.

Dr. Frank D. Dole, 1952
813 Gore Blvd.
Lawton, Okla.

Dr. Louie M. Doss, 1949
216 Leonhardt Bldg.
Oklahoma City, Okla.

Dr. Leslie E. Duncanson, 1952
405½ S. Main St.
Hobart, Okla.

Dr. William O. Haldeman, 1948
510 S. College St.
Enid, Okla.

Dr. Thomas F. Harmon, 1949
Sallisaw, Okla.

Dr. R. O. Hirschi, 1951
1524 W. Cleveland
Guthrie, Okla.

Dr. Frank C. Reisling, 1949
Box 607
Sulphur Springs, Ark.

Dr. H. L. Entriken, 1950
826 Bass Bldg.
Enid, Okla.

Dr. Bert W. Fesler, 1952
308 Petroleum Bldg.
Chickasha, Okla.

Dr. Charles A. Furrow, 1951
P. O. Box 223
Langley, Okla.

Dr. E. E. Sanger, 1951
109 N. W. 14th St.
Oklahoma City, Okla.

Dr. Fred D. Sparks, 1948
Box 479
Ponca City, Okla.

Dr. Andrew B. Walker, 1949
Norman, Okla.

Dr. Thurman H. Williams, 1950
309 Petroleum Bldg.
Chickasha, Okla.

Deceased Life Members

Dr. I. E. Cordrey, 1937
Blackwell, Okla.

Dr. James C. Devin, 1948
1103 S. Grand St.
Cherokee, Okla.

Dr. R. S. Parsons, 1950
801 Medical Arts Bldg.
Oklahoma City, Okla.

Dr. J. A. Townsend, 1950
Alva, Okla.

Dr. Lloyd E. Warder, 1950
1103 Broadway Tower
Enid, Okla.

Dr. William S. Williams, 1949
1027 W. Main St.
Durant, Okla.

APPENDIX Y

Code of Ethics

Since the natural tendency of man is not moral and his ideals are not always of the highest, it has become the custom among the professions to devise codes of ethics for the guidance of their members. W. A. Shumaker has said: "If there is such a thing in a profession as a concept distinct from a vocation, it must consist in the ideals which its members maintain, the dignity of character which they bring to the performance of their duties, and the austerity of the self-imposed ethical standards. To constitute a true profession there must be ethical traditions as potent as to bring into conformity members whose personal standards of conduct are at a lower level, and to have an elevating and ennobling effect on those members."

One of the earliest codes of ethics was established by Hammurabi, King of Babylon, about 2200 B.C., for the guidance of the physicians of his kingdom. Certain codes also existed among the ancient Persians, Jews, and Hindus. Among the Greeks, the first and only code for the guidance of physicians was that of Hippocrates. It is supposed to have been written by the "Father of Medicine" himself, although some authorities claim it was written later. This code was subscribed to by the Greek and Roman physicians, among whom were dentists, and has served as a basis for modern professional ethical codes. It has often been administered to classes of graduates in modern medical schools, and this custom still exists in some. The Hippocratic oath is tinged with the highest ideals of professional ethical thought and deserves the prominence it has been given:

I swear by Apollo, the physician, and Aesculapius, and Health, and All-heal, and all the gods and goddesses, that, according to my ability and judgment, I will keep this oath and stipulation: to reckon him who taught me this art equally dear to me as my parents, to share my substance with him and relieve his necessities if required; to regard his offspring as on the same footing with my own brothers, and to teach them this art if they should wish to learn it, without fee or stipulation, and that by precept, lecture and every other mode of instruction, I will impart a knowledge of the art to my own sons and to those of my teachers, and to disciples bound by a stipulation and oath, according to the law of medicine, but to none others. *I will follow that method of treatment, which, according to my ability and judgment, I consider for the benefit of my patients, and abstain from whatever is deleterious and mischievous.* I will give no deadly medicine to anyone if asked, nor suggest any such counsel; furthermore, I will not give to a woman an instrument to produce abortion. With purity and with holiness I will pass my life and practice my art. I will not cut a person who is suffering with a stone, but will leave this to be done by practitioners of this work. Into whatever houses I enter I will go into them for the benefit of the sick and will abstain from every voluntary act of mischief and corruption; and further, from the seduction of females or males, bond or free. Whatever in connection with my professional practice, or not in connection with it, I may see or hear in the lives of men which ought not be spoken abroad, I will not divulge, as reckoning that all such things should be kept secret.

While I continue to keep this oath inviolate, may it be granted to me to enjoy life and the practice of the art respected by all men at all times, but should I trangress and violate this oath, may the reverse be my lot.

Hippocrates swore to the gods that he would conduct his practice in an ethical manner. Less ostentatiously, Rabbi Moses Ben Maimon (A.D. 1135–1205), or Maimonides, as he is commonly known, offered a prayer to the one and only God for guidance as a physician. Maimonides was recognized as the greatest rabbinical authority of this time, and, besides, served as physician to Saladin of Egypt. As a matter of historical and cultural interest, and as an ethical inspiration, we present herewith the prayer for physicians by Maimonides:

O God, Thou has formed the body of man with infinite goodness; Thou hast united in him innumerable forces incessantly at work like so many instruments, so as to preserve in its entirety this beautiful house containing his immortal soul, and these forces act with all the order, concord and harmony imaginable. But if weakness or violent passion disturb this harmony, these forces act against one another and the body returns to the dust whence it came. Thou sendest then to man Thy messengers, the diseases which announce the approach of danger, and bid him prepare to overcome them. The Eternal Providence has appointed me to watch o'er the life and health of Thy creatures. May the love of my art actuate me at all times, may neither avarice, nor miserliness, nor the thirst for glory or a great reputation engage my mind; for, enemies of truth and philanthropy, they could easily deceive me and make me forget of my lofty aim of doing good to Thy children. Endow me with strength of heart and mind, so that both may be ready to serve the rich and the poor, the good and the wicked, friend and enemy, and that I may never see in the patient anything else but a fellow creature in pain.

If physicians more learned than I wish to counsel me, inspire me with confidence in and obedience toward the recognition of them, for the study of the science is great. It is not given to one alone to see all that others see. May I be moderate in everything except in the knowledge of this science; so far as it is concerned, may I be unsatiable; grant me the strength and opportunity always to correct what I have acquired, always to extend its domain; for knowledge is boundless and the spirit of man can also extend indefinitely, daily to enrich itself with new acquirements. Today he can discover his errors of yesterday, and tomorrow he may obtain new light on what he thinks himself sure of today. O God, Thou has appointed me to watch o'er the life and death of Thy creatures; here am I ready for my vocation.

About A.D. 700, the Japanese Emperor Mommu established a code of laws regulating education and the practice of medicine in his kingdom.

In the medieval period Arabian physicians, in the flower of their civilization, were deeply imbued with a high form of professional ethics, based on the tenets of Mohammed, although we do not know of the existence of any definite code among them. Complicated systems of medical ethics arose in the eighteenth century. The book of Thomas Percival (1740–1804) on medical ethics is an interesting commentary on the rules of etiquette and ethics laid down for the guidance of physicians in his day.

Today, codes of ethics exist among the medical, dental, legal, and other professions. The code for physicians is sponsored by the American Medical Association and that for dentists by the American Dental Association. In a communication from Mrs. Josephine P. Hunt, librarian of the American Dental Association, the following valuable information was contained:

"There are discussions in the literature previous to 1865 of the need of a code of ethics. The earliest discussion to be found in which a code of dental ethics was actually submitted was in the *Transactions* of the American Dental Association for 1865. This code was submitted by J. Allen and is contained in an article entitled, 'A Code of Dental Ethics for the American Dental Association.' A code of ethics was actually adopted in 1866, but the code adopted is not the same as that suggested by Dr. Allen in 1865. This remained unchanged through 1866, and few if any changes were made in this original code until 1922, when a new code was adopted. Revisions were made of the latter in 1926, 1927, 1929, 1930, 1933–34." (Reprinted courtesy McGehee and Walker, et al., Dental Practice Management [Chicago, Year Book Publishers, 1944.])

At the ninety-first annual session of the American Dental Association held in Atlantic City, October 30 to November 2, 1951, the House of Delegates adopted a revised Principles of Ethics. The text of the new instrument, which represents the combined thoughts of the Judicial Council and a committee of the Board of Trustees and which will serve in the future as a guide for the professional conduct of members is presented herewith.

Principles of Ethics

The practice of dentistry first achieved the stature of a profession in the United States where, through the heritage bestowed by the efforts of many generations of dentists, it acquired the three unfailing characteristics of a profession: education beyond the usual level; the primary duty of service to the public; the right to self-government.

The maintenance and enrichment of this heritage of professional status place on everyone who practices dentistry an obligation which should be willingly accepted and willingly fulfilled. This obligation cannot be reduced to a changeless series of urgings and prohibitions for, while the basic obligation is constant, its fulfillment may vary with the changing needs of a society composed of the human beings that a profession is dedicated to serve. The spirit and not the letter of the obligation, therefore, must be the guide of conduct for the professional man. In its essence, this obligation has been summarized for all time and for all men in the golden rule which asks only that "whatsoever you would that men should do to you, do ye so to them."

THE DENTIST AS A MEMBER OF A PROFESSION

SECTION 1. *Education Beyond the Usual Level.*
The right of a dentist to professional status rests in the knowledge, skill, and experience with which he serves his patients and society. Every dentist has the obligation of keeping his knowledge and skill freshened by continuing education through all of his professional life.

SECTION 2. *Service to the Public.*
The dentist has a right to win for himself those things which give him and his family the ability to take their proper place in the community which he serves, but there is no alternative for the professional man in that he must place first his services to the public rather than gain to himself.

374

SECTION 3. *Government of a Profession.*

Every profession receives from society the right to regulate itself, to determine and judge its own members. Such regulation is achieved largely through the influence of the professional societies, and every dentist has the dual obligation of making himself a part of a professional society and of observing its rules of ethics. The dentist's primary duty of serving the public is discharged by giving the highest type of service of which he is capable and by avoiding any conduct which leads to a lowering of esteem of the profession of which he is a member.

SECTION 4. *Leadership.*

The dentist has an obligation of providing freely of his skills, knowledge, and experience to society in those fields in which his qualifications entitle him to speak with professional competence. The dentist should be a leader in his community, especially in all efforts leading to the improvement of the dental health of the public.

SECTION 5. *Emergency Service.*

The dentist has an obligation, when consulted in an emergency by the patient of another dentist, to attend to the conditions leading to the emergency and to refer the patient to his regular dentist who should be informed of the conditions found and treated.

SECTION 6. *Use of Auxiliary Personnel.*

The dentist has an obligation to protect the health of his patient by not delegating to a person less qualified any service or operation which requires the professional competence of a dentist. The dentist has a further obligation of supervision of the work of all auxiliary personnel in the interests of rendering the best service to the patient.

SECTION 7. *Consultation.*

The dentist has the obligation of seeking consultation whenever the welfare of the patient will be safeguarded or advanced by having recourse to those who have special skills, knowledge, and experience. A consultant will hold the details of a consultation in confidence and will not assume responsibility for treatment without the consent of the attending practitioner.

SECTION 8. *Unjust Criticism.*

The dentist has the obligation of not referring disparagingly to the services of another dentist in the presence of a patient. A lack of knowledge of conditions under which the services were afforded may lead to unjust criticism and to a lessening of a patient's confidence in the dental profession. If there is indisputable evidence of faulty treatment, the welfare of the patient demands that corrective treatment be instituted at once and in such a way as to avoid reflection on the previous dentist or on the dental profession. The dentist has the further obligation of exposing fully at the request of appropriate authorities consequential negligence or incompetence in any form.

SECTION 9. *Rebates, Split Fees, and Commissions.*
The dentist has the obligation of disclosing to his patients all of the elements involved in the establishment of a fee, and he may not, therefore, secretly accept rebates, split fees, or commissions from any source associated with the service rendered to the patient.

SECTION 10. *Secret Agents and Exclusive Methods.*
The dentist has an obligation not to dispense or promote the use of drugs or other agents whose composition is secret. He also has the obligation not to dispense or prescribe except for limited experimental purposes any therapeutic agent, the value of which is not supported by scientific evidence. The dentist further has the obligation of not holding out as exclusive, any agent, method, or technic.

SECTION 11. *Patents and Copyrights.*
The dentist has the obligation of making the fruits of his discoveries and labors available to all when they are useful in safeguarding or promoting the health of the public. Patents or copyrights may be obtained by a dentist only when their primary purpose is the protection of the public and profession.

SECTION 12. *Advertising.*
The dentist has the obligation of advancing his reputation for fidelity, judgment, and skill solely through his professional services to his patients and to society. The use of advertising in any form to solicit patients is inconsistent with this obligation because it reflects adversely on the dentist who employs it and lowers public esteem of the dental profession.

SECTION 13. *Cards and Letterheads.*
A dentist may properly utilize professional cards, announcement cards, recall notices to patients of recent record, and letterheads when the style and text are consistent with the dignity of the profession and with the custom of other dentists in the community.

SECTION 16. *Use of Professional Titles and Degrees.*
A dentist may use the usual titles or degrees (Doctor, Dentist, D.D.S., or D.M.D.) in connection with his name on cards, letterheads, office signs, and announcements, but he may not so use his title or degree in connection with the promotion of any drug, agent, instrument, or appliance.

376

SECTION 17. *Use of the Term "Clinic" or "Group Practice."*
A dentist may participate in a regular established clinic or group service, but he may not apply the term "clinic" or similar designation to a dental practice when the use of such term may mislead the public directly or indirectly.

SECTION 18. *Limitation of Practice.*
A dentist may indicate the limitation of his practice to one of the approved specialties in dentistry on his card, letterhead, announcements, and office sign provided that such indication in style and text is consistent with the custom of the dentists of the community.

SECTION 19. *Directories.*
A dentist may permit the listing of his name in a directory provided that all dentists in similar circumstances have access to a similar listing and provided that such listing is consistent in style and text with the custom of the dentists of the community.

SECTION 20. *Education of the Public.*
A dentist may properly participate in a program for the education of the public on matters pertaining to dentistry provided such a program is in keeping with the dignity of the profession and has the approval of the dentists of a community or state acting through the appropriate agency of the dental society.

SECTION 21. *Official "Principles of Ethics."*
The statement will constitute the "Principles of Ethics" of the American Dental Association. Its constituent and component societies are urged to adopt additional provisions or interpretations not in conflict with these "Principles of Ethics" which would enable them to serve more faithfully the traditions, customs, and desires of the members of these societies.

SECTION 22. *Judicial Procedure.*
Problems involving questions of ethics should be solved within the broad boundaries established in the "Principles of Ethics," by the component dental society. If a satisfactory decision cannot be reached, the question should be referred, in turn, to the constituent society, the Judicial Council of the American Dental Association and House of Delegates of the American Dental Association, as provided in Chapter I, Section 40,H, of the By-Laws.

The Twin Territories

At one time the whole area now comprising the state of Oklahoma was designated the "Indian Territory." The Panhandle, or "No Man's Land," as it was called, was attached to the Indian Territory in 1889. The Territory of Oklahoma was organized in 1890. Thus the Indian Territory and Oklahoma Territory dental associations included the areas shown on the map.

Districts of the Oklahoma State Dental Association

At a special session of the Executive Council, January 24, 1915, seven component societies of the Association were established. This map shows the boundaries of these districts and of the counties which comprise them.

Index

UNIVERSITY OF OKLAHOMA PRESS

NORMAN